Penguins and Mandarins

Memories of Natural and Unnatural History

Penguins and Mandarins

Memories of Natural and Unnatural History

MARTIN HOLDGATE

The Memoir Club

First published in 2003 by
The Memoir Club
Whitworth Hall
Spennymoor
County Durham

British Library Cataloguing in
Publication Data.
A catalogue record for this book
is available from the
British Library.

ISBN: 1 84104 079 7

Typeset by George Wishart & Associates, Whitley Bay.
Printed by CPI Bath

*To Elizabeth, with love and thanks.
And for Robert, David, Karyn,
Katherine, Michael and Caroline.*

Contents

Illustrations

Photographs by the author unless otherwise acknowledged in the captions.

Acknowledgements

NO BOOK IS WRITTEN without a great deal of help from many people. My first and deepest thanks go to my wife Elizabeth for love, support and encouragement throughout the whole process. I am also deeply grateful to our sons Robert and David for their encouragement. Professor John Sheail kindly supplied copies of documents recently released in the Public Record Office. Dr Charles Moseley provided most helpful comments on early drafts of the text. Dr Barry Heywood, then Director of the British Antarctic Survey, Dr Duncan Poore, former Director of the Nature Conservancy, Dr David Drewry, then of the Natural Environment Research Council and Mr C.J. Meader of the then Department of the Environment were also kind enough to review sections of the text, and Mrs Tessa Stirling undertook the task of clearing the final version in Whitehall on behalf of the Secretary to the Cabinet, Sir Andrew Turnbull. I am most grateful to them all.

The sources of photographs are acknowledged on the individual pictures, but I am very grateful to Dr Klaus Toepfer, Executive Director of the United Nations Environment Programme, Dr Susan Sharland, Chief Executive of TRL Ltd, Dr Claude Martin, Director General of the World Wide Fund for Nature, Mr Achim Steiner, Director General of IUCN – The World Conservation Union and Dr Michael Dixon, Director General of ZSL for granting me permission to use photographs originally taken for or by their organizations.

Finally, it is a pleasure to thank Mrs Meg Ross of the Memoir Club for her help in editing and producing this volume.

CHAPTER ONE

Starting Points

LIFE IS A GIFT. Everyone's life is interesting, but some people are fortunate enough to go to special places, meet unusual people, and be there when exciting things happen. As life moves to its close, many of us look back and wonder how and why it all happened to us as it did. Then, as Chaucer's folk 'longen to go on pilgrimages' in the mediaeval springtime, so some of us in these later days feel drawn into writing down some of the things we have seen.

Some memoirs are written as contributions to history, by people who like to think that they have moved and shaken the world. Others – like this one – are perspectives from a more everyday level. Why write such a book at all? I suspect the honest answer is that people like me write to please ourselves. But what special perspective can I offer?

I am a biologist by training, and for ten years I was a naturalist-explorer in the Antarctic and Subantarctic at a time when science and politics were vying for supremacy there. The patterns of life – the way plants and animals spread in the remote past over the southern continents to give us the flora and fauna we now have – became a dominant fascination. But I was also brought up with a love of poetry, and a sense of a God who was 'under the world's splendour and wonder'. The interplay between people and nature, and the tragedy of human poverty in what should be a world of plenty, dripped into my awareness slowly but helped to turn me from the world of science into the world of policy, tinged with politics.

I moved from the clean world of the ice into the murkier world of human machination. I became a bureaucrat. As such I saw how science got blended with (and often subordinated to) the mixture of expedience and dogma that is modern politics. Conservation of nature was one of my goals, but so was action to halt pollution and to build a more equitable world. I got drawn into a vortex of international affairs, never as a decisive influence but possibly as a kind of lever that moved outcomes just that little bit. I helped to prepare the first two United Nations conferences on the human future, and sat in the stalls while world leaders delivered their carefully packaged oratory on stage. My earlier years had given insight into how the world of nature worked: later came a view of how the human world was superimposed, sometimes for good and often for ill.

That, I suppose, is the perspective of this book. If it has uniqueness, it is because I do not think that anyone else has had the same observer's opportunity. My life is the strand that links its episodes together but (despite the self-centredness of these opening lines) it is not about me. It is about what I have seen and heard, and what I think I have learned about 'the world, the universe and everything'.

Observers are conditioned by their background. I was a child of school and church. My father, Francis Wyatt Holdgate (always known as Frank), became a schoolmaster by accident, taking a temporary job at Brighton College while waiting to enter the Colonial Service in East Africa. But maybe the schoolmaster genes would have got him anyway, because his father, the Reverend William Wyatt Holdgate, was Headmaster of Sutton Valence School in Kent, and had married the sister of another Headmaster. Anyway, by the time I was born, Father had become a Housemaster at Brighton, where (among others) he taught my future boss, the Antarctic explorer Sir Vivian Fuchs. Father said that Fuchs got his lifelong nickname 'Bunny' because he kept rabbits at school, but I never confirmed that with the man himself.

Mother was a parson's daughter. Her father, Canon John Bebbington, was Rector of Slinfold, near Horsham, at the time of my birth in 1931, and that is why I was born in Horsham, close under my grandmother's wing. But Mother, with her two sisters and two brothers, had grown up in a rambling vicarage with a wild garden at Etchingham in east Sussex. Rudyard Kipling lived nearby, at Burwash, up a long hill, and Mother remembered turning out to watch his Stanley Steamer car chug by (occasionally with the aid of a push from the Vicarage children). She also remembered Kipling's son John roaring through the village on his motorcycle – and how the young man was taunted with cowardice when he failed to 'join up' for the first World War. It may have been this that led Kipling senior to press for a commission for his son, reversing the medical ruling which had excluded him because of his severe short sight. According to Mother, Kipling turned bitterly against the villagers of Burwash when John was killed, and asked Grandfather Bebbington to place his name on the War Memorial at Etchingham. It is there but I am assured that it is also in Burwash so maybe Kipling had a change of heart later.

We were not, by origin, a Sussex family, or a very distinguished one either. Both grandfathers were typical of the age, in escaping from back-grounds of trade and craft into Universities and the professions. The Holdgates were in iron, in Stoke on Trent, where my great grandfather Robert had had a successful business until – as my Aunt Evelyn put it, 'he got too fond of drinking madeira and playing whist at the Potter's Club and went broke.' Which left my grandfather Wyatt (Wyatt because of descent from the Staffordshire tribe of architects) to finance his way through Cambridge with the help of a scholarship and a loan from the Bishop of Newcastle-under-Lyme. The Bebbingtons were from Cheshire and from a long line of wheelwrights and carpenters. Grandfather John was the first to graduate (from London University), entered the Church, and 'married above himself': Mabel Edith Kynaston came of a Shropshire squirearchy ultimately descended from the Princes of Powys.

The 1930s were a time of dwindling families, probably in reaction to economic uncertainty, threats of war and relatively easy contraception. I was an only child, so cousins became very important as substitute siblings. But I was alone a good deal, and life was made more confining by poor health. I was supposed to be delicate, especially after a bout of rheumatic fever at the age of three led to the discovery of a heart murmur. For some years I was rather wrapped in protection, and turned in on books, jigsaws, Meccano and daily walks, usually on Brighton sea-front.

Brighton in the pre-war years seems, in retrospect, a place of glitter and romance, with life picked out in highlights. I know now that there was economic depression and a lot of poverty, and even the middle classes suffered – as Father did when his modest salary was cut ten per cent under the 'Geddes axe'. But we always had a comfortable home, ample food, a car and visits to grandparents in the country. We lived in a little terrace house on one of the many hills above the College, where the spurs of the South Downs fall steeply to the sea. Beyond a row of bigger houses at the top of the hill you came to 'Bedstead Alley' (named because it passed allotments, fenced off with old iron bedsteads) and so onto the Downs and the racetrack – or, if you turned right, onto open slopes that led towards Rottingdean.

The affairs of state intruded occasionally. I remember painting my wooden model bus red, white and blue like the real buses, in celebration of King George V's Silver Jubilee. I have a vivid little picture of the Abdication of King Edward VIII – because of a parental dialogue which must, I suspect, have been echoed in many houses throughout England:

> Father (entering from having listened to the news on the wireless):
> 'Well, the King's gone!'
> Mother: 'Oh, dear!'
> Father: 'Nonsense. Good riddance to bad rubbish.'
> Reign over.

It may well have been a mood of family relief that made Mother sit me down to listen to the Coronation Service of King George VI. But it was

Family picnic, 'somewhere in Sussex' in 1937. Frank Holdgate is on the extreme left,
'Bobbie' and Martin Holdgate are on the right. The large gentleman, Colonel Roberts,
was probably associated with Brighton College. Photograph from family album.

much more exciting to be taken outside to watch a big airship slipping
westwards down the Channel (Mother afterwards said it was the *Hindenburg*,
outward bound to the disaster which brought the age of the airship to an
end). From our hill, there were also glimpses of ships and more ships
endlessly passing, and great excitement when one was a battleship or even an
aircraft carrier. Mother's younger sister was married to a naval officer,
Lieutenant Commander Hugh Tollemache, and I remember an early visit to
them in Chatham, when we went aboard HMS *Emerald* – one of a pair of
cruisers eccentrically designed with two funnels forward and one way aft.
The adults enjoyed wardroom pink gins while I was taken on a tour: I
remember being fascinated by torpedo tubes. Across the dock basin lay rank
on rank of pale grey ironmongery, including odd vessels like the flat-
bottomed Monitor *Erebus*, designed to slip in over shoals and unloose
immense bombardment from her massive forward turret. I had a slim
version of Jane's *Fighting Ships* and (like many little boys of my generation)
knew the muster-roll of the Royal Navy pretty much by heart.

Father taught biology. I suspect that was a formative influence on me, for
I can remember as a very small boy going with him to the coastal rock pools
by Black Rock at Brighton to collect material for his classes. We also raided
ponds for fresh water life – which explains why I knew the Latin names of a

number of common aquatic insects like *Notonecta* and *Gerris* before I was aware they were known in English as back-swimmers and pond skaters. Once a whale was washed up beside the Palace Pier, and we queued up to see it (price 3*d*. – smell included). Grandfather Wyatt was also a biologist, but he was a keen amateur astronomer, a mountaineer and an archaeologist as well. He had a refractor telescope on a tall tripod through which I was later introduced to the mountains of the moon, the white polar caps of Mars, the changing silver phases of Venus, the rings of Saturn and the four great moons of Jupiter.

It was my first scientific interest. I was given a Planisphere, and twiddled it endlessly to watch the changing pattern of the heavens. I was given a book about the planets, and made little Plasticene models of them, dangling on strings from a light flex that ran across my bedroom ceiling – in the correct order from the sun, represented by the light bulb, of course. As a great treat, I was taken to see the family's most distinguished astronomer, Mother's uncle, the Reverend Theodore Phillips, who had spent years scrutinising and drawing the changing cloudscapes of Jupiter. He was President of the British Astronomical Association, and had what seemed to me an immense telescope – a 22-inch reflector. But it was cloudy.

In 1938 life was transformed. Father, who was then 37, was appointed Headmaster of Arnold School in Blackpool. Promotion had been a struggle for him, for unlike his father he was not a natural scholar. He had been at Trinity College, Cambridge, where he had played Rugby for the College First XV and had a lot of fun, but he had not worked all that hard and ended up with a Third – almost a kiss of death for a would-be headmaster of a Public School. But Arnold School, Blackpool, was not, shall we say, out of the top drawer. It had been founded only forty years previously by an entrepreneur named Frank Pennington, who had made it the best school in Blackpool but had died in harness, leaving the place as near bankrupt as didn't matter. Father got the job because of his direct manner and obvious competence – and because Mother, who was to be responsible for running the domestic side of the school, charmed the Board. Father always used to say that the turning point came at the end of his interview.

Chairman of Governors (Alderman Tom Masheter, the most important butcher in Blackpool): 'Mr Holdgate, is there anything you would like to ask us?'

Father: 'Well, yes, Mr Chairman. I take it this School is meant to pay?'

Chairman (warming to a businesslike fellow): 'Of course.'

Father: 'Well, does it?'

They protested it did, and gave him the job on a year's probation, commencing in September 1938. Halfway through the year it was obvious that the school, down to about a hundred boarders and only a slightly larger number of day boys, did not pay. They confirmed Father in office hastily. The rumbles of war speedily brought more boarders, refugees from the Manchester business community. Money came rolling in. The school has never looked back – as I know because, by one of those turns in the wheel of fate, I am now the Chairman of its Governors.

Moving from Brighton to Blackpool was quite an experience for a seven year old. Not so much geographically as culturally. Blackpool boys spoke differently. I was quickly known as 'cut glass' at school because of my south-country accent (later, somebody noticed that my first name rhymed splendidly with 'fartin', and the association, especially to describe the Headmaster's son, was much too good to ignore). I knew nobody, of course. So Mother did the obvious thing – she found out who among the members of staff had sons of the same age (it was assumed that boys of 7 only played with boys of 7 or 8). That brought Alan Haythornthwaite, whose father William (nick-named 'Bumps') taught Latin, and his friend John Rothwell into my life. Soon afterwards it brought John Holt, whose father George ('Thistle') taught English. John became my closest friend for the following four or five years.

The move to Blackpool transformed my life, because it took me to Asby. George Holt had married a co-heiress of Breakells Brewery in Preston, and served as its managing Director alongside his job at Arnold. The firm owned several inns in the Eden Valley of Westmorland, including the Three Greyhounds at Great Asby, five miles from the County Town of Appleby. George Holt was a fine shot, and rented the sporting rights over seven or eight farms. Finding that Father also enjoyed shooting, he invited us to join the Holts for the half-term break in the middle of our first autumn.

I had never seen country like it – the stone walls, the grey stone houses strung along the beck that flowed through the village, the endless vistas over rolling, wrinkled, green countryside, and the great hills far off, grander than anything I had ever seen in my life.

The beck was a particular excitement. Much of the drainage in that limestone country is underground, and the stream bed through Asby was often dry above a big spring about two thirds of the way through the village, which served as a well and water supply. The well was protected by stone walls so that cattle did not foul the pure water. But after heavy rain, the upper beck would 'come down'. A rushing sound would herald the sudden arrival of trickles along the stony bed, building swiftly to a strong stream or even a torrent. If you walked upstream, you would come to the 'kettles' –

great, sinister, round excavations in the stream bed, four or five metres deep, cut by swirling stones – and above them to a cave mouth from which the stream issued after heavy rain. Above that it was always dry, all the way up past the farms and the small enclosed pastures to the moors – divided by immense lengths of stone wall into summer grazings or 'allotments', each going with a particular valley farm.

Those moors were another surprise. The land south and west of Asby rises to a low ridge, only about 300 to 400 metres above sea level, but much of it covered by great sheets of bare limestone pavement, fissured with deep clefts or 'grikes' in which a mass of ferns and flowers lurk. I know now that this is one of the finest examples of this kind of landscape in Europe, and that the flora that I slowly got to know there is special. Today, those uplands are a National Nature Reserve. But as a child, I saw only a great, sinister expanse, shining under the moon and haunted by an ancient past.

War was in the air, and Mr Chamberlain had returned from Munich with the famous scrap of paper. Men like Mr Holt and Mr Haythornthwaite, veterans of the trenches, began to murmur about the future. But peace hung on. That first winter in the north took us to Scotland for Christmas. Uncle Hugh and Aunt Eve Tollemache had moved to Greenock, where Uncle Hugh was supervising the fitting out of a light cruiser, HMS *Bonaventure*, in which he was killed off Crete in 1941. Father had a Ford V8 car of which he was immensely proud (and indeed, it was a splendid vehicle for its period, well able to top 60 m.p.h.). The journey to Scotland was set to be exciting anyway – but it turned out especially exciting because there was snow. Father stopped at Kendal and asked whether he could get over the notorious Shap Fell. He went on cautiously, stopping to fit chains. I vaguely remember the dip and rise of the road at High Borrowbridge on the old Shap road, the white slopes either side, the line of stranded heavy lorries, and how with a slither or two Father and his splendid car topped the rise and ran down easily towards the long down-slope to Carlisle. For some reason the second area of high ground around Beattock was nothing in comparison – and he was delighted to be told that his was the last private car to get over Shap that night.

That Christmas was, for my parents, a time of naval revelry – lots of parties, dances and jollifications. An era was ending: the era when the Royal Navy was a big, confident, club with a lively social life. Hugh and Eve had been stationed in Malta, and looked back with nostalgia. Now, as the inter-war years came to their close, their generation faced the end of their carefree youth. It touched my parents, too. Those who knew Father later as a stern, rather overpowering Headmaster found it hard to discern the cheerful young man-about-town, sportsman, horseman, dancer and party-goer – but he had been all of those. I think he looked up to Hugh Tollemache as a more confident, more glamorous personality and felt uplifted in his company and in the naval circles in which Hugh and Eve moved. Mother, too, as a lively and pretty young woman had loved the party-going, the tennis and the tranquil summers of the thirties. They all knew that the world was changing: in his first Speech Day at Arnold, Father commented that 'whether we like it or not, civilisation has packed its tents and is on the march.' They all knew that Christmas 1938 was likely to be their last chance of peaceful partying, and they made the most of it. For me, it was a period tied to my young cousin Ian's nursery. But I enjoyed looking out over the Clyde at ships twinkling with lights, among them a big four-funnel transatlantic liner, and visiting the shipbuilder's yard, where new hulls towered up above the stocks and slipways.

Back home, preparations for war were evident. The First War veterans on the School staff designed an air raid shelter in the gardens. It was a slit trench, lined with timber, roofed with corrugated iron, and covered with three feet of sand. We boys persuaded Father to allow the gardeners to dig us a little trench, also lined in old wood and roofed over. We called it the 'H's Line' (Haythornthwaite, Holdgate and Holt) and used it as our retreat. The LDV (Local Defence Volunteers) – precursors of the Home Guard – began drilling on the school field.

Blackpool had a quiet war. It was too far from mainland Europe to be easy to raid, and had no targets of strategic importance apart from the airfield, where the RAF trained aircrew in sedate old Avro Ansons. One or two sticks of incendiaries were dropped on the school fields and gardens, one of them landing a couple of metres away from Father as he was shepherding boys into the slit-trench shelter. He heard it fizzling, and turned to shove earth over it with his gumboots. More damage was done by souvenir hunters invading the playing fields and digging up bomb fragments. Air raid alarms were for us boys more in the nature of an exciting excuse to go out into the night, supported by steaming Bovril, served in 'unbreakable' glasses which sometimes shattered explosively on being filled with hot liquid.

We were aware, of course, that things could go wrong. I suppose I was about eight when I asked Mother what would happen if the Germans came. She paused, and was quite truthful:

'Well, they might shoot Daddy, because he's an important man and wouldn't work for them. But you and I should be all right . . .'

Once in a while the war came nearer. Grandma Holdgate had died in 1937, but after a period of retirement Grandpa went back to active parochial service, as Vicar of Tong in Shropshire, with my aunt Rene to keep house while Uncle Jim (a professional soldier) was away on service. We had two family Christmases there, while we still had a car, and in 1940 we listened to wave after wave of German aircraft droning northwards. It was the time of the Christmas blitz on Manchester. Then Uncle Hugh Tollemache was killed and Aunt Eve, with my cousins Ian and Rosemary, came to live in Blackpool. And once we went to Liverpool to visit my godfather, Owen Fulljames, who was Chaplain in HMS *Rodney*, an oddly truncated battleship with three huge forward gun turrets but only a single one aft. Like her sister ship *Nelson*, she had been designed to be bigger: the truncation was due to a Treaty which restricted the size of battleships – a provision of which Hitler took no notice. *Rodney* was in a mess, following action which had severely damaged her midmost forward gun turret, and made a tangle of the deck armour plating. Liverpool was our nearest big city, and the nearest scene of serious blitz: there were times when we could see a glow in the southern sky from Blackpool and knew that fires were raging.

The School went through inevitable vicissitudes. We had a Manchester school evacuated on us, sharing the classrooms in shifts. We had rationing: I still remember the horror when Father held up a one-pound jar of jam and told the boarders that would be their personal limit for a month! But he had one dominant goal – keeping academic standards up. He had himself suffered at Sutton Valence in the first World War, when almost all the permanent teaching staff had joined up and been replaced by the retired and the inadequate. He was determined this would not happen with us. So when key staff started to leave for the services he looked around for academically competent replacements. The best were women – all good teachers and disciplinarians. Some of the men were eccentric. The cleverest, Ivor Stoyel, who came to teach maths, had a first class degree from Cambridge. His drawbacks were that he could not comprehend how difficult maths can be to the non-mathematician, and that he was easily sidetracked into discussing religion (he was a fundamentalist) or astronomy. We egged him on with enthusiasm. Sometimes he walked right into it.

'Holdgate,' said Mr Stoyel one day, knowing I had care of Grandpa Holdgate's telescope, 'have you seen Uranus?'
Voice from the back: 'He does it with mirrors, Sir.'

He could also be provoked over discrepancies between Biblical accounts of the Creation and the findings of science, for example regarding the age of the Earth and the history of the dinosaurs. But he had a perfect argument-stopper:
'But if we believe our Bibles, these things cannot be.'
End of digression.
Mr Passey – Hiram B. Passey as he became known – was a pacifist, a

conscientious objector, and a brilliant teacher of Shakespeare. His enthusiasm was compelling, and he could work himself into a frenzy, frothing at the mouth as he declaimed great speeches. He had no truck with the mealy-mouthed. Witness one day in form Five A when a boy was hesitating over a naughty word.

'DAMNED!' yelled Passey.

The Headmaster walked in.

Father supported Mr Passey, but the Chairman of Governors did not. Bert and Elsie Grime had three sons in the services – one a prisoner of war, taken like so many others from west Lancashire when Singapore fell; another a bomber pilot making regular sorties over Germany and the third a pilot in the Fleet Air Arm. They did not look kindly on conscientious objectors. Hiram B. P. departed after a year. English became a duller subject.

Although Asby – and the hills – were my ideal world, Blackpool was not a bad place to grow up in. It was vibrant, full of entertainment and top entertainers. It had the Pleasure Beach, great for excursions with visiting cousins. And it had the sea.

The shore of almost-anywhere-on-sea is a place of contrast – contrast taken for granted by most of us. On the landward side you have a town full of hotels and houses, cafés and fish and chips, and even towers and big dippers. On the other side of the sea wall you have the greatest wilderness on earth, the untamed waters that cover seven tenths of the surface of the planet. When the gales blew out of the west, as they often do at Blackpool, the wilderness invaded the townscape in surging, breaking swell and driving spray (we had a dangerous wave-dodging game, played on South Promenade, darting from shelter to shelter and trying not to be soaked by the full force of a driven breaker). When it was calm, at low tide, especially on an evening of full moon, it was a delight to walk out across the sand bars to the tide's edge, dropping the lights and the sea wall hundreds of yards behind and savouring the wilderness. You could do practical things too: John Holt and I made several long night lines which we baited with lugworms, catching a fair number of small and delicious flatfish to supplement the rations. We got to know the tides and the shifting sandbanks really well, and I am sure that the experience made the modest risk well worth taking.

One benefit of living in a school was that the rations could be bulked, and were much easier to manage than the weekly pittance for an individual. And as a catering establishment, we got some special deals too. They were augmented by eggs from the seventy hens that were installed in the gardens in about 1940. And by crates of rabbits which Father ordered from a rabbit trapper near Appleby – four dozen rabbits, delivered by rail in a big, ventilated crate, once a fortnight. In those days the railways would collect and deliver almost anything door to door, from school trunks and bicycles (sent 'passenger's luggage in advance') to live calves which would often be seen sitting on the platform, sewn into sacks with just their heads and necks protruding, waiting to be lifted into the guard's van.

But we did have Culinary Sensations. The best was the Adventure of the Soyagetti. This was a kind of rice-substitute made of little plugs of soya flour. You simmered it in milk, slowly, and it came out looking and tasting not unlike rice pudding (which was a school staple). Unfortunately, one batch had been diverted to nourish other creatures before it got to us.

I was quite a senior boy by then, which suggests that this was a post-war interlude, probably around 1948 (when the rationing was more difficult, anyway). Father sat, as usual, at the head of one lunch table doling out portions (other staff, Matron and Mother presided over other tables). Suddenly there was a voice of horror:

'Sir, Sir, there are bugs in the pudding!'

'Nonsense, boy! Eat your lunch!'

I ranged three small brown beetles, a few weevil pupae (chrysalises) and six white grubs with brown head capsules tastefully on the side of my plate and passed it to him.

'It looks as if we have a weevil infestation, Sir.'

'My God! So it does. Oh well, what doesn't sicken will fatten. Eat it and we'll investigate afterwards.'

So we did. There was a bin of soyagetti and about one in five of the little sticks of hard flour had a neat round hole in the end. Many contained small maggots. As a weevil culture it would have graced a laboratory. Some, indeed, was used as a biology demonstration, while the rest was returned to the supplier, doubtless with pithy comments.

The food store also had a thriving mouse culture at times (we didn't mind mice all that much, but if anyone saw a rat, the local Council officers were speedily summoned). Mice were dealt with by trapping and especially by the cats, among which Bubbles was the champion (her brother, Squeak, had quite missed the mousing gene). Bubbles' great day came when the housekeeper heard squeaky noises from a metal dustbin that had been filled with plates and other crockery, piled in a manner that left plenty of spaces. Clearly it had become Musopolis. Bubbles was placed on top of the highest plates and we let her down slowly by removing the crockery from under her. It was rather like cutting a field of corn with a reaper-binder that went round and round a diminishing island in the middle, until all the rabbits, hares and whatever that had taken refuge had to rush out past the waiting throng of men with sticks and guns. Bubbles caught fourteen mice in that bin . . .

Headmasters in those days were stern, dominant, figures and Father's six foot two of height and strong personality fitted the part admirably. He was a strict disciplinarian of the old school, punishing misdemeanours and idleness with what he judged to be a fitting number of whacks of the cane. He argued that this was the best way – the matter was dealt with swiftly and was then over and done with. But this strict discipline was only one side of his personality. He was also a very caring man who took a deep interest in the futures of his pupils and tried hard to steer them into the right careers. He could get deeply emotional when saying 'goodbye' at the end of the year, or when he had to announce that an Old Boy had been killed in action.

His forceful leadership did sometimes go wrong. There was, for example, the Incident of Annie and Mrs Wainwright.

These two redoubtable ladies were school cleaners. And what cleaners. None of this vacuuming stuff – they got down on hands and knees and scrubbed the planked classroom floors, then swabbed them over with a mop. Unfortunately, they couldn't stand one another. It got to the point where they would mark a line down the middle of a classroom and each take a half. Even then, warfare was not uncommon.

We were about to leave for Asby. Father was just strapping some suitcases onto the rack at the back of the car (which places the incident in 1939 or 1940). Enter Mrs Wainwright, fair flustered.

'Mr 'Olgate, Mr 'Olgate, Annie's thrown t'scrubbing brush at me. What should I do?'

'I don't give a damn what you do. For all I care you can throw a bucket of water at her. I'm going on holiday.'

Exit a happy Mrs Wainwright. Five minutes later Annie encountered the bucketful of cold, soapy water and the news that she was receiving it on the Headmaster's strict instructions.

Neither was there when we returned from holiday. Which was a loss, for they scrubbed floors magnificently.

In 1943, Father decided that it was wrong in principle for his son to be educated at his own school. I think this was partly a reflection of experience, for he had been a boy under his father's headship at Sutton Valence, ending up as head of School as I was eventually to do at Arnold. But possibly he was influenced by two other factors. First, those were the days when having been to a well known public school helped you to university and to a job afterwards. Second, he himself was getting restless: the war was clearly moving to its close and he thought about moving on to another job – in which case it would have been easier were I settled in a boarding school. So, in September 1944 I was on my way to Oundle.

I should have loved it. Oundle is a charming little town in pretty country.

There were good walks. My housemaster, Mr Hewett of Laundimer House, was a biologist and noting my interest, took me into the labs from time to time to help him prepare class material. But I didn't like it, partly, I think, because the teaching did not grip me and was frankly inferior to that at Arnold. It was the end of the war (we celebrated VE day by running riot over the countryside, hitching lifts on various military vehicles and nearly getting into serious trouble when a group of older boys found that the tarpaulins they were sitting on covered crates of bottled beer, which they proceeded to sample). The Headmaster, Kenneth Fisher, was elderly and ill (he died in September 1945, soon after retirement). It was rather a sporty school, and I was not sporty. It had an emphasis on cross-country running which my doctor didn't want me to do (I was still going to a specialist because of my heart murmur). I came top of my class in English and science, and slithered down in other subjects. As I began my second year at Oundle, Father discovered that I had been moved down from the fastest stream to the third stream. He went to talk to Harry Mayall, his Second Master.

'Look, Harry, you know the boy. You've taught him. If he was your son and he got these reports, what would you do?'

'Do you really want my opinion?'

'Yes.'

'I'd ring up his housemaster and tell him to put the boy on the next train home!'

Father did – after rather difficult conversations with the new Headmaster, and with Mr Hewett who was upset, seeing it all as a criticism of him. He summoned me, told me, and handed over a letter from both parents. 'I think he's making a mistake,' he said. I tried to be non-committal. I then had my first experience of a Confidential Operation. I was not to tell anyone. Mr Hewett was to announce at breakfast next morning that he wanted to see me. I was to stay in his sitting room while the others left for lessons. I would then be taken to the station and put on the train to Northampton, where Mother would meet me. The House would be told that evening. It all worked like clockwork, and I reappeared at Arnold leaving a seven days' wonder behind me.

Blackpool was home and school. Asby was escape, and almost paradise on earth. We went there twice or three times a year, right through the war, first by car and then by train. Always, the Three Greyhounds was the goal, and almost always we were the only guests (we felt vaguely cheated if the other sitting room and bedrooms were let to someone else).

Mrs Hayton, who was a widow, kept the inn. She was not an Asby woman, but a foreigner from Crosby Garrett, four miles away across the moors. She was helped by her two daughters, Madge and Dorothy, and by Jack Alderson, an even more remote foreigner from Swaledale, twenty miles away, who attended to the farm and the stock. For like many country inns in that part of the world, and like many of the cottages along the Asby street, the Three Greyhounds was also a smallholding. Its four fields – no more than fifteen acres in all – ran as a narrow strip up the slopes to the south. Most of the fields were hedged – cut and laid by Jack from time to time, to keep them trim and stock-proof – but there were drystone walls of grey limestone around the top fields rich in shelly fossils. The inn kept four or five milk cows and raised calves, selling off bullocks at about a year old to go for fattening on the better lowland pastures. The Eden Valley was the kingdom of the Northern Dairy Shorthorn – pretty, red roan beasts, giving a moderate amount of fairly rich milk and yielding a good carcase. A few people kept chestnut and white Ayrshires with short, upward-curving horns. They got more milk, but worse meat. The invasion of what are now the universal black and white Friesians did not happen until well after the war.

The bar at the Three Greyhounds was quite small, and John Holt and I often had the back bedroom immediately above it. It was quite the nicest room, for it looked across the fields to rising ground southwards, and there was always something going on. Kittens were sometimes born in the interstices of the woodpile, and would emerge to play. Pigs would grunt from the sties behind (they killed two a year, and the dairy was hung with muslin-swathed hams and sides of home-cured bacon). At night one lay drowsily awake hearing the rich, deep, burr of heavily accented voices down below, and the clack of dominoes being snapped down on the tables. They spoke proper Westmorland in those days, before the BBC and universal travel eroded our national diversity of tongues.

We got to know that countryside inside out. Even now I can remember virtually every field and hedgerow, and make a pretty good guess at what was grown where during the wartime period when ancient pastures were ploughed and sown with wheat, oats, turnips, swedes or kale. We dammed the little stream, Burneybeck Sike, that came down from the fields behind the inn, and floated little boats whittled out of willow sticks or made of matchbox trays. In summer we even managed to bathe in the pools we had made. And we hunted rabbits with catapults made by Father (I cannot remember ever hitting anything, but the stalking was fun). Later we learned to set rabbit wires, and did catch quite a few (and I'm glad to say that Father not only taught us the most humane way to set them but also made us go round them twice a day, whatever the weather, so that no animal would suffer for long if it was not killed instantly when it ran into the wire). Later still we were promoted to guns – and in my case, a .22 rifle. By then John's and my lives had diverged, because his father had fallen ill (he died of lung cancer in 1946), and the Holts came only rarely to Asby.

One of my jobs was to get rabbits for dog food. We had two black labradors, and keeping them supplied meant delightful forays before breakfast, best of all on crisp frosty mornings when the puddles were iced over and the leaves hoar-fringed. It was a matter of pride to stalk carefully upwind behind a wall or hedge, ease yourself slowly into view, choose the tenderest-looking three-quarters grown young rabbit out of a group nibbling peacefully in the grass, and drop it instantly, without alarming the others too much. And to walk back for breakfast with maybe two couple of victims – no more than needed (for there was no refrigeration) – perhaps dropping one or two off on the way for the old ladies at the alms-houses by the village well.

Father's best dog was Jumbo – the cleverest dog I have ever known. He was an accident – the result of the escaping skills of Entwistle the gunsmith's pedigree labrador bitch and the opportunism of a neighbouring Airedale terrier. Jumbo combined the keen nose, retrieving ability and gundog's temperament of his mother with a terrier's hunting instincts and – unfortunately – hard mouth. He was a wizard at locating rabbits in the base of drystone walls. You would walk along on the downwind side of a wall – and Jumbo would halt, quiver, sniff and signal vigorously with his tail. If you lay down, you could often see the rabbit sitting in a cavity in the wall base. If you worked one or two small loose stones out you could slip your hand in, extract the rabbit and despatch it. He often found his supper like this. And he was not averse to richer game. I remember George Holt (who kept pedigree spaniels and affected to despise Jumbo's ancestry and ruffianly disposition) once dismissing his enthusiasms over a patch of bushes as 'it'll only be a rabbit – let the dog go in.' There was a heave and a flutter and Jumbo returned triumphantly with a cock pheasant – which, unfortunately, he killed (as he always did live game) by biting too hard on the rib cage – his sole defect as a gun dog.

Jumbo also had his Airedale father's opportunistic enthusiasm when it came to bitches. In Blackpool he often vanished for hours, and as often as not would be found by the search party (usually me) in the midst of a throng of fellow-enthusiasts making sure that somebody would be more careful about securing their bitch next time she came into season. In Asby he excelled himself one fine, warm, Sunday evening. The village was at church and because of the heat they had left the door open – unaware that Jumbo was meanwhile pursuing his pleasures with a sheepdog bitch among the tombstones. Coupled tightly together, they wandered into the church. Tom Cleasby, the Churchwarden and biggest farmer in the village, evicted them with a broom. Jumbo staggered reluctantly back over the bridge towards the inn. His owner could be seen making himself scarce on his bicycle.

Jumbo once embarrassed Father in another way. It happened in Shropshire. Father had had the excellent notion of taking a party of maybe thirty senior boys to help a group of farmers with the harvest. Each year from around 1942 to 1946 we went to Calverhall, south of Whitchurch, where we were based in the village school. Mother and a group of local ladies did the cooking, and the boys slept in wooden huts, while we lodged at a local farm. It was en route to that farm – Cloverley Farm – that there befell the Incident of Father, Jumbo and the Bull.

Like many others in that country of big estates and wide parklands, the farm was approached through iron gates and along a tree-lined avenue that crossed an expanse of pasture. The herd of seventy-five Friesian cows often grazed there, accompanied by Old William, an immense (but peaceful) bull. One afternoon Father was cycling back as usual, with Jumbo at heel. A cow noticed the dog and began to trot after him, as cattle will. Jumbo did not like it and crowded close to Father's rear wheel. Father quickened his pace. The cows accelerated. Before long, there was a regular stampede: one Headmaster in full flight, pursued by one dog trying to take refuge somewhere under his chain guard, pursued by seventy-five large cows and one very large bull. Of course when he came to the inner gate by the farm and had to stop, the whole stampede also stopped, in a snorting circle. Nobody was bruised except one Headmasterly ego, when he realized that Mother and I and Mrs Parker the farmer's wife had been watching the performance from an upper window.

It was in Calverhall that we got our second labrador, Tiger. Because I was only 13, and not of full size to work in the fields (though I remember lending a hand setting up corn stooks quite often), I was surplus to harvesting requirements and sent out to walk around the estate with the gamekeepers, counting coveys of partridges in advance of the shooting season in September. It was good exercise and I learned many useful bits of country lore. Old Dawson, the head keeper, looked after the Shavington Estate gundogs, in kennels behind his cottage. One of his favourites was old Biddy – and she produced a litter of ten pups, when herself at least eight years old. These were too many for her, and rather than destroy the surplus, Mrs Heywood-Lonsdale offered us one to raise on a bottle. So Tiger came home – at about eight days old, a little squeaking thing with eyes still shut, needing feeding every few hours with a fountain-pen filler until he was big and strong enough to suck from a normal baby's bottle. Mother made a padded box (I think it started as a barley sugar box), complete with compartment for a hot water bottle, and exercised him on a sheet of green waterproof oilcloth, across which the widdles ran in rivulets. But Tiger grew fast and became a very big dog indeed.

Getting from Blackpool to Asby during the war, once Father's beloved V8 had gone to serve its country as a staff car, was quite a carry-on. We changed trains at least twice, and sometimes three times. Blackpool to Preston, the main junction on the LMS west coast line. Preston to Blackburn. Blackburn up the valley of the Ribble past Clitheroe to Hellifield. There one waited – sometimes for over an hour. Then a smudge of smoke would appear on the horizon, and the long train, maybe of a dozen carriages and often drawn by two steam locomotives, hove into sight. And then through the central Pennines on England's most spectacular main line railroad – the Settle to Carlisle line, built as a rival to the east and west coast routes in the days when the free market and the railway boom combined to festoon the country with tracks. Many men died in its building, raising viaducts across the dale heads and tunnelling through the fells. Ribblehead, Dentdale, Garsdale and then alongside the upper Eden, with marvellous views over Mallerstang to the great escarpment and gritstone cliffs of High Seat. Kirkby Stephen. Appleby. Out . . .

And then . . . Mother was duly enthroned in Mr Robinson's taxi, with three suitcases, two gun cases, and her bicycle on the roof, and Father and I took to our cycles, the dogs running behind. Down the slope, across the stone bridge into Appleby market place with its tall, white pillar of a market cross, past the old Church of St Lawrence and the Moot Hall, across the grand, tree-lined street of Boroughgate, and so round the Castle and up and down along the hilly road to Asby. It was a switchback road, and the trick was to freewheel the down slopes, pedal furiously as you came near the bottom and attacked the further rise, and be prepared to get off and walk if your three-speed gearbox proved inadequate to the task on the steepest ascent. Five miles of hedges and woods and farms and rough fields full of rabbits and birds, with the long, bubbling calls of the curlews telling you that you were in the enchanted lands again.

The limestone hills had a special atmosphere, and over the years I had some strange moments there. One evening, when I must have been fifteen, I was out with the rifle on the great 'allotment' called Royalty. Turning a corner I saw before me what seemed for a moment to be a village – a row of little huts or shelters of piled stone under a low cliff. It could have been a trick of the light; it could have been a set of miner's shelters (the next 'allotment', Coppermines, was pierced by old and dangerous tunnels), but on that occasion in the twilight it felt strangely haunted and sinister. I did not linger. Legends lie heavy on those hills, which are scattered with burial

The limestone ridge above Great Asby – one of the finest sweeps of bare pavement in Britain, now a National Nature Reserve.

mounds and the ruins of the villages where the Brigantes lived at the time of the Roman occupation. Amidst the greatest area of limestone pavement, on a little knoll, lies the remotest of them all, Castle Folds, maybe used as a place of refuge. The Hollin Stump tumulus is said by some to be the burial place of Llewellyn or Lluel, who gave his name to Carlisle, Caer Lluel, and the name would fit: 'Hollin' for 'Llewellyn' and 'stump' for 'tump' – any mound, including a grave. He is said to ride out at season, as does the strange Man of the Moors who challenges strangers to wrestle, while the fords and crossings have their animal 'boggarts' – white calves or hounds.

'Old men dream dreams, and young men see visions.' I saw another vision of a different kind one winter evening on the Drybeck road. That road runs across a slope of land, patterned with dry-stone walls and with ashes, hollies, birches and straggly hedgerows. It had rained all day, and we had rushed out when the clouds lifted and broke. To our right the slope dropped towards the Eden – a wide vale of treetops with the keep of Appleby Castle catching a gleam of westering sun. Beyond, there was a wall of fells. Bold pointed and humped hills thrust forward before the main escarpment, which lifted to a long plateau. Highest of all, the cap of Crossfell, nearly nine hundred metres high, soared above the plain. Snow streaked the summits. The wind had turned north-westwards, driving the tatters of cloud and letting through that pale, clear, winter's light that seems to come from beyond the edges of the world.

Suddenly I was seized by hill-fever. I mark that as one of the turning points of my life. From then onwards, I seized whatever opportunities there came (and to start with there were not many) to drag my parents up whatever hill was to hand, and after that to start exploring on my own. The path to Gough Island, to the far south of Chile, and to the Antarctic began there, on the Drybeck road, in 1942.

The climbing excursions started very gently – cycling beyond Appleby to the Crossfell Pennines and walking up modest hills like the shapely cone of Murton Pike, less than 600 metres high, but a marvellous viewpoint. Later, when Father was again motorised (with a new 1947 Ford Prefect), I was able to drag my weary parents up higher hills like Wild Boar Fell above Mallerstang (re-named 'consummate bore fell' by the old man, obviously in response to my over-enthusiasm). But they finally rebelled on High Street, when I tried to lead them up the Long Stile in wind and driving cloud. I thought it was exciting. Father thought it was just too much, and led the retreat. After that I had to make my own excursions.

In a way, I had the wrong generation for parents, for Grandpa Holdgate had been a keen mountaineer. As a young man he had gone for many summer seasons to the Alps – mainly in France, but occasionally in Switzerland, around Zermatt. He had taken Father as a young man and they crossed the Breche de la Meije – which cured Father of mountains, but which I, of course, would have loved. Looking at Grandpa's photographs of the Matterhorn from the Rothhorn, or of the Ecrins from the Pic Coolidge, and hearing about scrambles on the Aiguilles d'Arve, I really despaired of Father's lack of vision. Why on earth had he preferred rugger?

It was in Westmorland that I began to learn some natural history. Father was good at birds and skilled at finding their nests (in those days, egg collecting was still commonplace, though I gave up quickly). We had a fascinating book called *Woodcraft*, designed to teach Boy Scouts about tracking and living off the country (somebody should reprint it for, although dated, it is full of keen observation and old lore). We hunted plants, then in profusion before the days of universal herbicides and nitrogenous fertilizers. That limestone country had rich, flower-filled meadows such as you now see only on nature reserves or in countries like Switzerland and Scandinavia – globe flowers and fragrant orchids and vetch and cranesbills rampaging amid the grasses. Sometimes we walked over the limestone ridge to a little lake, Sunbiggin Tarn, set amid heather moorland but with all manner of lime-loving plants in amidst the heath-clumps where the limier substrate cropped out. There were springs with rare sedges, and fens intermingled with acid bogs: Great spearwort and Saw sedge and Marsh potentilla and Water avens and Meadowsweet and campion and scabious. In June the limy ground was pink with the little Mealy primrose – a plant virtually confined to the limestone of northern England. Later I published my first scientific papers on that vegetation.

The countryside of those years has gone. The depression of the 1930s had left the land under-grazed and poorly-drained. 'Rough' pastures dotted with bushes, rushes and miry places were commonplace. Hedges often straggled into trees, including vast, ancient hollies under which you could shelter in a downpour. The flower-rich fields had never felt the plough or received more fertilizer that comes from the backside of a cow. After the war, it all changed. Determined never again to put the country to the risk it had suffered when, with run-down agriculture, it was unable to feed itself, Government poured money into farm support. New fertilizers and new seed mixtures allowed pastures to be re-seeded and boosted so that the old, grey, flower-rich grasslands gave way to bright nitrogen-green, productive monocultures. The roan Shorthorns were superseded by Friesians, and Jack Alderson, back from the war and married to Madge, was another agent of change.

Jack had been in the livestock transport business before the war – with one small truck. Now he saw an opportunity. Horses. Before and during the war all the main farm jobs were done with horses, mostly Clydesdales or stocky Dales ponies. After the war tractors came roaring in. Jack and his business partner, Arthur Huddart of Hadderdale Farm, a couple of miles along the Appleby road, bought up the surplus horses and transported them for conversion to steaks and sausages (this was a meat-hungry time). Before long they ran four or five trucks conveying all manner of livestock and had built a big garage and depot at the end of the village. Then, in the prime of his success, and at an age of little more than fifty, Jack was smitten by a stroke which left him unable to speak beyond the one word 'aye'. Awful, understanding everything but only able to indicate assent.

Appleby was Asby's local metropolis, and we often cycled in for morning coffee and a chat with friends. Roger Garfitt, the vet. Arthur Eggleston the ironmonger and breeder of pedigree pointers (called by Landie Garfitt 'Artie Egg', which suited his round, bald, happy face but struck me as daringly impolite). And Jimmy Whitehead, 'Mr Appleby', owner of the bookshop and stationers, Alderman and several times Mayor. A dapper little man, always welcoming, always full of local news, always interested in wider things. His shop was full of maps, books about the district, table mats, ornaments and pictures and – one reason for our frequent visits – it housed the lending library where parents could get their westerns or whodunits or romances for holiday reading.

Appleby was the smallest County Town in England. In the twelfth and thirteenth centuries it had been an important place, commanding the old Roman road that ran from Carlisle southward over the Pennines into Yorkshire. Six hundred years ago, the town had some three thousand inhabitants, with rights and privileges on an equal footing with those of York. It nestled in a crook of the Eden, which gave it natural defences on three sides. On the fourth the castle, with immense earthworks, blocked the approach. From castle to church ran Boroughgate – the 'town street'. At the top, outside the Castle gatehouse, and at the bottom, outside the Church, stood two tall white-painted pillars: the High Cross and the Low Cross. On the upper was the inscription, probably placed there by the most redoubtable lady of the Castle, Anne Clifford, Countess of Pembroke: 'Retain your Loyalty. Preserve your Rights.' Not a bad injunction for the citizens of today.

Appleby seemed a quiet backwater. What was odd, when you looked into its history, was how many of the scholars of its ancient grammar school had moved away to influence the world. An archbishop, sundry bishops, many Provosts and Fellows of Queen's College Oxford, at least one Lord Mayor of London (Jimmy Whitehead's grandfather), and George Washington's half-brothers. George Washington himself would probably have gone there, had not the family emigrated to the American colonies. William Pitt had been the town MP in the years when it was a 'rotten borough' controlled alternately by two powerful local families, the Tuftons (heirs to the Clifford estates) and the Lowthers (later Earls of Lonsdale).

Jimmy Whitehead got me interested in Appleby's history. Later on, when I was an undergraduate, I told him (probably rather rudely) that I didn't think much of the little book about it that he had helped to write and now sold. 'Write me a better one, then!' came the riposte. Very well. There followed many enjoyable hours in my College library and among my own small collection of books – and I duly delivered a text. My first book – and it stayed in print for forty-five years.

The year 1946 changed my life. Up to that point I had been a very run-of-the mill, unathletic and not particularly clever schoolboy, with most of my enthusiasm outside school. Getting back to Arnold and finding myself well behind others who had been level with me before I had gone to Oundle had been a jar. But suddenly learning began to come right. In 1946 I sat School Certificate (this was well before the days of GCSE and A-level). I remember those exams, partly because Blackpool airport hosted the first post-war Air Pageant and we had aircraft screaming all around during the exam period, which took place in hot weather. A Gloster Meteor, at that time the fastest aircraft in the world, zoomed over at around 600 m.p.h. The choice was between open windows and bedlam or closed windows and stifling heat. But somehow concentration held up, and the results were surprisingly good. That meant a choice of specialization for Higher Certificate. English or biology? Father (as always) had some clear, firm advice:

'If you go in for science, you will get qualifications that are in demand and they'll help with a good job. English specialists are two a penny. You will always enjoy reading and writing – it's important to be well-read – but you can do that for fun. You study science. You'll be far better off.'

I suppose I have been, though I sometimes wonder what would have happened had I gone the other way. But it would have taken a stronger boy than I was to argue.

So, suddenly, I was specializing in zoology, botany and chemistry, with a bit of maths and a little French 'to keep my hand in'. It meant preparing for University – which of course had to be Cambridge, and preferably Trinity. Father and Grandpa had been there; so had Grandma Holdgate's second cousins the Butchers, two of whom had been Fellows and one of whom had been MP for Cambridge.

I think it was then that we had a fire. They had been re-wiring the main school building and, as happens all too often, some electrical connection had been messed up and smouldering turned to flame. It burned through from the kitchens into the upper floors, just next to a dormitory of sleeping boys. It also, fortunately, billowed smoke into the alleyway at the back of the school. Our regular policeman, on his regular beat, saw it and blew his whistle, waking several staff up before running across to a telephone box on the street corner. Suddenly the night was full of bells. Suddenly there was a banging on Father's and Mother's door.

'Mr 'Olgate, Mr 'Olgate, get up quick. Senior School's on fire.'

Everyone was out swiftly, and the fire brigade dealt with it all very fast. But if it had happened today, with no policemen on the beat, would it have been different?

It was certainly around 1947 that we had our most memorable School Prize Day. Arnold had no hall big enough for this annual gathering, so we hired the Palace Variety Theatre on the Promenade, right beside the Tower. We had it just for the afternoon (plus an earlier rehearsal), and you could never be quite sure what kind of act, with attendant props, was going to be in evidence backstage. On this occasion there was an act involving lions – three of them. There they were behind the curtains, in screened cages. The boys, having received their prizes, were expected to exit left, turn backstage and pass the cages to return to their seats. There was some nervousness and hesitation at rehearsal, when the lions started roaring shortly after the first, rather small, prize-winners disappeared behind the scenes. Father rose to the occasion and summoned the Keeper of the Beasts.

'Can you keep those animals of yours quiet?' he demanded.

'Oh, aye. Reckon I can.'

'Right. There's a quid for you at the end of Speech Day, and every time I hear one of those brutes roar I'll knock a bob off.'

The Lion Keeper got his pound (a tidy sum in 1947). And that night the act lacked its normal fierceness. Well fed lions prefer to sleep.

In the spring of 1948 I was taken to Cambridge for an Indoctrination Visit. We stayed with Mother's brother, Nick Bebbington, recently appointed Chief Constable, his wife, universally known as Dilly because she hated her real name, Daphne, and their sons Dru and Bruce. There was no official Chief Constable's house, and they hadn't the money to buy one, so they had been put in a little terraced house in central Cambridge, in Park Street, while something more dignified was built by the Council. At least it allowed the new police chief to see the town from the inside. There were noisy pubs not far away, a theatre close at hand, and a house of doubtful repute a few doors the other way. Nothing seemed to faze Nick and Dilly, who lived in a much more relaxed, bohemian style than my parents did. Their house was full of young people, forever dropping in to chat with them or call on the Dutch art student, Lizzie Noordhof, who lodged there and helped look after my young cousins. I sensed then that Nick and Dilly were going to be a new influence on my life.

But the visit was planned as Serious Business. I still remember Father's reverent tones as we halted before Trinity Great Gate, with its figure of Henry VIII holding a chair-leg for a sceptre.

'That, my boy, is *the* College, of which I hope you will soon be a member.'

I had, after all, been entered at birth (they did that sort of thing then). But the tutor for admissions hummed and ha'ed. 'I think it will be all right,' he said. Father was worried. If not Trinity, then where to guarantee a Cambridge place? He went on with his 'milk round', visiting other admissions tutors. At Queens' he saw Arthur Armitage. 'Have you any good biologists?' he was asked. 'Well, only one, and he's my own son and he's entered for Trinity.' 'Well, if we like him, and Trinity won't have him, we will.' The next day I reported for interview with the Director of Studies in Biology, Dr Arthur Ramsay (a sinister figure at that time, wearing a black eye patch because a bit of grinding wheel had gone the wrong way in the Zoology Department workshops). I was cross-examined in Arthur's high, dry, Scottish voice. Next thing I knew was that I was definitely heading for Queens' not Trinity, but was asked to sit the entrance scholarship that December. Next thing I knew after that was a telegram:

HEARTIEST CONGRATULATIONS ON AWARD SIXTY POUNDS SCHOLARSHIP QUEENS = ARMITAGE TUTOR.

It made Father's Christmas. And Grandpa's too – just six weeks before he died. He wheeled out the fizz and made a speech – proclaiming that I had been valued at £10 a year more than him. And so back for two last terms as Head of School to Father as he had been to Grandpa.

And so to Cambridge and the wider world.

It was a good time to be there. Though the war had been over for five years by the time I arrived, there were still quite a few older men (the University was predominantly a male establishment in 1949) who had been in the war, and many others coming on after National Service, making it a diverse and sophisticated place. Not that I led a very social life. I was rather too shy and unsure for that. I studied and passed the various exams well enough, and even landed the odd prize. I enjoyed visiting Nick and Dilly (and it must have been in that period that I met a very attractive girl called Lizzie, who made me dance in the kitchen). I flirted with Serious Religion in the shape of CICCU – the Cambridge Inter-Collegiate Christian Union – and fell back on the gentler, less strident Anglicanism of the College Chapel. But I was hedged about with science. The problem was – which science to specialize in?

Cambridge was unusual – and, in my view, commendable – for the breadth of its natural science courses. For two years you had to study three main subjects – in my case zoology, botany and human physiology – before concentrating on a single subject for your third year. The choice was difficult. My heart still lay in field ecology, mainly as a pathway to wild country. I had been with the botanists to study vegetation on the Lizard and in the Cairngorms. The Botany School was the scene of exciting new research that used plant pollen trapped in the peat that had accumulated over thousands of years in fens and bogs in order to unravel the history of the flora and the climate. But the atmosphere in the Zoology Department was special. The place hummed with intellectual creativity. Professor Sir James Gray, who headed it, was a world expert on how animals moved and a founding father of modern experimental biology. Around him he had built a team of outstanding researchers. Ten members of the Department were Fellows of the Royal Society. Professor (later Sir) Vincent Wigglesworth was arguably the most distinguished insect physiologist alive. My own supervisor in my second year, Dr Jimmie (now Sir James) Beament, was a world authority on the structure and properties of insect eggshells, a good biophysicist, a clever engineer who made things like electronic organs in his spare time and a musician who composed the incidental music for various amateur dramas. I went where the intellectual excitement was, spent my third undergraduate year in the Zoology Department, and stayed there to do research.

It was at about that time that I joined (or rather, was elected to) the Cambridge University Natural Science Club. This was an after-dinner discussion group in which members read papers to one another about their studies, or about topics that interested them. It thought rather a lot of itself – you didn't get in unless you either had a First or were expected to get one – and candidates had to prove their calibre by reading an original five minute paper (timed to the second by the older members, watches to the fore). It took pride in the high proportion of past members that were elected to the Royal Society. It has gone now – maybe it was too elitist and too old-fashioned for later generations – but it had two features that I still find admirable.

First, it was truly multidisciplinary. Astronomers, chemists, biologists, geologists and all other 'ologists' took a keen interest in one another's subjects – and demanded papers that were exciting but also comprehensible across the topical divides. Second, it was stimulating. Many a time someone from another branch of science would come up with a question, an analogy or a suggestion that altered lines of specialist study. It certainly made me keen to move into research.

But what research? I had burned my ecological boats by opting for Zoology, for that Department was solidly experimental and although there was a short summer course in ecology (which I later helped to teach), it was really no more than a nod in the direction of field science. I compromised by going off to Westmorland, first with a fellow undergraduate, John Haines, and then on my own, to survey the vegetation around Sunbiggin Tarn. The work led to two not very distinguished descriptive papers that duly appeared in the *Journal of Ecology*. Perhaps more importantly, it alerted the youthful Nature Conservancy to this complex of fens, springs and calcareous heaths. It is now a Site of Special Scientific Interest and has all the qualities to make it a National Nature Reserve.

But the Zoology Department in Cambridge was dedicated to experimental zoology, and that meant agreeing a subject with Professor Wigglesworth, my supervisor. I decided to look at what governed how insects were wetted by water. Surprisingly, there had only been a handful of scientific papers on the topic, despite its obvious importance in ecology and pest control. I had to start by building an apparatus (designed by Jimmie Beament) to measure the angle of contact between an insect surface and clean water.

In those days the Departmental tradition was that people made their own apparatus. There were excellent workshops, and having drawn your design and consulted the lecturer in charge of workshops, Dr Ralph Brown, you went in and got to work. One good thing about Oundle was that every form in the school spent one week a term in 'shops', learning metalwork, woodwork and the operations of foundry and forge, so I did know how a lathe, metal planer and drill worked. My apparatus worked, too. Making it was a good discipline – now rendered impossible by the mass of Health and Safety regulations that keep unqualified people out of workshops, sparing them from the remote risks of improbable errors.

Somebody once described research as 'one per cent inspiration and ninety-nine per cent perspiration'. Others seem to think that scientific research proceeds by cold, logical deduction, hypothesis, devising of experiments to test and disprove the hypothesis, and so on until some new construct is proven. It isn't quite like that. The rigorous process of testing is certainly there, but the research scientist also has room for – indeed a need of – intuition and creative ideas. I don't claim to be much of an experimental scientist, but I can illustrate what I mean by something that happened in my first year of research.

Insects have waxy outsides. That's not surprising, if you recognize that an insect is really a small drop of water, wrapped in an armour of jointed plates. It has a lot of surface for a small volume, and is always in danger of drying up. It waterproofs itself with wax. Clean insect surfaces therefore resist wetting by water – their surfaces have more or less the same properties as a block of paraffin wax. But soft wax layers are at risk of scratching, and many insects protect them with a surface layer of hard 'cement' – something my supervisor, Vincent Wigglesworth, had discovered. Now I was looking at how chemical composition, surface roughness, and various other factors determined just how wettable insects are.

I was working with mealworm beetles. This because they are easy to keep in the laboratory. I made a special study of the broad, gently curved, front of the beetle pupa (chrysalis), because it was big and smooth enough for easy study and didn't want to walk around all the time: you could stick it with wax onto a clean glass rod and manipulate it as you wished. It went on developing quite happily in an incubator while you worked on it. And I found that at about eight hours after pupation that broad front end stopped being shiny and became dull and matt in appearance. The contact angle shot up in a way that suggested it had become much rougher. I deduced it was extruding a surface wax layer. But it was too small to see in any microscope we had.

One day early in 1953 I went to have tea with an old Arnold schoolfellow,

Geoffrey Dearnaley, then at Pembroke College and doing research in nuclear physics. With him was another research student, Michael Seal. Michael was studying the surfaces of diamonds, observing them directly, using a modified electron microscope – modified by putting a wedge-shaped collar into the housing, so that the beam hit the diamond surface at an angle and bounced off. This, the invention of his supervisor Jim Menter, was the beginning of the reflection electron microscope that became commonplace a decade or so later and is now universal. I was intrigued. Could we use the reflection electron microscope to look directly at my rough insect surface? No, because the beam would melt the wax. But they had a technique of coating surfaces with silver in a vacuum, and that should preserve its configuration.

We tried it, and it worked. It showed the newly-moulted insect smooth and shiny. It showed it eight hours later covered with filaments of fine extrusion. It showed that if the insect was washed in a wax solvent like chloroform it went back to the smooth, shiny, condition. Finally, we crystallized out the material washed off in the chloroform and used another technique, electron diffraction, to show that the crystal structure corresponded to that of a wax. This was the first time reflection electron microscopy had been used to study an insect surface, or electron diffraction to characterize an insect wax. And it all came about because two people working in quite different disciplines had time to meet and chat over a cup of tea. Lesson – try to ensure that people do have time to meet and chat, and do try to mix up people from different disciplines. Do we still do it in today's cost-conscious world, I wonder?

My three years as a research student in Cambridge taught me that I was not cut out for laboratory experimentation. I am not methodical or patient enough. But I do sometimes wonder what might have happened had I gone on to work with the people in the Physics and Chemistry of Surfaces Unit to look at other animal and plant surfaces. I also got interested in the actual waterproofing of insects – that became the bulk of my doctoral thesis – and toyed with the notion of looking at the role of waterproofing waxes in plants. That could also have been a good area for research. Indeed it could have led into a fascinating academic career.

In October 1953 I was invited for a chat with the Senior Tutor of Queens', Dr Graham McCullagh. He came to the point. 'I am happy to tell you that the Governing Body of the College has decided to elect you as a Research Fellow for three years. Congratulations.'

This was my first paid job (for as a research student I had been on a grant from the Agricultural Research Council). It meant signing up for a pension scheme, which at the age of 22 seemed an investment in an infinitely remote future. It meant moving back into College from digs in the same house as my friend Peter Croghan. It meant a touch of Collegiate formality, beginning with the swearing of a Latin oath in Chapel. It meant getting to know the dons – the senior members of the College, of whom I was now the most junior. It meant delirious delight from Father, who saw me launched on the academic superhighway. The Head Porter, Mr Chessum, clearly thought likewise, hailing me as I went back to my rooms in a Jacobean brick wing of the College where my name was now painted on the wall as *Mr* Holdgate, to show that I was a fellow and not a mere student:

'There, Sir. To think that you may be here for the rest of your life.'

He meant it very kindly. I remembered Wordsworth's lines about 'shades of the prison-house'. I still yearned for the hills and the wild places.

In the spring of 1955 my life was transformed. It happened when Peter Croghan drifted into my room at the Zoology Department and asked:

'Martin, are you interested in going to Gough Island?'

CHAPTER TWO

Unsuspected Isles in Far-off Seas

GOUGH ISLAND is a dependency of St Helena, and an outlier of Tristan da Cunha – all lonely volcanic islands way off in the South Atlantic Ocean. But I had never heard of it, and said so.

'Well,' said Peter, 'you'd better come and meet John Heaney, who's leading the Expedition.'

John Heaney, surveyor and engineer. Robert Chambers, mountaineer and historian. Roger LeMaitre, geologist and mountaineer. Michael Swales, ornithologist and agriculturalist. Nigel Wace, ex-Royal Marine and botanist (and from Oxford, moreover). Philip Mullock, mathematician and radio enthusiast. James Hall, ex-RN, ex-medical student, cine-photographer. Johannes van der Merwe ('call me Van') – South African meteorologist. Martin Holdgate, invertebrate zoologist, part-time botanist. Average age, 25. Nine people who, despite widely different temperaments, were to become friends for life. Between us we seemed to have the 'ologies buttoned up – and John was adamant that this was to be a scientific survey.

For very little was known about Gough Island. It had been discovered as long ago as 1505 by the Portuguese navigator Gonçalo Alvarez, who gave it his name and placed it not far from its true location at 40 degrees south and 10 degrees west. It was 're-discovered' in 1731 by Captain Gough of the British ship *Richmond* (who got its position wildly wrong). That was the time of British ascendancy and the second name stuck. A few passing expeditions, mostly coming back from the Antarctic, had called there and published short descriptions. We knew that the island was about 13 kilometres long and five wide, and rose to about 800 metres, but there were no good maps. We read that although it lay in roughly the equivalent latitude to Lisbon or New York, the southern hemisphere was so much colder that it was classified as Subantarctic and icebergs had occasionally been seen not far away. We knew that it lay in the 'Roaring Forties' – the zone of westerly gales that shrieked their way incessantly around the southern end of the world, making it like one of the circles of Dante's Inferno. We were told that it rained all the time, and that the seas were so rough we probably wouldn't be able to land. And if we did, so the stories went, all the higher ground, though grassy, was so steep and slithery we'd need crampons on our boots to keep a grip.

Why was such a small and apparently inhospitable bit of land worth the

The Gough Islanders in London in 1955. Martin Holdgate, on the right, is using the expedition mascot, Prudence, to illustrate a (probably indelicate) point about penguins. Others (from left) Roger LeMaitre, James Hall (standing), Michael Swales, Philip Mullock, Robert Chambers (standing), Nigel Wace, John Heaney. Photograph: Anglo-American Press.

effort and expense of a scientific expedition? Chiefly because remote oceanic islands are specially interesting places. Almost all of them rise from mid-oceanic ridges – submerged mountain chains where molten magma wells up from within the Earth. Almost all of them are volcanoes. It follows from this location and origin that the islands have never been joined to any continent, and everything that lives there has had to immigrate across a wide expanse of ocean. Land plants and animals are bad at this, so that the islands have relatively meagre floras and faunas – to use modern jargon, they have low biodiversity. Land birds, flying insects, and things like spiders that drift on air currents find it easiest to make the crossing, as do plants like mosses, fungi and ferns with tiny spores or plants with seeds that drift on the wind or hook a lift on birds. Once there, the immigrants are cut off from inter-breeding with mainland relatives and they often evolve into distinct island forms. At the same time, seabirds find such islands secure breeding grounds because predators like cats, dogs, foxes or rats cannot get there.

We knew that parties of sealers had lived on Gough Island for periods of many months during the nineteenth century, but there was no record of any attempt at permanent settlement. While the sealers had brought some weeds with them, and had introduced mice, we had every reason to believe that the island was rat-free and retained a largely undamaged natural flora and fauna. Indeed it was one of only three or four islands in the southern temperate zone to be in a more or less undamaged state. That made it exciting for biologists like Nigel, Michael and me. For geologists like Roger its volcanic structure and history demanded study. For all of us, it was new land to explore and map – and mapping was John Heaney's speciality, since he had been a surveyor on the icy Subantarctic island of South Georgia.

We read avidly in the library of the Scott Polar Research Institute, and decisions followed. We ought to take a hut as a base rather than try to live in tents in all that wind and rain (though we'd need tents for working on the high ground). We'd need to be able to keep plant, bird and insect specimens dry (Roger's rocks could take their chance). We'd need plenty of paraffin for cooking (trusty old Valor oil stoves at Base, and primuses for the camps). We'd need a diesel generator to provide electric power for the radio. We'd need to be able to bake bread (memo – don't forget the yeast). We'd need warm clothing and strong boots. We'd better have mountaineers' anoraks against the cold winds. And very warm sleeping bags . . .

But – there wasn't enough money. We couldn't go out and buy enough gadgets and goodies to ensure comfort whatever the weather and whatever unexpected things turned up. Like most expeditions of the day, we had to scrounge. Scrounge sea passages to Cape Town (only the rich went by air in 1955). Thank you, Union Castle. Scrounge a passage from the Cape to Tristan and Tristan to Gough. Thank you, Royal Navy and Tristan Development (fishing) Company. Scrounge food (thank you, almost everyone – we spent £52 on goods that would have cost £800 in the shops, both figures in 1955 money). Ask for special things to test. Thank you, Huntley and Palmer for some splendid oatmeal block biscuits, and thank you, Ministry of Food experimental station for freeze-dried vegetables, potatoes and meats, then a novelty (and in the case of the meat a tough one at that). Scrounge clothes, and buy what had to be bought as cheaply as possible. Persuade John Dickinson's to make you waterproof notebooks (an excellent design, later used by many expeditions). All the files of this mighty scrounging are carefully preserved in the archives of the Scott Polar Research Institute in Cambridge, which served as our organizational base. We established a model others followed avidly.

We had to raise money by grants and donations. The Scott Polar Research Institute. The Royal Geographical Society (an important accolade, and backed up by the loan of surveying instruments). What about nature films for television (then just starting, with Peter Scott's LOOK series as the leader)? John tried to get David Attenborough (another Cambridge zoologist) to come along, but he was married with a family and would have had to have a salary, which although very modest was beyond our means. James Hall came instead, and we did get an advance for the film that he was to shoot. And even then the money wasn't enough. Come June, deadlines neared and prospects looked doubtful. Nigel had a contact with a friend of the Queen Mother, who said, 'That sounds just the sort of thing Philip would be interested in!' John and Nigel went to see Prince Philip's Treasurer, General Sir Frederick Browning. HRH was interested and gave us a generous donation (even forty-eight years on, I mustn't reveal the amount). It got us there.

Even so, the road to the islands was long and had its upsets. The most serious came when John, undergoing a medical examination in preparation for joining Shell after the expedition, was picked up with tuberculosis. He made good progress, but the doctors would not agree to his going. Robert Chambers took over as leader, with me as senior scientist (we switched leadership twice more in the months that followed). We sailed in two parties to the Cape in September.

I think that we miss a lot today by air travel. Oh, yes, I know that it has made things possible that never were before. You can pack meetings on three or four continents into a fortnight's trip away from business base. But sixteen days from Europe to South Africa in a ship plugging across the trade wind belts and the doldrums, names familiar from old romances of the sea, was vastly more comfortable, without worries over adjustment to changing time zones. And the fact that travel was slow meant that it was not lightly undertaken. Even a North Atlantic crossing of four days would be planned to allow at least a week or so for business on the other side, with a thorough agenda. None of these breathless dashes by Concorde to arrive in New York before you left London (according to the clock) or seven-hour nights further eroded by dinner and movies, returning after a hectic day's discussions.

Our trip to Cape Town was made livelier by an eccentric Captain with endless yarns and a habit of handling an 8000-ton fruit ship like a private yacht. One day he stood close inshore off Cape Verde to show us the local fishermen working the reefs in flimsy craft, bobbing amid the swell. Travel between the Cape and Tristan da Cunha in a Royal Navy frigate, HMS *Magpie*, was very different. The ship – by happy coincidence, formerly commanded by our Royal backer, Prince Philip – was not in her first youth, and was grossly overcrowded with passengers. Besides ourselves there were one Archbishop, two dentists, two expatriate families returning to the island after spells of home leave, and the Port Meteorological Officer for Cape Town, Allan Crawford, who had himself surveyed Tristan with a Norwegian Scientific Expedition in 1937-38 and had been our own adviser and agent in Cape Town. The First Lieutenant was beside himself, for he simply did not have the accommodation, so when it came to us they just handed out hammocks, and gave us a corner of the mess decks to sling them in.

I am glad to have seen how the Navy used to live, for it has all changed now. The mess decks were simply big spaces extending from one side of the ship to the other, walled off fore and aft by bulkheads. Pipes and electric trunking wriggled across what passed for a ceiling. There were hooks from which hammocks dangled by night, swaying to the motion of the ship. Every morning the Petty Officers burst in with the traditional call: 'Wakey, wakey, wakey. 'Eave-oh, 'eave-oh, 'eave oh. Rise and shine, rise and shine, Lash and stow, lash and stow!' Down came the hammocks, clearing the way for the sixty-odd men in each mess-deck to sit, chat and eat in groups of ten or so on plastic-padded benches around plastic-topped tables. We often went on deck (sometimes of urgent necessity, for we hit quite a westerly swell, and the ship, despite stabilisers, allegedly fitted in HRH's time for the comfort of his Royal wife, had a queasy motion). Our diary records laconically at one point: 'Martin left too late . . .'

From the Cape to Tristan is about 2700 kilometres. It took about a week in *Magpie*, but can easily take twice that time in the smaller, slower, fishing ships that work Tristan waters. A week watching the great Wandering albatrosses soaring around the ship, circuit after circuit, fast upwind along the port side, rising across the bows, swiftly downwind along the starboard side, a sweep across the stern and so round again – unless, of course, the cook's mate threw buckets of tasty kitchen scraps over the stern, when the graceful gliders dropped to the water to scrabble over the goodies like ungainly, outsize, farmyard ducks. A week in which Michael made us familiar with the other sea-birds of the Southern Ocean – the Sooty albatrosses and the mollymawks, smaller and more graceful than their Wandering cousins, the bulky Giant petrels, the dapper black and white Cape pigeons, the various other petrels and shearwaters.

Robert, meanwhile, ordained a stranger form of exercise. 'We ought to practise some rope-work,' he said. So a climbing rope was dropped from the upper forward gun turret to the deck – a drop, I suppose, of about three metres. Prussic loops were attached. This permits motion not unlike that of a sloth through a rain-forest canopy: feet and hands in different loops; one foot raised and its loop slipped vertically up the rope; weight transferred; other foot upwards; hand grips eased upwards and so forth. Simple, effective, and slow – but it could have been useful had we had to drop a rope over a small overhang when fixing a route up the broken terrain of Gough. We never had to. It was fun while it lasted, especially as the ship was never still. I don't know what the First Lieutenant thought. He was probably past caring about the antics of his passengers.

And then – a blob on the radar changed into a pale grey pyramid against the cloudy western sky. The island of Tristão da Cunha, discovered in 1506 by the commander of a Portuguese fleet taking the sea road to the East Indies. It loomed up as a tall, shapely volcanic cone, rising just over 2000 metres from the sea. Snow streaked the upper gullies. As the slopes fell from the Peak, they became more gradual, flattening into a girdling plateau called The Base, from which cliffs dropped steeply. As we drew nearer, we saw that there was a green shelf of land at the foot of the cliffs, and on it lay the cluster of cottages that made up the Settlement of Edinburgh, sole inhabited place on the island. To the left, at the foot of sheer cliffs and fronting on a beach of black basaltic sand, stood a white building – a crayfish canning factory.

As *Magpie* slowed, we saw longboats rocking gently on the smooth swell. They were white-painted, and although they had strong wooden frames the outer coverings were of canvas. In these islands, driftwood is the only shipbuilding timber, and light boats are anyway best for beach landings. We scrambled down swaying ladders, trying to step neatly into the longboat as it rose on the swell, and were soon heading for the shore. In through the fringe of giant, trailing kelp, red fronds dimpling the translucent water and smoothing the choppy sea. A pause in the shallows as the swells gathered and lifted the boats, to roll by and break foaming on the black sand. Debate among the crew, the co-partnership of boat owners. 'Foine smooth toime now, Johnny?' 'No, wait a bit, swelly toime coming.' 'Now!'

There was a heave of oars, to run the boat in on a small wave, the grate of the keel and a leaping of barefoot men into the foam to heave the boat clear of the following wave. We had arrived on Big Beach, largest of the landing places, just beside the crayfish cannery. Now for Gough.

We waited a month. The fishing ship *Tristania*, which was to carry us on the final leg, was delayed with engine trouble. But we had a splendid time on Tristan. While the Navy was there, all manner of jollifications took over. Sports (I won a donkey race for the only time ever). Dance. Parade. Church service. Getting to know the islanders – helped immensely by Allan Crawford, who knew everybody. We lived in 'the station' – the war-time naval hutments – and visited around. Allan stayed with Martha Rogers, daughter of the legendary Tristan matriarch, Frances Repetto, and her husband, Arthur, who later came down to Gough with us. We went to visit them, in their whitewashed cottage under its thatched roof. The little front garden was bright with marigolds.

'Come you all in,' said Martha. 'We's werry glad to see you all.'

We got to know many other families in the scatter of cottages separated by green swards, across which the little streams or 'watrons' meandered, serving for water supply and drainage. We made excursions, to collect peat samples from a wet expanse, aptly named Soggy Plain, halfway up the mountain, to sample insect life and study birds and to climb the Peak (frustratingly enveloped in cloud just as we reached the highest point). Roger and Robert got embarrassingly cragfast in full view of the village while exploring the rock structure of a rather unstable cliff: night caught them short of the way off, and we had to lower ropes from above. Nigel and I wrote an account of the zones of vegetation on the mountain – the first scientific publication from the expedition.

Tristan is the largest of a group of three islands, arranged in a roughly equilateral triangle forty kilometres on the side. The others? Inaccessible, just a quarter of a once larger volcano, named from its girdle of sheer cliffs, and Nightingale, a little green humpy mass named after an English sea-captain, Captain Gamaliel of that ilk. Gough lies some 350 kilometres away to the south-south-east. All three northern islands are rich enough in their original wildlife to be very interesting to the visiting scientist, but they also show the devastation that people can so easily cause in such places.

People have been coming to the islands for over three hundred years. We do not know whether the Portuguese discoverers ever landed, but the Dutch East India Company investigated their natural resources in 1643, finding 'Sea Lions as large as oxen, and abundance of Birds'. Sealers – mostly Americans – were there from the 1790s onwards, taking thousands of Fur seal skins from the Tristan islands and Gough. They also brought potatoes (which still grow wild in a few places) and inadvertently introduced the mice that still abound on Gough. Pigs and goats were introduced to Tristan, where they ran wild. But permanent settlement did not start until 1811.

It began when an American whaler, Jonathan Lambert of Salem, Massachusetts, took up residence on the site of the present Tristan Settlement with two companions. His plan was to provide passing ships with fresh water and fresh food. It was not as wild an idea as it sounds, for those were the days when sailing vessels bound from Europe to the Cape or the East Indies steered across the south-east trade winds to near the coast of Brazil, where they hoped to pick up the westerlies and run back cross-ocean to the Cape. Tristan lay near their path (that was how the Portuguese navigators came to discover it) and Lambert doubtless hoped that some

*On Tristan da Cunha, 1955. A typical island house can be seen in the distance:
the 1961 volcanic eruption burst through the slopes just to the left of the picture.
Photograph: Gough Island Scientific Survey (GISS).*

ships would choose to get their victuals from him and miss the Cape
altogether.

He was a man of big ideas. He constituted his little group into a kind of
commonwealth, with a co-partnership agreement. He announced that they
had taken possession of the islands 'on the sure and rational ground of
absolute occupancy'. He designed a flag. He renamed the islands 'the Isles of
Refreshment, with the Settlement of Reception, on the north west side by
the cascade'(where it still stands) 'as our chief seat'. And to start with they
lived pretty well, carving out cultivation plots in which they grew potatoes,
cabbages, maize, radishes and pumpkins, and raising pigs and poultry. No
doubt they also hunted the wild pigs and goats released by earlier visitors.

We can deduce from early accounts and from what is left today what
Tristan must have been like when Lambert arrived. Low down by the sea
there were areas of giant grass tussock among which Elephant seals – indeed
'as big as oxen' for the big bulls can be 5 metres long and weigh almost four
thousand kilogrammes – bred in early spring, and wallowed in moulting
time in the summer. Yellow-crested Rockhopper penguins also nested
among the tussock, and there were probably some remnant colonies of dark,
agile, Fur seals among the rocks and grassland at the southern end of the

island. In more sheltered parts of the lowland plains and on the girdling cliffs, there was scrubby woodland made up of the only tree that has succeeded in colonising the three northern islands, a low-growing bush related to the buckthorn and called by scientists *Phylica arborea*. Its mainland home is in the Cape. Among the trees and on the slopes of the Base above tree line there was a dense growth of tree ferns (*Blechnum palmiforme* to botanists), looking for all the world like a pineapple plantation. They intermingled with heathy and peaty ground, covered in mosses, grasses, sedges and a red-berried crowberry (*Empetrum rubrum*). Higher up, tussocky heath and grassland merged into an alpine zone where patches of open stony ground alternated with moss mats and lichen covered rocks.

At least fifteen kinds of sea birds, including three kinds of albatross, nested on the island. Large numbers of Wandering albatrosses and Yellow-nosed albatrosses (mollymawks) built their mound-nests of earth on the mountain heaths and among the tree ferns (and the mollymawks also bred in the woodland zone), while Sooty albatrosses nested on the cliffs. And there were three kinds of land bird unique to the island – a small, black, flightless moorhen looking very like the European species, a speckled 'hermit thrush' or 'starchy' (*Nesocichla eremita*) and an 'island canary' (*Nesospiza acunhae*). There must also have been lots of insects and spiders, but there are few records of these from early days.

Like most island communities, Lambert and his companions preyed on the wildlife around them. While they were struggling to get established, they fed themselves and their pigs on the meat of the Elephant seal. Even when the pigs had plenty of plant food, Lambert 'gave them an elephant every now and then, to keep them in heart'. And the group enjoyed eating the flightless moorhen which they found 'very fat and delicate in the Fall'. The bird is now extinct.

The little colony collapsed within two years. Lambert and one companion were lost at sea in 1813 leaving Tomaso Corri as the sole survivor. He has come down in legend as an old man who told vague stories of treasure buried under the sea cliffs, and who got more tangible income from rendering down the blubber of Elephant seals at 'Tommy's oil-house' – a name corrupted in Tristan vernacular as 'Tommy's eyeloose'.

The second occupation came in 1816, when the British garrisoned Tristan, some say to stop it being used as a base for the rescue of Napoleon from St Helena, 2000 kilometres away, but more likely to deny it to privateers. In 1817 Higher Authority took the troops away again. Corporal William Glass, from southern Scotland, and his Cape wife, Mary Magdalena Leenders, stayed behind with two other men, six horses, four cattle, fifteen sheep, about forty pigs and some ducks and turkeys! They built cottages that look unsurprisingly like Scottish crofts, using a volcanic ashstone that is soft enough to be shaped by scraping with an axe, but hard enough to resist wind and weather. One of the first sketches, made by Augustus Earle who was stranded there in 1824 but went on to become artist in HMS *Beagle* and Darwin's shipmate a decade later, shows 'Governor' Glass, pipe in mouth, leaning on his garden fence outside a long, low, thatched house with a red ensign streaming in the wind.

From that beginning came the people of Tristan. The founder population, apart from members of the garrison, included shipwrecked or deserting seamen, and the first crisis arose in 1827 because five of the fourteen men on the island lacked wives. Their saviour was a Cornishman, Captain Simon Amm of the sloop *Duke of Gloucester*, plying between Rio de Janeiro, St Helena, Tristan and the Cape. He agreed that he would try to get partners for them at St Helena. He consulted His Excellency the Governor and posted a notice asking for 'sound and healthy volunteers . . . to proceed to the Island of Tristan d'Acunha as servants'. He got them (did he explain what 'servant' meant?). As he neared Tristan, he appears to have suffered pangs of doubt. Anyway, instead of waiting for a hero's welcome, he landed his human cargo one cool dawn when nobody was up, fired a signal gun, and sailed away. It is reported that Tom Swain, an English seaman who had served in Nelson's *Theseus*, vowed to marry the first woman ashore and stood by his promise. The others found some other way of deciding who got who. All are said to have lived happily ever after. So, one hopes, did Captain Amm, whose descendants still live in Cornwall. I am godfather to one of them.

As the decades went by the little Tristan colony grew, and at first it did well. Cattle flourished, and there was plenty of milk and butter. Trade was good, especially in the 1830s when peace brought many American whalers to the South Atlantic, and Tristan became a favoured victualling point. The main thing the people felt they lacked was a teacher and clergyman, and this need was met in 1851, when the Reverend W. F. Taylor arrived, to be succeeded in 1881 by the Reverend Edwin H. Dodgson, brother of 'Lewis Carroll'. Sometimes I have wondered whether letters from Tristan played a part in the moulding of that masterpiece of expedition narrative, 'The Hunting of the Snark'. For in one of the early verses there is a splendidly accurate description of arrival at Tristan:

> But the danger was past – they had landed at last
> With their boxes, portmanteaux and bags:
> Yet at first sight the crew were not pleased with the view,
> Which consisted of chasms and crags.

Some Lewis Carroll scholar should investigate whether any letters from Edwin to Charles Dodgson survive, and whether they throw light on the origins of the 'Hunting'.

The new colony had its problems. Tristan, though green and fertile and surrounded by waters rich in fish and crayfish (a kind of lobster without the massive front claws) is also exposed to violent weather. Between 1821 and 1877 there were nine shipwrecks in the three Tristan islands, and Queen Victoria signed a letter of appreciation for the help given by the community to over 200 survivors. As the numbers grew, the livestock began to graze out the pastures and their productivity declined. In 1857, Mr Taylor persuaded forty-five people – more than half the population – to resettle in the Cape (some came back in 1902, two of them bringing young Irish brides – the last infusion of legitimate new blood for decades). Mr Dodgson took ten more with him when he left, forecasting the evils of in-breeding in so small a community. His strictures upset Peter Green (a Dutch seaman, formerly Pieter Willem Groen, by then the most prominent resident and spokesman for the islanders). 'Mr Dodgson say we are going to form a new link between man and animal. So for us the motto is "eat, drink and be merry for tomorrow we shall be apes",' he wrote bitterly. And in 1886 there was a real disaster when fourteen men – almost all the able-bodied boatmen, all married – were lost after putting out in a new longboat to a ship that never stopped.

Things went from bad to worse. As the nineteenth century wore to its close, fewer sailing vessels took the old route to the Indies. Steamships made direct voyages that passed nowhere near Tristan. In the early years of the twentieth century the standard of living declined and trade with ships became little more than begging. But the community hung on, staunchly self-reliant, devout and united. The seven surnames that remain today – Glass, Green, Hagan, Swain, Rogers, Repetto and Lavarello – were established, while other families like the Cottons died out. Men (or women) of strong personality became accepted 'headmen' or 'headwomen' even though all the islanders were regarded as equals and there was no formal structure of government. Between 1920 and 1943 Frances Repetto, widow of Andrea, a shipwrecked Italian, was dominant in the community although her bachelor son, Willy, was nominal 'Chief'.

We get many snapshot pictures of Tristan from the narratives of visiting warships and scientific expeditions. HMS *Galathea*, commanded by Queen Victoria's second son, Prince Alfred, Duke of Edinburgh, called in 1867 – and that is why Tristan Settlement is named Edinburgh. The *Challenger* oceanographic expedition visited in 1873, the Scottish National Antarctic Expedition in 1904, and the Shackleton-Rowett Expedition in the *Quest*, after Shackleton's death in 1922. But the first full account by a sociologist was provided by a Norwegian, Peter Munch, who was a member of the Norwegian Scientific Expedition to Tristan da Cunha in 1937-38 (Allan Crawford was their surveyor). The Norwegians were originally bound for Gough, but their shipping arrangements went wrong, leaving them to spend five valuable months in the three northern islands of Tristan, Inaccessible and Nightingale.

Peter Munch described a community with strong family ties and generous loyalty. All heads of family were equal, and none ruled the others, but property was not in common and the hard workers and those with many cattle were respected more than the slovenly, idle or poor. Life was based on fishing, growing potatoes, and raising livestock. Sheep and cattle ran on the plain near the settlement, and there were donkeys and pigs. The donkeys were ridden and used to carry burdens, while bullocks drew small carts made of stout driftwood timbers. No attempt was made to regulate the number of grazing stock, even though in winter the grass was eaten smooth as a billiard table and beasts starved. From cattle came milk, meat and hides: cow's hide moccasins served for shoes. Mutton was the luxury meat and 'big 'eaps' – a feast of roast mutton with potatoes roasted in the oil they extracted from young Greater shearwaters – was the great way of celebrating a 'barthday'. Wool was washed, carded and spun and knitted into long white stockings and 'garnsays'. Coloured wool was rare, being obtained only by barter or charity, so that coloured rings were used sparingly to adorn the tops of socks – a couple or so for the everyday wear of husband or children, but up to four broad ones for a sweetheart!

The Tristan Islanders (they call themselves 'Islanders' by the way: 'Tristans' is an English Press invention) also depended on barter or charity for clothing such as jackets and trousers. The main goods for trade were models of the island longboats and 'tossel mats' bearing rosettes of the head-plumes of Rockhopper penguins. Driftwood was essential for boat frames, house timbers and furniture, though the straggly, crooked island tree could be used for fuelwood. Almost every book on Tristan records the maiden's prayer: 'Please, God send us a good shipwreck so's Johnny and me can build a house and get married.'

As human numbers grew, the Islanders had an increasing impact on Tristan's wildlife. The Wandering albatross was exterminated from the Peak in the nineteenth century, along with the flightless moorhen. Sooty and Yellow-nosed albatross were greatly reduced in number. The Rockhopper penguin colonies were cut to small remnants. Although wild pigs and wild goats were destroyed, rats (from a ship, wrecked in the 1880s) and cats caused further devastation amongst the bird life, and it may have been they that finished off the flightless moorhen. Elephant and Fur seals were also eliminated. The main sources of eggs and birds were the two smaller islands – Inaccessible Island, forty kilometres to the south-west, and especially Nightingale Island, a similar distance to the south. Longboats would take parties over in fine weather, to camp on Nightingale and collect penguin eggs and the young of the Greater shearwater, which breeds there in immense numbers. The fat, rendered down, was the staple cooking oil. It has a strong, musky, flavour and is an acquired taste.

The 1939-45 war heralded major changes to this simple way of life. A Naval Garrison was established, with a weather station which Allan Crawford ran for several years. And after the war came commerce – to exploit the crayfish which teemed in shallow waters around the three Tristan islands and Gough, recognized as a part of the Tristan group. At the time we arrived in 1955 there were two fishing ships – *Tristania*, a steel-built vessel of some 650 tons and *Frances Repetto*, a wooden ex-motor minesweeper of 350 tons. The fishing company also employed islanders to work from the Settlement, bringing their catches to the cannery, and paid fees to the Island Administration. This meant money to buy imported goods, a store, and even luxuries like radios.

Tristan social life at that time centred on occasional dances, house to house visiting and rare excursions by the young people to Sandy Point in the east of the island, to gather apples (and get away from their elders). Major trips to the smaller islands for 'h'eggs and buds' were in the nature of island holidays. Tristan dances were formality writ large (at least, on the surface). The 'band' was a gramophone, occasionally relieved by two men with accordions. The dance floor was the village hall (another relic of the Navy: the big Prince Philip Hall was not put up until several years later). The drinks were monotonously soft (the bar came with Prince Philip Hall). At the outset, sexes were strictly segregated, men on one side and women on the other. The music provided a signal for a kind of dive to grab chosen partners. Sometimes the choice was more individual and public, as in the pillow dance when a cushion passed from person to person as each holder laid it at the feet of his or her chosen one and they knelt to kiss on it before taking a few turns on the floor. There was a handkerchief dance, with some movements reminiscent of the Chilean *cueca*. There was 'Black Tom' – a two-man jig in which one participant, full of mock rage, hopped after his partner who retreated in mock horror. We were told that they used to dance it with knives in their teeth.

We had been asked to record songs. There was an epidemic of shyness. 'Oi don't know no songs,' said someone. We persuaded on, and came home with several tapes. 'Shoo fly, don't borrer me.' 'Ah's goin to be a sportin' boy upon the Orgadie.' 'Polly Perkins.' And a gruesome refrain about 'when the blood runs streaming, streams and streams at Bunker's Hill.' A collection of seamen's, whaler's, European and North American ditties, half remembered over the decades and translated into the distinctive Tristan dialect with its odd tenses ('I done dig my patch'; 'When you done went down Gough'), its aspirated 'a'('hashmere' for asthma, an inherited scourge despite the pure air), 'w' for 'v' so that Violet became 'Wi'let', and so forth.

Above all, the sincerity, the piety, the gentleness, the community spirit, the hospitality and the sheer warmth that glowed through every imperfection and atoned for the depleted grazings, the wasted resources, the unwillingness to try new things, the unconcern over time, and all the lesser matters on which outsiders were apt to seize. I am glad to have known Tristan before it was convulsed by volcanic and social upheavals. It was a very special place.

On 13 November 1955 we landed on Gough Island. The passage from Tristan took twenty-four hours, and we sighted the island at dawn. It was as unlike Tristan as could be. It towered up in serrated cliffs, mantled in greenery. There were spires and pinnacles of rock, and dykes of grey stone standing like ruined walls out of the forested slopes. Above, mountain peaks lifted tawny and black masses to lowering clouds. And – again unlike Tristan – it ran with water. Plumes dropped down the ravines, and waterfalls leaped from the valley mouths to the beaches below. 'I'm so glad it's not just a smaller Tristan,' said Robert. 'This is going to be *fun!*'

It wasn't, as far as he was concerned.

Tristania came to anchor off the main valley on the east side – The Glen, so named by William Speirs Bruce of the Scottish National Antarctic Expedition in 1904. There was a good, calm, lee although vestiges of swell ran towards the stony beach we knew to be the best landing, partly sheltered by a conspicuous Archway Rock. Boats were heaved out – thirteen foot clinker-built dinghies used by the fishermen. We went to investigate, with Arthur Rogers and John Lavarello, our two Tristan Islanders, as the experts in charge. It seemed surprisingly easy. The biggest waves were only around a metre high, crashing among the rounded stones in harmless foam. We leapt ashore and the stores – all packed in wooden crates we had deliberately kept light to make handling easy – flowed after us. Robert heaved energetically at the painter of a dinghy to run it up the beach – and collapsed with acute back pains. Three days later he was evacuated, trussed up in a spinal splint. 'Buried at sea, was he?' asked someone to whom I showed the photograph afterwards. A miserable start.

Two leaders down and we hadn't even begun our serious work. I found myself in nominal command, and facing a severe problem: the Expedition

Landing on Gough Island from Tristania, *13 November 1955. Robert Chambers lifts the bow of the white dinghy while Martin Holdgate pulls on the painter. Michael Swales holds the painter of the boat on the right. Photograph: GISS.*

now lacked a qualified surveyor, able to record those valleys and pinnacles and surprising complexities of terrain we had glimpsed as we arrived.

But the first thing was to get established. The sectional wooden hut – braced with stout wire ropes against the fierce gusts that pounded down The Glen – went up quickly. Philip soon got the diesel generator and radio system up and running. The stores were sorted into heaps of this and that (thank goodness for the trouble taken in colour-coding and numbering back home). Water was piped through a hose from a pool up a side-rivulet that cascaded down peaty and bird-burrowed slopes (analysis, after we left, suggested that it was quite unfit for human consumption – but there were no human bugs on Gough)!

The fauna was all around us as we worked. We had to evict a few wallowing Elephant seals from hollows by the hut – pits left from a bizarre and fruitless diamond-prospecting venture of the 1930s. They were young beasts, only two or three metres long, and although they gaped, roared and lunged at us, in between threats they backed off and soon slithered into the stream and away. Rockhopper penguins with bobbing yellow head-tassels hopped to and fro between the sea and their breeding colony a couple of hundred yards upstream. Every now and then we heard the 'chack-chack'

Gough Island. The Expedition Hut and Archway Rock are visible left of centre, in the mouth of the steep-sided Glen. Photograph: GISS.

call of the Gough Island moorhen, a flightless bird very similar to the extinct Tristan species, and glimpsed one or two as they scurried among the clumps of tussock grass. The other special island bird – a greenish yellow finch with puzzlingly diverse plumage patterns – fluttered around. Yellow-nosed mollymawks, on their earthen nest mounds, dotted the ferny and scrub-covered slopes that towered steeply and craggily from the valley floor. Brown skuas, almost identical to the bonxies of Shetland, held their territories up the valley, screaming defiance at intruders and swooping by your head if you came too close. And at night the whole place cooed with birds – the calls of petrels, guiding their mates to the nest burrow. When we turned on the film-maker's floodlights in the evening, to speed up work on the hut, disorientated birds crashed into us, the hut walls and the illumination.

The hut stood between the mountains and the sea. The main stream poured down The Glen, leaping over falls and seething among stones, to reach the shore by the Archway Rock. The Archway flung out a protective arm across the stream-mouth, part of whose waters ran to the sea through its piercing tunnel. Fierce little Antarctic Swallow-tailed terns nested among clumps of tussock grass on the Archway's flanks. Beside it lay the landing beach, its rounded pebbles grading into boulders and reefs as you passed westward under mounting cliffs to where a pinnacled sea-stack – Dell Rocks, named after Shackleton's boatswain – marked the limits of the view. A big, shallow cave, really no more than a dry but windy overhang, gave shelter to Michael, with his work-bench and nails on which to hang bird skins, and served all of us as an open-air kitchen during the first days before the hut was operational

All these surroundings were known ground, familiar from photographs and explorers' narratives. We wanted to get into new country. That meant heaving and hacking our way up The Glen, sometimes following the stream, hopping over boulders and circumventing waterfalls, and sometimes scrambling up steep places and thrusting through tangled thickets of the 'island tree'. A kilometre or so inland, after the stream had divided twice and become a shrunken remnant, we hacked a steep way up the valley sides, dipping among the ravines until, eventually, we emerged from the ferny bush to the zone of stumpy tree-ferns.

The Hag's Tooth dominates The Glen. It is a plug of hard rock filling one of the extinct volcanic vents. It towers up like a ruined castle (or a broken tooth stump), apparently inaccessible until you work your way round it to find smooth slabs of rock slanting upwards in an easy staircase. Behind it, the land rises steeply, in short grassland over slippery shallow peat, to the wall of banded lava that bars the valley head and rises to the triple peaks of Mount Rowett, named for Shackleton's school friend and patron. We turned the northern corner of the Rowett ridge and were truly on new ground. A vast soggy plateau, red with *Sphagnum* moss and dotted with pools, stretched either side of a narrow, wind-scoured ridge that ran for a mile to the base of a higher hill which was evidently a young volcanic cone. It proved to be the top of the island, just over 900 metres high, and we named it Edinburgh Peak after our Royal supporter.

And beyond that? Great domes of almost bare trachyte lava, rising to the second summit only a little lower than Edinburgh Peak. We named it Expedition Peak, although many years later, at Nigel's instigation, the Governor of St Helena approved a change to Gonçalo Alvarez Peak, so restoring the name of the island's discoverer to the maps of the world. That peak overlooked further soggy plateaux, dotted with white specks that were adult or chick Wandering albatrosses at their nests. From the central highlands, ribs of hill jutted out to divide a series of six valleys, each about a kilometre and a half long, radiating to the northern and eastern coasts. All deep, rough, tangled places which we had not thoroughly explored even after six months (some, so far as I know, have still not been walked through, although they are unlikely to hide any lost and mysterious beasts).

The first, brief, sally onto the high ground brought home to us how much varied and beautiful scenery Gough Island packs into its tiny area of sixty-five square kilometres. It sprouts all manner of bizarre rock forms – pinnacles and walls and domes and teeth. There are three 'Hag's Teeth', though neither of the others rivals the massive, towering, canine in The Glen. There are deep green valleys, down which streams pour in tumultuous cascades. There are shadowy, secret gorges in dark contrast to the wide plateaux open to the sky and the soaring albatrosses. There are bare rock domes, maybe kept plant-free by their chemistry. And all around, towering cliffs drop to boulder beaches fretted with roaring surf, where the great swells driven by the westerly winds of the 'Roaring Forties' burst violently on the land.

Such terrain needed mapping. Philip and I, with help from James and a last-minute briefing from a horizontal Robert, got the theodelites out and worked out how to use them. We set up two tented camps on the high ground – one close under Expedition Peak, giving access to the northern summits and ridges, and one in a wide, wet, albatross-filled valley dipping to the gentler, wooded, southern slopes. We named it 'Gonydale' from the old sailor's name for a Wandering albatross – a 'goony' bird because it lets you walk up to it and wring its neck (goons should beware of sailors). But our inexperience was very evident. Fortunately, early in 1956, we had a telegram:

DOCTORS APPROVE HEANEY GOUGHWARDS FEBRUARY ACTION PENDING POSSIBLY FLY...

John, fully recovered and newly married, arrived in mid-month. He brought Harold Green and Ernest Repetto with him, Arthur Rogers and John Lavarello having gone home at Christmas. John took over the survey – and showed what a trained and experienced person, gifted with a great deal of determination, could do. From top to top, he marked the angles between the peaks. We measured a baseline on the long and fairly level crest of the youngest of the island's lava flows. We mapped the detail in the valleys using on the spot measurement of distances by rangefinder, angular differences by clinometer, conversion to map distances and height differences by slide rule, and direct plotting of form lines (we did not dare to call them contours) on a plane table. The coasts were mapped using the dinghy to gain access to headlands and islets. It all worked amazingly well and we were delighted when, a few years later, a long-range RAF reconnaissance aircraft took vertical photographs that confirmed our work. Allan Crawford was also happy: his map of Tristan got a good mark, too.

Mapping the interior, and studying the birds, plants and insects of the uplands, was done from the tented camps. Here we were at very close quarters with the only significant introduced animals on Gough – mice. Vast numbers of mice. Originally House mice, no doubt transported by sealers in the eighteenth or nineteenth centuries. They were (and still are) everywhere. We don't know what they have done to the ecology, but they eat seeds and insects so must have upset it in many subtle ways that nobody has yet worked out (a problem that I dismissed far too lightly forty-eight years ago). They were very happy to abandon their wild ways for richer pickings when we set up camps in their homeland. They would nibble their way around the tents at night, gathering crumbs. They would nibble your hair as you lay in your sleeping bag (no doubt it was pretty tasty, for we had only primitive bathing facilities). They would even queue up to die by mousetrap, if you set one between your feet and sat quietly near the tent door. They were all around the main hut in The Glen too, but our relationship was less intimate there. Even so, they were a nuisance. James made an ingenious water trap and caught three hundred in a couple of weeks (it was this material that allowed a specialist at the Natural History Museum to demonstrate that the Gough animals were both larger and darker than mainland House mice). The catch also led to an informal experiment: how many dead mice could a skua swallow?

The skuas were easy to attract to the base hut for they are scavengers as well as predators (they kill many small birds, leaving the wings, joined by the breastbone, as tokens). One bold bird stood by as James lobbed the first mouse over. Gulp. A slight flicker of the eyes. Next mouse, next, next . . . I think it was at about the seventh that the process slowed. The tail of the eighth slid slowly out of sight. 'Letting the mouse's tail go down' has become a saying in our family, when pausing, replete, at table.

We had some rough weather on Gough, though generally the summer was warmer, sunnier and easier to work in than we had ever expected. Certainly the person who suggested crampons for grip on the steep grass slopes was talking nonsense. We had lots of rain, but no snow (that starts around April but does not lie until June, and then only on the uplands). But we were buffeted by wind and rain. Philip was washed over a waterfall when he and I were descending The Glen after heavy rain; fortunately our short length of rope and handhold on a nearby tree were good enough safeguards. At Gonydale, a 3-man bell tent (ex RAF, ex Scott Polar) collapsed on us, leaving a choice of getting soaked by rain from without or equally soaked through putting our sleeping bags in polythene covers that retained the sweat. At the High Camp in the north we lost our best lightweight theodolite when a stores tent blew violently from its moorings (I read, much too late, that a good field surveyor uses his theodolite as a pillow). But our specially made tents stood everything and could even be left unattended for days at a time. Someone once wrote: 'I think that a shipwrecked sailor could live on this island in reasonable comfort.' I agree – you could find shelter in coastal caves, there is plenty of food if you don't mind birds or seals and have the means to cut them up, and plenty of wild celery that is a pleasant, though stringy, nibble and would be good against scurvy. There is plenty of driftwood, and some of that cast up in a cave or overhang will be dry enough to kindle fire.

We did sample native food occasionally. Fish were easy to catch if you rowed the dinghy out into the kelp, and we borrowed a crayfish net from the ships and baited it with fish, pulling up a good haul of succulent crustaceans in exchange. When Michael took a Fur seal or two as scientific specimens, we dissected out the shoulder muscles to find that they made excellent steaks – and the liver was also very good, if fried with reconstituted dried onion and then simmered in water to make a rich gravy. One night we had a disaster when some petrels put in a crate to await banding suffocated before we could attend to them – so the skins went to the Museum and the meat went into the pot. Not so good. We had pot-roast young Wandering albatross for an excellent Christmas dinner, but deterred the Tristan Islanders from taking any more. And we did try penguin casserole – which is excellent if you strip off the breast muscles, blanche in boiling water to extract the oil, and simmer very slowly with onions and beer. We wrote to the editors of the *Penguin Cookery Book*, which was our constant handbook, criticising them for failing to tell you how to cook penguins. They were not amused.

But even if the island is relatively kindly to the shipwrecked, it has claimed its victims. Sealers lived rough in past years, dropped by their ships in parties of half a dozen or so to kill what they could, scrape the blubber from the pelts, and store them for collection when the ship came back – if it did. One favoured haunt was a great, square-cut, cave at the north end of the island, known as the 'Baker's Oven' because it looks like one. They got very dirty, and no doubt smelly – as a fastidious Naval Lieutenant said when he came upon a gang in 1811: 'all in a most ragged plight, full of grease and filth and clothed chiefly in seal skins.' And in 1869 one man, José Gomez, 'perished in the snow' crossing the island. There is an oval mound by the side of the ridge (Michael's Ridge) that makes the obvious path from The Glen to Gonydale, and it may be his grave. More recently, after we left, no fewer than three young, fit, South African meteorologists who ventured on the mountain on warm summer days, lightly clad, fell victim to the island's fickle weather and severe wind-chill. We had no problems, but we were well-clad and used to the chill wetness of the British hills.

Our riskiest moments were at sea. You cannot get very far round the coast of Gough on foot, for the beaches are broken by massive bluffs of sheer cliff. Traversing from beach to beach overland is a slow and exhausting business (that was probably what did for José Gomez). We therefore used boats. The Fishing Company had lent us a miniature Tristan boat – a canvas covered dinghy – but it proved too vulnerable on the rougher beaches of Gough and instead we borrowed a 13-ft wooden fishermen's dinghy from Captain Otto Mohr of *Tristania*. This took us to headlands and islets to survey, study marine life and count seals. It was potentially dangerous – for we were in the middle of an ocean six thousand kilometres wide, driven by fierce winds and notorious for its turbulent seas. We stayed in the lee of the island, and took no chances. Even then, there were interesting moments when a 'willy-waw' down-draught of wind from the cliffs spun the spray into whirling columns thirty metres high and came racing across the water. You just had to turn the boat's bows into it and get ready to bale.

The two fishing ships were a real safety back-up. Both captains knew the coasts and the weather of the island intimately. Captain Morris Scott – 'Scotty' – 'Scott of the Atlantic' – of *Frances Repetto* had landed on many an islet and beach and given his own names to many features. As the weather changed, the ships shifted their fishing grounds to stay in the lee. While we always went prepared to bivouac ashore in case the wind freshened against us and stopped our return to base, we often found that those very conditions brought a ship to lie offshore from where we were. The captains were invariably welcoming and we spent many nights with our air beds and sleeping bags in some secluded corner between decks. And they were very generous with their drink – indeed I think they tried to drink us under the table.

You would arrive. You would put your things where indicated. Then came the summons:

'Come and have a liddle trink before supper, ja?'

A 'liddle trink' was often half or a third of a cabin tumbler of neat whisky. We discovered that a standard 70 cl whisky bottle can just be squeezed into three cabin tumblers and goes easily into four, so that the empty can go straight out through the scuttle. Water? Not on those ships. You had to be ready for the post-supper invitation. 'And now perhaps we get down to some serious drinking, ja?'

I think it was partly a have-on, and I do not remember ever seeing any of them drunk on board, even when snugly at anchor for the night. The weather was too fitful for that. But we did get our revenge – rather naughtily. We invited them back for a party at the hut, and served rum. Excellent rum. Smooth and strong. Indeed, it was over-proof naval concentrate, almost twice the strength of their whisky. We gave them a 'liddle trink' each in a tumbler. It was raining – quite warm rain, with an outside temperature of around 16 degrees Celsius. Not surprisingly, our

guests needed a pee. Our custom was simply to go down to the beach –
bringing back a boulder to shore up the revetment at the end of the hut (so
that the process became known as 'going to fetch a stone'). Greggy
Gregorsen, Chief Engineer of *Frances Repetto*, needed to go desperately, but
didn't want to get wet, so he stripped off. The beaches were slippery, and he
stumbled as he turned to come back. A penguin bounded out of the surf and
hopped the rocks past him. It is the only time I have ever seen a Norwegian
ship's Chief Engineer, clad only in a long fair beard, crawling up a boulder
beach in the rain in pursuit of a penguin.

But we were on Gough for Serious Science. What did we find to make
the venture worth while?

Roger LeMaitre made a detailed study of the structure of the island and
the chemistry of its rocks. His work was later extended by Cliff Ollier from
Australia, who went to the island with Nigel Wace in 1976. As we knew even
before we went there in 1955, Gough is the eroded remnant of a volcano
built up from the mid-Atlantic Ridge. This marks where magma wells up
from deep within the Earth, adding to the floor of the South Atlantic and
making it spread, slowly moving Africa away from South America. The
three northern Tristan islands are other volcanic peaks associated with the
same ridge. Their different state of erosion is enough to indicate they are of
different ages, and radioactive dating of rock samples confirms this. No
rocks on the young volcanic cone of Tristan are more than a million years
old. Gough's oldest rocks are about 2.6 million years old. Most of
Inaccessible has slumped into the sea, but what remains goes back some
eight million years. Nightingale Island is no more than the worn-down
stump of a volcano, with rocks up to 18 million years old.

What is odd is that despite these different ages, all four islands show signs
of recent – and possibly even continuing – volcanic activity. Many of the
little volcanic cones that stud the slopes of Tristan are only a few thousand
years old, and it erupted again in 1961 to demonstrate that it was still in
active business. That is not surprising, given its youthful shape (though it
surprised some learned volcanologists who should have known better). But
what is truly surprising is that all three of the older islands have youthful
features. Edinburgh Peak, summit of Gough, is a young cone, possibly only
20,000 years old. Banded sediments suggest that it once had a crater lake,
now drained by a stream that has cut into its northern flanks. A young lava
flow pours from its base, and Nigel found an ash band in the peat on nearby
Albatross Plain that was deposited only around 2400 years ago. There are
several other youngish-looking volcanic features on Gough, and several
young cones also jut from the slopes of Inaccessible, while lavas and ashes
on Nightingale lie over peats that appear to be only about 36,000 years old.

The implication is that the islands still lie more or less over the 'hot spot' from which they were formed, and that any one of them could erupt again at any moment.

It is quite clear that these oceanic volcanoes have never been linked to any continent, although the South Atlantic was considerably narrower when the first eruptions took place over 18 million years ago. Lying close together as they do, and in much the same climatic zone, it is not surprising that they have very similar floras and faunas. The most obvious differences between Gough and Tristan reflect the fact that Gough has a more or less undisturbed vegetation pattern. But there are subtle differences, some of which probably arise because Gough is both cooler and wetter. For example Gough has two kinds of coastal tussock grass, one the same as on Tristan but the other being the Subantarctic tussock (*Paradiochloa flabellata*), widespread on many islands around the southern ocean. Gough also has a second tree, *Sophora*, growing in one small patch in a single valley. And Gough, of course, preserves the full richness of seabird life that people and introduced predators have destroyed on Tristan.

The plant and animal life of the islands has three particular features that interest naturalists – and are typical of remote islands the world over. First, despite the temperate climate and fertile volcanic soils, there are very few species of plant and animal on the islands, and whole groups we take for granted on the continents are missing. Second, quite a lot of species are distinctive island forms – so-called endemics, found nowhere else in the world. Third, many of the insects and two of the land birds cannot fly.

On Gough Island, there are only 62 kinds of flowering plant, ferns and their allies that we are confident 'belong' there, having arrived without human aid. People have brought another 11 species. In the whole Tristan group the tally is only 78 native plant species – plus about a hundred imported by humans, mostly to Tristan itself. Compare that with the English county of Cumbria, with 945 species of native higher plants and a further 428 species introduced by people. It is much the same with the invertebrate animals. On Gough, by 1976, 81 kinds of land invertebrate had been recorded, of which 19 are definitely introduced. Later surveys by scientists at the University of Sheffield have added a host of introduced species, but found relatively few more genuine 'natives'. There may still be more species to find, but the fauna is certainly poor compared with even relatively sterile mainlands. And there are gaps – for example the larger earthworms, slugs, centipedes and millipedes and at least eight major groups of insects appear not to have reached the islands by natural means. Other groups, such as woodlice, are represented only by one or two species.

What about endemics? It is not as easy as one might expect to be definite about these, because we still do not know as much as we should about the species of South America, where many of the closest relatives of the island forms live. But we do know that all the eight land bird species found in the group are endemic. As for the invertebrate land animals, when I did an analysis many years ago, 35 out of 239 recorded species seemed to be endemic to single islands (8 to Gough), and 29 to the group as a whole (14 of them occurring on Gough).

Many of the insects endemic to Gough and to the other Tristan islands are flightless. So are two of the land birds – both ground-living landrails. The Gough Island moorhen is closely related to the extinct Tristan 'little black cock', and can flutter a metre or two to help descent from a rock-top (rather as a farmyard fowl will flutter down from a roost). Inaccessible has an even stranger, tiny, primitive, rail that is totally flightless and looks like a little black fluffy chick with ruby eyes. It scurries secretively about in the tussock grass like a mouse. Flightlessness may well have been selected for in evolution because remote islands are windy places. Flying may be a good habit if you want to be a colonist, but it is dangerous if every time you take wing you are liable to be swept away from the new home to perish in the surrounding ocean.

The other land birds do fly. Gough has an endemic finch-like species, *Rowettia goughensis*, that seems to be related to a bird common in the Falkland Islands and South America. On Tristan there used to be a 'canary' as well as the 'starchy' which survives on all the three northern islands. Both Inaccessible and Nightingale have two kinds of 'canary' – one (*Nesospiza acunhae*) with a small bill, and the other (*Nesospiza wilkinsi*) a large-billed species that feeds on the fruits of the island tree. The Inaccessible and Nightingale forms of both species are distinct, and as a whole the four forms demonstrate in miniature the kind of evolutionary radiation that entranced Darwin in the finches of the Galapagos Islands.

There are no native vertebrate land predators in the islands apart from skuas and Giant petrels. This is one reason why the seabird colonies are so vast, even though the smaller species nest underground, burrowing into the peaty soils and so safeguarding themselves from the skuas. Michael Swales estimated that about two million pairs of Rockhopper penguins nest on Gough, along with almost the whole world population of the Tristan sub-species of Wandering albatross, a smaller relative of the great white bird of the oceans to southwards. There may still be 2000 to 3000 pairs of this bird, although there are disturbing reports nowadays of their slaughter by long-line fishing boats, whose baited hooks they gulp only to be dragged down and drowned as the line sinks. There are a few thousand pairs of Yellow-nosed and Sooty albatross, the former also with its world headquarters in the

Wandering albatross pair at nest on Gough Island.

Tristan group. There are literally millions of many of the smaller petrels. Nightingale and Inaccessible also have vast seabird populations – it is only on Tristan where humans, dogs, cats and rats have proved lethal predators that numbers of birds have plummeted. Taken together, Gough, Inaccessible and Nightingale are the most important island group for naturalists in the southern temperate zone, and I like to think that our expedition started to put them on the world conservation map.

There are lots of puzzles about the life of the islands. One is why the four have such similar floras and faunas despite their disparate ages. Another is why there are so many similarities between the life on Gough and that on the three northern islands – even to the point of sharing some flightless species. How on earth did the same endemic snails evolve on or exchange between Gough, Inaccessible and Nightingale? It is, of course, possible that some species colonised several islands in a single wave of immigration, and then evolved in parallel in the closely similar habitats they provide: the flightless moorhens of Tristan and Gough probably fit this pattern. Some similarities may result from inter-island transport by birds. But the detailed inter-relationships and evolutionary history merit a lot more research.

Any student of island floras and faunas, recognizing that they got to their islands by immigration across the oceans, is bound to ask the question 'where did they all come from?'

Analysis reveals that the South American relationship is the strongest – as might be expected as that continent is upwind and up-current in the prevailing westerlies. Some species immigrate before your very eyes – as did a big orange and yellow Brazilian moth (*Othreis apta*) I caught one night as it fluttered around a floodlight. Some plants and insects appear to be island specialists, since they are widespread in the southern temperate and Subantarctic zones. Yet others have distributions that suggest travel by sea.

Among them is the second small tree found on Gough – a yellow-flowered bush belonging to the sweet pea family, called *Sophora* by scientists, but 'Yellow kowhai' in New Zealand. There are only a dozen or so specimens on the island, all in one valley that converges with The Glen at the Archway Rock. The species also grows in Chile and the Juan Fernandez islands in the Pacific: it has close relatives in New Zealand, Tasmania and Hawaii and it once also grew on Easter Island in the crater where the giant effigies were carved. Its seeds float well (Nigel successfully germinated some after they had been in sea water for many months), and it is likely to disperse that way. Other plants may hitch a lift on birds (he found hooked seeds of a sedgelike plant, *Uncinia*, in the neck feathers of a young mollymawk, and the burrs of *Acaena*, called 'dog ketcher' by the Islanders, are also liable to entangle themselves in anything).

We could ask these kinds of question on the island, but the detailed evaluation of our results could only be done after we got home. And we had taken one big gamble when we went to Gough – we had no certain means of return. The fishing ships would leave long before we wanted to (John's late arrival meant that we ought to stay until late April if the map was to be finished). That would also make us too late for the one expedition ship known to be passing – *Theron*, in which Dr Vivian ('Bunny') Fuchs was returning from the Weddell Sea after setting up the Atlantic base for the Commonwealth Trans-Antarctic Expedition. Parents, in particular, thought this irresponsible and were not readily consoled by the knowledge that we could survive on the seals and seabirds and wild celery for an indefinite period. Catherine Heaney no doubt had even stronger views. But diverting ships is expensive. We needed a free lift.

Allan Crawford, again, did the critical deal. The South African Weather Bureau was interested in setting up a station on Gough because the island is upwind of the Cape in the westerlies, and can therefore gather information about South Africa's weather before it arrives. Also, the International Geophysical Year was upon us and a base on Gough would be a useful one for international data-gathering. We received 'an offer too good to refuse' – a payment for our hut and surplus stores and a free trip back to the Cape in a South African frigate, *Transvaal*. So there it was. On 13 May 1956 we left.

Back to Tristan for a farewell dance. Back to South Africa. Back to England. Back with – extraordinary to relate – a profit on the Expedition. We were able to create the Gough Island fund at the Royal Geographical Society, to pass on some of our gains to future expeditions, and when book royalties had been added it rose to over £1000, which was a tidy sum in the late 1950s. It still exists.

So we all came back to a mix of reunions, analysis of results and job-hunting. Expeditions are like research: you spend a lot longer planning and preparing and biting your fingernails in uncertainty, and a lot longer evaluating your results afterwards, than in doing the exciting business in the middle. It took John Heaney eighteen months to plan the Gough Island Scientific Survey. We were away from Britain ten months, of which six were spent on the island. Some of the papers describing the results did not come out until twenty years afterwards. And some of us – especially Nigel, Michael and me – are still working on Gough Island affairs. We were hooked for life. The expedition was, in different ways, the making of us all. As Prince Philip said in his foreword to the book I wrote in 1956, 'if every man has to face his Everest some time during his life, I strongly recommend him to get his Gough Island in first. There is no better preparation.'

I spent the northern summer of 1956 in Cambridge, as the final months of my Research Fellowship at Queens' went by. Most of the time was occupied with book-writing, getting collections to specialists and sending research papers to journals. Then I was off to Manchester University as a Lecturer in Zoology.

I didn't really like Manchester. To start with, I had no girl friend or close circle up there, and I was not very good at getting started. And I was warned that LECTURERS DID NOT GET OFF WITH STUDENTS even if the age gap was only a little over five years. I lived in a Hall of Residence, St Anselm's (commonly known as 'Slems'), which was rather churchy. The teaching was a bit old-fashioned and the departmental buildings highly so. I was therefore a bit depressed – until, by luck, I met Jim Cragg on a railway platform in London.

Jim was the Professor of Zoology in the Durham Colleges of Durham University (at that period, Durham also included what later became the University of Newcastle-upon-Tyne). He was a dynamic animal ecologist who had built up one of the best Departments for that sub-discipline. Many of his students worked on the high Pennine moors, just over the top of Crossfell from Appleby. Jim was typically direct:

'How do you like Manchester?'

'Not all that much.'

'Not surprised. Not your scene. Lewis Davies is leaving me and going to

Canada. I need someone to teach invertebrate zoology, and we may be getting involved in Antarctic biology. Would you like to come?'

'I think I'd like it very much.'

There were interviews, of course. The formalities had to be observed. But come September 1957 I was ensconced in Durham, living as a resident Tutor in University College with rooms high in the Castle Keep, looking south over the wide lawns of Palace Green to the great mass of the Cathedral – 'half Church of God, half fortress 'gainst the Scot'. It was to be an enjoyable home base for three years, which brought another major expedition and brought me into contact with some of the top people in British science.

But the islands are terribly possessive. Over the succeeding years they drew me back twice (and it should have been three times). Let me jump forward to those visits now.

In early October 1961, I was visiting my parents in Blackpool. The Press carried reports of earth tremors on Tristan, strongest close to the Settlement and hardly perceptible on the other side of the mountain. Peter Wheeler, the Administrator, had asked for advice. The Royal Society National Committee on Volcanology was dismissive. 'Just natural tremors on a young volcano – maybe landslips,' they said. I was not so sure. There were lots of very young-looking volcanic features on the island; I had seen them and the Committee hadn't. 'Wouldn't be surprised if it's going to erupt,' I said to Father, before taking the road to the Lakes. That evening, his opening greeting was 'Are you psychic?' The BBC had just reported that the islanders had been evacuated. A plug of red-hot lava had burst through the Settlement plain only a few hundred metres from the nearest houses. The dazed population, after a night spent huddled at the Potato Patches five kilometres away, was trans-shipped to a passing liner, and so to South Africa and England.

The plug of lava burst, emitting a fast-moving flow of basalt from its side. It engulfed tanks of diesel fuel in a mighty explosion. It swallowed the crayfish canning factory and thrust across Big Beach as a four-lobed fan, jutting over a hundred metres into the sea. Passing ships saw the glow of it thirty kilometres off, and the plume of smoke and sulphurous vapour rose thousands of metres, blighting the vegetation downwind. Warships landed parties to tidy up and search the abandoned village: other ships landed parties who took what they could steal. A Russian whaling fleet came in and killed almost all the rare Southern Right whales which had been such a delight to watch in the shallows around the island.

Almost everyone in England who had ever been to Tristan went to visit the Islanders soon after their arrival at a rather cheerless ex-army camp in

Surrey. I remember finding 'Big Mary' Swain – last seen when she had hosted a wonderful 'big eaps' for us on our way home from Gough – in bed with a cold, and in deep misery. Two newspaper reporters entered and were persuaded to go away again. Mary was blunt.

'The people is sick and toired of these newspaper reporters,' she proclaimed. 'They comes here, they talks to us, they goes away and they writes lies. Why doesn't they stay in London and make up their lies there and leave us in peace?'

Most of the Islanders did not like England, even after their move to better conditions at Calshot near Southampton. They were very much opposed to the idea of sending them to Shetland – though they might well have found it a home from home when they got there, apart from the dark, cold winters. As it was, they were suddenly dropped into a big, bustling community with alien values. Their social order was disrupted. On Tristan the older men were respected leaders because of their experience. In England those men were of little account, their knowledge of Tristan's winds and seas an irrelevance. They had little education, no certificates, and only a few had marketable skills. Success went to the young and adaptable. And many Islanders were not used to working for a boss, or to a set forty-two hour week. On Tristan, even if they worked for the fishing company, they were masters of their own dinghies and could fish on the days they chose – and dig their potato patches or go to Nightingale for eggs or guano when the mood took them.

Crime, too, was a jar. Of course there had been some petty thieving and dishonesty on Tristan. People spoke rarely of it. Somebody had been found on the factory roof in suspicious circumstances. Somebody was seen as a lazy sloven, parasitic upon the Administration. Somebody was said to have offered his daughter as a bedfellow to clear a debt. Such offenders met with severe social sanctions, and the slur worked in a small community with little room for undetected crime. But in England crimes of violence were matters of everyday report. 'Big Gordon' Glass, whose one arm made employment difficult, was robbed by youths as he sat by his brazier watching a road works in the darkness. Small wonder the older generation wanted to go home, especially as there were reports that those homes had been spared, it seemed by a miracle.

Scientists were interested in the impact of the eruption. We met at the Royal Society, the Committee on Volcanology surprisingly unchastened by the confounding of their earlier dismissive remarks. Haroun Tazieff, world-famous Belgian volcanologist, who liked nothing better than to be in the thick of the lava fountains and the bounding boulders, came over. A Royal Society Expedition to Tristan da Cunha was mounted, led by Professor Ian

Gass of Leeds University, with Roger LeMaitre as one of the geologists and
Allan Crawford as meteorologist. I couldn't go, because I was committed to
an Antarctic season, and Nigel Wace had a new job in Australia, but Jim
Dickson, an able botanist from Cambridge, and Donald Baird, zoologist
from Oxford, went to attend to the biology. I was in HMS *Protector*, on my
way home from the Antarctic, when the party was picked up in late March
1962.

We were off Tristan at dawn. The Settlement lay unchanged. But behind
the white crofts, the cliffs that soared to the edge of the Base were blackened
with scorched vegetation. Below them lay the black fans of new lava, with
the stubby new cone above them, fuming gently. Big Beach and the Factory
were gone. Little Beach, the other landing, was also obscured by the new
lava.

One familiar sight lay at anchor round the corner of the island – *Frances
Repetto*, squat and unkempt as ever. We steamed round to join her. Scotty
was rowed over and clambered, puffing somewhat, to *Protector*'s bridge.

'Hey, Mister,' he said, addressing Captain Robin Graham as he sat in the
conning seat, four rings of gold braid gleaming on his sleeves, 'what do you
want to come round here for, interrupting my fishing. And' (catching sight
of Holdgate) 'what the hell did you bring this bugger back for? We had
enough trouble with him and his lot six years ago!'

Which was, in its way, an endearing greeting – made more palatable by a
present to the Wardroom of two boxes of succulent crayfish tails. Scotty's
bark always belied his real generosity. He gave a most helpful briefing on
conditions ashore, and then disappeared. The First Lieutenant reappeared,
frantic.

'That man Scotty!' he said. 'He's down at the stores buying things and I
can't get him to leave. We've got to move back to the Settlement and take the
Expedition off. You know him – can you shift him?'

'Don,' I said. 'There's only one way. Use lower deck language. Slap him
on the back and say, "Scotty, old man, please eff off out of it because we've
got to sail."'

Scotty grinned. 'Sorry, Mister,' he said and sidled off like an amiable bear.
We moved back to the Settlement and soon the helicopter was zooming
between ship and shore. With Peter Baker and Roger LeMaitre I climbed the
new cone – yellow with sublimed sulphur and showing incandescent red
gleams where cracks opened deep into the lava. Down there, only a couple
of metres away, the temperature was still around 800 degrees. We descended
and explored the Settlement.

It was amazing. All the houses except one stood unharmed. That one,
nearest to the new cone, was gutted by fire, the blackened walls rising as an

Tristan da Cunha in 1962. The fans of lava thrust into the sea from the new volcano have left the Settlement unscathed on the right. Photograph by author from a Royal Navy helicopter.

empty shell floored with charcoal and debris – a perambulator frame, some glass bottles fused by the heat, and a distorted knife and fork. The cause of the fire was obviously a volcanic 'bomb' – a lump of lava which had fallen red hot through the thatch. But the rest of the houses stood unharmed in a kind of embayment – almost a protective wall – of new lava. The longboats lay undamaged beside the track to Little Beach, which dipped grotesquely into black, jagged, basalt. There was a bay – almost a natural harbour – between new and old cliffs. 'It'll be foine for the people returning,' said 'Little' Joe Glass who, with Adam Swain, had accompanied the Royal Society party. Allan Crawford agreed. Just a few pictures shown back in England and the votes for return rose to an overwhelming majority. God himself had clearly shielded their homes, and they must show their appreciation of His bounty. They went back, their futures secured by a new harbour built by the British Government.

My last visit to the islands was in 1968, with Nigel, Clive Elliott the ornithologist son of Hugh Elliott the first Administrator, Harold Green and Herbert Glass. We arrived at Gough in the South African supply ship *RSA*, on an astonishing day of sunshine, violent wind and white-capped sea, the seabirds driven like snowflakes with the spume. We saw for the first time the new South African Weather Station, white-painted and four-square round a little grassy courtyard, standing atop the southern cliffs. (As we found later, landing there usually meant sitting in a cargo net and being winched up the thirty-metre cliff by crane!) We landed at The Glen, where our old hut had long-since vanished, replaced by a clutter of smaller huts built by the fishing company. There was even a flush lavatory and a wash basin, using water piped from the stream. Mouse droppings lay everywhere. I picked up a coil of rope and a mouse shot out of each end. Harold Green looked anxiously (and unsuccessfully) for a hammock. The night was full of scrabbling and nibbling noises.

The aim of our visit was to find out what had changed after twelve years of continuous human habitation. For it is the isolation of remote islands that both causes and protects their distinctive life forms. In today's world of universal human travel and trade, this isolation is being eroded and we live in an era when mainland species are being carried to islands in increasing numbers. Once there they prey on, compete with, and frequently supplant the native species – especially if the habitat is being disturbed by human agency. Three quarters of the extinctions known to have occurred throughout the world since the year 1600 are of island endemics. We wanted to know whether the process was beginning to affect Gough.

Nigel hunted weeds and I looked for snails and other smaller animals. His report was good – the only things to be seen had been there in 1956. I was less happy. In 1955 there were no slugs on Gough Island. Now they were common among the sedges and in the damp, peaty soil and litter – and I blamed us for importing them. With them around the huts, but less widely dispersed, were centipedes – also new, and also probably due to us. They joined a British millipede, a European woodlouse, and the common English Garlic snail that had been everywhere in the lowland litter in the 1950s following introduction by the sealers (to whom we also ascribed a patch of wild potatoes growing by the stream up The Glen).

The good news was that when we moved round to stay for some days at the new South African station we did not find new weeds or invertebrates. Since then one weed – a creeping pearlwort, *Sagina procumbens* – has established itself near the Weather Station and a massive operation has been mounted to eliminate it. Otherwise, quarantine measures seem to have paid off, though there was one alarm in 1968 – we found a dead rat in a crate. Horrors! Rats are notoriously the most destructive of all animals imported to remote islands, and almost impossible to control once established. Fortunately this one seemed to have been dead a long time, and repeated studies since then, including an attempt by Nigel on a later visit to seduce any established rats by attracting them to caged females, had negative results.

The mice, however, are doing their best to turn into rats: the Gough animals are larger than normal House mice and given a few thousands of years may evolve into a damaging predator on their own account. Mouse eradication may be impossible but in 1995 Nigel went back with ideas about how at least to cull the population heavily.

The uplands were unchanged in 1968 – except that, in April, they were cool and we saw veils of snow sweep over them from a passing squall. It had been a stormy autumn, and strange birds appeared in many odd corners. A grey duck about the size of a mallard, with a dark bill, burst from a clump of grass as we tramped around the soggy plateau of Tarn Moss. There were at least two white egrets (and another when we got to Tristan). There was an emaciated Grey heron flapping slowly down The Glen. Very possibly there were American Purple gallinules, relatives of the island moorhen, for we saw two on Tristan where they are so common that the Islanders have given them a name – the Guttersnake. All these birds were vagrants, driven (almost certainly from South America) by the storms. Could they establish themselves? Certainly herons and egrets could not – there is no food of the right kind. Ducks might – they have on Subantarctic South Georgia – but Gough may not be a big enough habitat. The gallinule just might establish itself on Tristan, but the Gough Island moorhen, probably descended from two pairs which Michael released in 1956, is now spreading among the scrubby woodlands on the eastern side and is likely to exclude its relative.

There was one obvious change in the twelve years – Fur seals were everywhere. Michael Swales had counted 13,000 in 1955-56, mostly on the western coast. He had also established that the Fur seals of Gough Island are not the same species as those of the Cape and South America, but a Subantarctic species (*Arctocephalus tropicalis*) that also occurs in several other island groups, including Kergnelen Island in the South Indian Ocean. In 1968 there must have been at least twice as many as in 1956, and they lolloped and barked around areas of tussock grass close to both The Glen and the new Weather Station. Their recovery is a great testimony to the resilience of animal life, for they had been virtually exterminated by sealers in the nineteenth century: the last sealing party on Gough, in 1892, commented laconically that 'the seal had deserted the island'. Where the tiny remnant hung on we cannot tell, but I would guess that it was on the most inaccessible part of the west coast, near the mouth of the immense ravine we had named Deep Gulch, very hard of access overland and almost impossible to reach by sea. In contrast, the Elephant seal population, also devastated by sealers, remains quite tiny.

Our two week stay was over all too soon, and it was back to Tristan.

Bright sun and onshore wind made the Settlement clearly visible and totally inaccessible. The ship went round to the lee. 'Let's walk over the top,' said Nigel. Harold and Herbert agreed enthusiastically. They wanted to get back to their wives and families. So off we went – landing in the south-west of the island near the little cone of Hill-With-A-Hole-In-It (almost certainly scene of the eruption immediately preceding that of 1961, probably about 300 years ago), with a view up to Ridge-Where-The-Goat-Jump-Off. We tramped across the bare grazings at Stony Beach (cropped by a small herd of semi-wild cattle), and looked out over Cave Point where Fur seals were said to be breeding once again. Up the steep flanks of the Base, and across the winding path through tree ferns and across gulches and so – at last – to the other side and the welcoming lights of Prince Philip Hall and that 1960s innovation – the bar, with refreshing South African lager!

The bar was a product of exile. Before that, Tristan was kept 'dry', partly for paternalistic reasons. One was told that the islanders were 'not used to drink (true) and that it sent their unhardened heads berserk (nonsense). English pubs scuppered that myth, and beer now flowed in Prince Philip Hall. The houses looked very different too. The painted, boarded walls of Martha Rogers' house gleamed as they did when she and Arthur had welcomed us thirteen years earlier, but there were china ducks displayed in flight on Harold's walls and his tables bore ornaments like any in Southampton. Clothes, tableware, furniture – all were conventional English suburban rather than traditional Tristan. And new water closets, linked to a sewer system, stood by every door. The little roads were tarmac: down in the factory the equipment was modern, and above the harbour, with its twin, curving walls of stones held in massive metal mesh cages, Basil Lavarello operated a neat little crane to load and off-load from the boats. And the boats were changed. The old white-painted, canvas-covered longboats still lay about the village but large motor launches served for traffic with ships, while yellow fibreglass motor dinghies had taken over the fishing.

A money economy had come to Tristan. Peter Munch the sociologist, who came back for a visit after the resettlement, described the conflict over the building of the harbour. Administrator Peter Day demanded that the men working on it followed the pattern they had been used to in England – contracts to work a set number of hours for an agreed wage. Those who refused were dismissed and not taken on again for three months. Likewise the new crayfish freezer plant went through a strike before a new pattern of employment emerged. Peter Munch, looking back to 1938, deplored this commercialization of Tristan. He rejoiced when the traditional way of life seemed to triumph, virtually the whole male labour force downing tools to go on a 'fatting' trip to Nightingale. But by the time we arrived a compromise seemed to have been reached. Wages and work were regular, but the Administration and factory management had accepted that trips to Sandy Point for apples, to Stony Beach to kill wild cattle for meat, or to Nightingale for fat and the dirt and feathers mis-named guano were a therapeutic necessity.

The Administration in 1968 itself seemed to suffer from delusions of grandeur. The old, easy-going, family style had given way to formality. There was a Sergeant of Police with two part-time Special Constables. Our passports were stamped! The Administrator's lawn had been enlarged – allegedly to allow Garden Parties. One day a small wooden hut appeared by its far gate, and a Boy Scout mounted guard 'to carry messages to Government House'. Puzzling, for such messages were usually word-of-mouth on Tristan. On Day One there were plenty of volunteer Scouts, but the novelty soon wore off. On Day Two the Administrator's son performed intermittent duty. On Day Three a gale blew the sentry box over, and on Day Four a hefty cow used it as a rubbing-post and knocked it apart. The remains were last seen being carried off like a buckled giant coffin to the Administration Store.

Thirty years later, all was set for me to pay a return visit – but another ship's engine failure put paid to the plans and I doubt if I shall make it now. But Nigel Wace and Michael Swales have been back several times. Michael, indeed, organized three expeditions from Denstone College, where he headed the Biology Department – two to Inaccessible, where they made the first good map and described vegetation and wild life, and one to Tristan where they did a census of the expanding population of moorhens and established that the birds were the Gough Island variety rather than a recovery of the original Tristan sub-species. He and Allan Crawford have also created a Tristan da Cunha Association as a 'supporters club' in Britain, and its periodic Newsletter has chronicled the changing pattern of island life. It is clear that the island community has regained the control over its affairs that was eroded by the coming of the Navy in 1942. The teachers are islanders. The Administration is much smaller. The elected Council has more authority. The elected Chief Islanders (man and woman) have many of the roles of Leader of a Council in England. There is still a Policeman, but there are many more commercial operations to police. There are many more links with the outside world.

And there are cars! In January 2002 there were about fifty – status symbols bought on hire-purchase and used mainly to chug along the three kilometres of tarmac road between Settlement and Patches. But having a car brings an imperative to use it, so children are driven the two or three hundred metres to school, and proud owners drive comparable distances to work at the Factory. Obesity is becoming a problem among the young as well as the old.

On Gough, every effort has been made to halt change. New conservation laws adopted in 1976 made the island a Nature Reserve (Nigel and I became members of the Gough Island Wildlife Reserve Advisory Committee). In 1995 the island was added to the World Heritage list, as one of the most beautiful and precious remote islands on Earth.

It deserves that status. I still think of Gough as the most enchanted place that I have visited. The enchantment goes deeper than beauty: it is somehow touched with the freshness of the Garden of Eden. When he was carried off in 1955, Robert Chambers handed me a paperback copy of the works of Gerard Manley Hopkins, and they evoke this intertwined loveliness and wonder, and the feeling that God is present behind it all 'with a sovereignty that heeds, but hides, bodes but abides'. For me, Gough was a high point of life, and I would give much to walk its hills again.

CHAPTER THREE

In the Footsteps of Darwin

IT WAS ASSIZE SUNDAY in Durham. The two judges, Mr Justice Salmon and Mr Justice Edmund Davies, full-wigged and gowned, paused as they emerged from the great north-west door of the Cathedral. Two trumpeters of the Durham Light Infantry blew a fanfare. Then . . .

'Paara parara pa pa Paa . . .'

The strains of 'Colonel Bogey' rang out from a window somewhere below mine in Abbey House. A student was clearly 'taking the mickey'. Across Palace Green, a posse of police led by a Chief Superintendent marched resolutely at the head of the judicial procession towards the Judges' Lodgings in the Castle, but their eyes darted daggers. There was a pause, and then a sound as of snorting buffaloes bursting in through the front door. I went to investigate.

'Good morning!'

'Who are you?'

'I am the Tutor in charge of this house.'

'Oh, are you? Then let me tell you, young feller, that we've come to have words with one of your students. He's been blowing a bugle in a derisory manner, and insulting Her Majesty's judges. And let me tell you, young feller, that anyone who insults her Majesty's judges insults Her Majesty the Queen in person. And that's a very serious offence. Now where is he?'

The bird had flown, leaving the offending instrument on his bed. Two days later he was sent to apologize to their Lordships, who kept commendably straight faces during the interview, and enjoyed recounting it over the College port afterwards.

Durham was a good place to work. It was pleasant to live in the Castle, with its collegiate atmosphere and magnificent architecture, and to walk to the Department every day down the steep wooded banks of the Wear and across the graceful span of Prebend's Bridge. But late in 1957 there were stirrings of new distraction.

I had a letter from Dr Carl Pantin, Reader in Invertebrate Zoology at Cambridge. The Royal Society – Britain's premier scientific institution – wanted to mark the centenary of the publication of Darwin's *Origin of Species* in 1959 by something more than the usual conferences, lectures and publications. They resolved, in addition, to send 'a small expedition to investigate problems of animal and plant distribution like those which the young Darwin met on the voyage of the *Beagle*.' The organizing committee decided to focus on the relationships between the flora and fauna of New Zealand, southern Chile, and the islands of the south Pacific. They hoped that a scientific party would travel between these places in the New Zealand vessel *Endeavour*. Carl Pantin knew of my experiences in the South Atlantic islands and thought that I might be a suitable member of the expedition.

That meant journeys to London and interviews with Dr Pantin and the South Pacific Expeditions Committee he had been appointed to Chair. It was an immensely distinguished group. Sir Lindor Brown, Biological Secretary of the Royal, Dr (later Sir) Gerard Thornton, its Foreign Secretary, Sir Julian Huxley, Sir Alister Hardy (former biologist on the *Discovery* investigations and visitor to Gough thirty years earlier), Professor Harry Godwin, eminent Cambridge botanist, the Hydrographer of the Navy... and many more. Plans changed suddenly when it became clear that the New Zealand ship was not available. The Royal Society decided to send a 'pilot expedition' to the cold-temperate regions of Southern Chile instead. Darwin had spent a good deal of time there, but there had been very little biological research since then. I was asked to organize the expedition, working with the Society's staff and especially with George Hemmen, who had been in the Antarctic during the International Geophysical Year and now worked for the Crown Agents. What he didn't know about expedition logistics was hardly worth knowing.

The plan? To send a party of five people to the forested island of Chiloé in southern Chile in around October 1958. Darwin had been there in 1835. To travel south, possibly with the Chilean Navy, to the islands and fiords of western Patagonia and then to the region of Tierra del Fuego where Darwin had met canoe-Indians he described as 'the most abject and miserable creatures I anywhere beheld'. The party would include two or three New Zealanders, both because the Royal Society of New Zealand wanted to participate and because one of the few well-known things about the biology of the far south of Chile was that it was very like that of the South Island of New Zealand – similar forests, of similar trees, with similar peat bogs, and similar insects. Darwin's friend Sir Joseph Hooker had noted these resemblances during his voyage as naturalist with Sir James Clark Ross' Antarctic expedition in 1839-43. George Knox, a marine zoologist from Canterbury University in Christchurch, was to head the New Zealand contingent.

Jim Cragg was encouraging. 'It's a great honour for you and for the Department,' he said. 'Of course we'll give you leave. I'll have to get someone else to give your first year lectures, but you may be back in time to do some in March. And you'll be here for examining in May. I'll speak to the Warden, but you go ahead.'

Early in September 1958 I left the clutter of war-time buildings grandly described as the Heathrow North-side Terminal for a ten-hour flight to New York in a piston-engined DC 6C. From New York a now-vanished airline, Panagra, took me to Miami, Panama, Guayaquil, Lima and Santiago. Those were the days when aircraft had limited endurance, and city-hopped their way around the world. I watched the lightning flickering among piled up clouds in the Caribbean night, making them glow from inside like incandescent lamps, and saw the dawn behind the long wall of the Andes. Robin Duke and John Wilson of the British Council met me, and our expedition owed an immense amount to their kindness and support. They were busy people and we must have been a confounded nuisance. As we were to the British Embassy, for although we had had diplomatic assurances from the Chilean Ambassador in London that we would be most welcome, nobody had instructed the customs to admit our stores. The harassed Commercial Secretary at the Embassy, and Leo Borax, Vice Consul, were frantically trying to persuade somebody to issue a *decreto de liberación*. But it was holiday time, and there had just been a Presidential Election . . .

The election was much in evidence. Streets and houses were plastered with slogans. ALLENDE, ALLENDE, ALLENDE . . . BOSSAY SERA PRESIDENTE . . . FREI, FREI, FREI . . . ALESSANDRI – HECHOS NO PALABRAS (deeds not words). The supporters of Alessandri (who won) had rolled his name out as a new central white line along the highway, and it was almost mesmerising. ALESSANDRI . . . ALESSANDRI . . . ALESSANDRI – we turn right here – ALESSANDRI . . . ALESSANDRI . . . – slow down for the traffic lights . . . ALESSANDRI . . . ALESSANDRI all the way home. And the event had been marked by the most severe earth tremors that the city had felt for years. After-shocks were still making the glasses tinkle in the cupboards. Shakespeare might have written the copy:

> I say, the Earth did shake when I was born.

> And I say, the Earth was not of my mind
> If you suppose, as fearing you it shook . . .

I spent nearly a month in Santiago. The New Zealanders arrived. George Knox, aged 38, married with five children, cheery-looking and unflappable. Eric Godley, botanist, 39, thickset, grinning, dark. Bill Watters, geologist, 32, tall, fair, studious-looking. We met our Chilean member, chosen by the Rector of the University. Father Dr Guillermo Kuschel, probably the leading entomologist in Chile, was a rather disconcerting first sight – very tall, clothed in a long priest's habit. He soon dispelled any aura of solemnity. 'Call me Willy,' he said. The habit went into the suitcase long before we took to the field. He was a fine naturalist, and superb liaison officer. And we changed his life (as I will tell later).

Santiago lies in a deep basin between the Andes and the lower range of mountains along the Pacific coast. It is one of the few capital cities in the world from which (if the traffic smog lets you) you can see perpetual snow, on El Plomo, an ice-mountain over six thousand metres high. From the coastal cordillera on the way to the seaport of Valparaiso you can sight Aconcagua, nearly a thousand metres higher and the tallest peak in the Americas. A long spur of hills sweeps into Santiago, culminating in the Cerro San Cristobal, covered in a park of trees and flowers, and capped by a great white statue of the Virgin with a funicular railway crawling to her feet. In the very centre there is a little hill, the Cerro Santa Lucia, capped by a Spanish colonial fort. Darwin (who was here in 1834) found its ascent 'a never failing source of pleasure'. Riding out one evening, he found the view of the city across the plain at sunset 'pre-eminently striking: the dead level surface, covered in part by woods of acacia and with the city in the distance abutting horizontally against the base of the Andes, whose snowy peaks were bright with the evening sun.' In September 1958 the snow lay far down the nearest slopes, and the smog was not dense enough to obscure that view. It was all murk when I was back in 1982 . . . !

Santiago in 1958 was in transition. There was still a Spanish colonial city with baroque façades and ornaments. There was a modern city of tall concrete and steel office blocks. There was a genteel flowery city with clean streets and a profusion of trees. There were squalid and sprawling slums. There were precise, ordered shops (English spoken) and muddled, picturesque, gabbling stalls. We savoured it, and made abortive journeys to Valparaiso to argue about our stores. When we got into the warehouse at last, we found that our bedding and weatherproof field clothing had disappeared. A half-empty case of whisky was less of a problem: it was, after all, also half-full, and the bottles were useful as presents to customs men and our agents. There was a noticeable warming of relations and acceleration of action.

We were taken for a two day trip into the Andes by Jack Ewer, University lecturer and former Antarcticist. Several hours on horseback up the valley of El Manzano, the valley of the apples – which in its higher and drier parts was actually a valley of tall, many-branched cactuses and spiny acacia bushes. A trudge up steep and barren slopes streaked with snow, to a bivouac at about two thousand metres, in a little cave that commanded a stunning view. Eagles and a condor drifted above, and the sun set through bars of cobalt and gold. We slept well, but the earth shook again at breakfast – not a

The Royal Society Expedition to Southern Chile in the Andes above Santiago. George Knox leads the group, followed by Martin Holdgate, Eric Godley, Bill Watters and guide. Willy Kuschel did not come on this trip. Photograph by Jack Ewer.

comfortable experience in a cave. We trekked across snowfields scattered with dead bees, flies and moths, obviously blown on the wind from the country below, and so down through cactus land to the suburbs.

We were still in Santiago for national independence day, the *dieciocho*, 18 September. There was a great march-past on a wide parade ground, flanked by trees, with the snowy ranges soaring beyond. The outgoing President took the stand, under a high black and gold canopy. The Chilean flag, scarlet, blue and white and set with a single star, was broken at the masthead. A group of *huasos* – the Chilean cowboys – trotted up and offered the President a horn of wine in which to pledge the health of the nation. Infantry goose-stepped. Long files of mounted lancers, spears extended and accoutrements gleaming, trotted past, with horse artillery following. Aircraft flew over. And after the formalities the town burst into revelry. Under the trees there was one enormous picnic. There was dancing, and especially the swift, merry, national *cueca*. There was drinking, aided by wine booths set at intervals along the roads. The aftermath lasted several days. The milkman – *el lechero*, to give him a title that in English does look a little ambiguous – who normally trotted past the Wilsons' house decorously, blowing a whistle to attract attention and stopping often, burst down the avenue like a tornado.

There was a hammer of hoofs, a roar of wheels, a clatter of cans and a derisive whistle as he shot round the corner. As the dust settled, dozens of white-aproned figures were revealed, clutching empty cans and looking to the west, where a faint cloud marked their escaping quarry.

Possibly lubricated by the whisky, we escaped from the customs house with most of our stores, filling the gaps by local purchase. Willy made contact with Contralmirante Balaresque of the Chilean Navy, who offered help with our travel among the western Patagonian channels, and General del Aire Bobadilla who assured us that the FACh (Fuerza Aerea de Chile) would fly us into Chiloé – for the road shown on the map as crossing the island was no more than a rough planked track, and the 'village' we wanted to go to was a single house, although it had an airstrip. We had an incapacitating lunch with the Commandant of the Instituto Geográfico Militar, Colonel Eduardo Saavedra, who stocked us up with maps and – most valuable of all – aerial photographs of our chosen study regions. We said goodbye to the British Ambassador, Ivor Pink. And finally, we took a long train journey on the crack express, the *Fleche del Sur*, arrow of the south.

We stopped at Frutillar, the place of strawberries. Willy's brother was waiting for us on the platform – a tall figure draped in a poncho and surmounted by a soft hat. Soon we were at the Kuschel home, a wooden house with broad eaves looking for all the world as if it had strayed from Bavaria. Which it had, for this whole district is German-settled. By the bay of Frutillar, on a wide lake that runs thirty kilometres to the feet of the lovely, symmetrical, snow-capped peak of the volcano Osorno, the wooden, multicoloured houses stood around a slender church tower capped by an onion-shaped spire typical of the Alps. Willy's family spoke German as easily as Spanish and often leaped from one to the other sentence by sentence. Benjamin Subercaseaux, a lively writer of Chilean geography, summed it up (in the 1930s):

> The Germans, once installed in the south, began to create everything for a German life. The first factory in the country was built here – the brewery of Anwandter. The stock-raisers began to breed pigs so that Hoffman could make his delicious sausages and other *delikatessen*. The cattle and sheep farmers produced the hides from which Rudolff made his excellent boots. The fields had to be cleared for the growth of barley and wheat, two essential ingredients in the manufacture of beer and of the delicious *kuchen*.
>
> The streets of Valdivia have a markedly German aspect. Among the inhabitants, German is spoken. The signs and the shops are German,

the schools also. The sports clubs display the swastika, set in the middle of a sun rising behind the volcano Osorno . . .

It had changed in 1958, and we certainly saw no swastikas, but the culture remained – and the finest beer we drank in Chile was served in the Hotel Club Alemán (the German Club Hotel) in the little town of Puerto Montt.

The Kuschel family introduced us to a great Chilean custom. From a little hut behind the house, wood smoke billowed.

'Come and see the *asado*,' commanded Willy.

Inside the hut sides of mutton sizzled on two long spits, ranged on either side of a long bar of glowing embers. It smelt magnificent. Saliva flowed!

'That is the idea,' Willy explained. 'You come to savour the *asado*, and so get an appetite.'

Soon we were all sucking at juicy strips of superbly-flavoured mutton, washed down with red wine. It was the first of many such celebrations, as we munched our way through the south.

Puerto Montt was the jumping off place for Chiloé. In 1958 it was an old-fashioned town with many wooden houses. And the fish market, with its open stalls and a strong aroma of what used to be politely termed 'ozone', was remarkable. There were some ordinary-looking fish, but they were in the minority. There were big red spiny spider crabs called *centolla* – a great delicacy. There were sea-urchins, *erizos*, whose yellow ovaries, eaten raw with lemon juice, taste like sticky-sweet sea water impregnated with iodine. There were many kinds of shellfish, including giant mussels and the limpet like *locos* (I never found out why they were mad). There were small sea-cucumbers and sea-squirts, the latter removed from their outer tests and sun-dried in strings, like desiccated plums. There were cakes of green seaweed, oozing gently at the edges and looking ideal for ploughing in under the spring cabbages. And there were piles of leaf-stalks of *pangue*, the giant rhubarb-like *Gunnera chilensis*, which peeled and eaten raw has a refreshing, tangy-sweet astringency (it grows quite well in European botanical gardens where they protect it by pretending it is poisonous). 'We must eat *mariscos* (sea-food) in Chiloé,' said Willy. 'And *mariscos* without lemon are nothing. You must buy a sack of at least a hundred lemons.'

Hawks and vultures haunted the waterfront. A medium sized brown hawk (*Milvago chemango*) scavenged rather as red kites are reported to have done in medieval Britain. Black vultures and red-necked Turkey vultures soared in the upcurrent along the sea wall and sat in a row on the slaughter-house roof. Black-backed Dominican gulls fought with the hawks over tasty morsels in the outfall of the town drain.

We didn't know it, but this was a scene soon to be obliterated. In 1960 there was a violent earthquake and this whole coast was devastated by a tidal wave. The steep slopes behind the town slid, destroying buildings and killing about five hundred people. Over half the town was flattened in a few minutes. The little seaport with its low wooden houses and frontier atmosphere vanished for ever.

We woke to wind and rain, and I wondered whether the FACh would be able to take us to Chiloé.

'Don't worry,' said Willy, 'the pilots down here are very good.'

His further explanation was less reassuring.

'You see, the country is so dangerous that they have to be, or they would soon die.'

An Air Force Otter took us and our stores to Chepu on the west coast of Chiloé, and as we flew we crossed the frontier. First, there were cleared lands, near to Puerto Montt. Then came dense, sombre, dark-green carpets of forest into which the cultivation of the advancing settlers cut salients and islands, linked by narrow roads. On Chiloé Island, the new farms were strung along ridge crests, and burning seemed to be the main means of forest destruction: blackened tangles of prostrate logs made a funereal border to the woods.

We knew that in Darwin's time the whole of the eastern side of Chiloé was 'thickly covered by one impervious blackish-green forest'. We had read conflicting accounts of the present situation. Some reports said that the climate was so wet and the forest so dense that clearance had proved impossible. The climate was blamed: Darwin had written that 'in winter the climate is detestable, and in summer it is only a little better. I should think that there are few parts of the world within the temperate regions where so much rain falls.' On the other hand, we had learned that the rainfall in northern and eastern Chiloé was only around 1000 mm a year – less than at Great Asby – and one correspondent had written: 'so far from being covered in impenetrable forest, Chiloé is a thriving agricultural area suffering from over-production of potatoes.'

As we went westward it became obvious that both reports were right. By 1958 much of the east of the island had been cleared and farmed. But as we flew low over the western hills towards Chepu virgin forest spread everywhere below us. Hillsides, ridges, narrow ravines and riverside flats were tangled in a confusion of trees. The leaf canopies in early spring were a deep, dark, green with a few paler splashes where the young buds were breaking. Bamboo hung in long festoons from the crowns, twenty metres or more above the ground, while the river hollows were choked with low-growing, smooth-topped thickets giving way to reddish bogland in the wettest places.

Bygone wilderness. The forested hills of the Cerros de Metalqui bar the horizon, beyond Chepu sands, Chiloé.

At a few points we glimpsed the track marked on the map. It was indeed a planked road just as Darwin described: 'a curious affair: it consists in its whole length of great logs of wood which are either broad and placed longitudinally or narrow and placed transversely. In winter, when the wood is rendered slippery from rain, travelling is exceedingly difficult.' When we explored on the ground we found that today's planked roads were mostly of small, transverse, logs that were not only slippery but rotten, with gaps through which a horse could easily drop a leg into the soft earth.

We turned towards Chepu, following a sluggish river that wound through lakes and swamps to enter the Pacific in a broad bay of white sand. The Otter lurched, and swung over a green strip with a hut at the seaward end. A man on a horse appeared and could be seen driving the cattle off the landing ground. We bumped down and stacked our stores in the little hut for later collection and transfer by bullock cart to the single house that was Chepu.

That house was a substantial wooden building owned by the national settlement agency, the *Caja de Colonisación*, but occupied only by one family – Alfonso Muñoz, his wife and children. They gave us a large empty room to work and cook in, and another couple of rooms in which to spread our air mattresses and sleeping bags. It was all very comfortable. The only problem was that right outside there was a small hut into which a vast number of hairy, brown-mottled, long-bodied pigs tried to crowd at night, when the temperature fell sharply. One realized the aptness of the collective noun 'a sounder of swine'.

Chepu was really a communications centre. Dotted in the forest to the south there were dozens of small, new homesteads for which Alfonso Muñoz acted as some kind of back-up. It was clear that we were seeing a land in transition, and we worked to describe the forest and its life while there was yet time.

We travelled along the coast, following the broad and beautiful beaches. There were great expanses of sand, where the long swells out of the west broke in regular bars of foam. There were towers and pillars of rock – volcanic lavas, quartzite, schists and coarse-grained sandstones. Offshore, the cold Humboldt current, sweeping northwards, brought seabirds typical of the Subantarctic (we saw at least one Giant petrel). And on the beaches we saw the solution to a Gough Island puzzle.

There was a lot of 'Yellow kowhai', *Sophora*, along the river banks inland. The same species as on Gough. Eric soon established that the big corky pods split open on the tree and shed their seeds into the river. We later found the round yellow seeds in the sand at high tide mark. Clearly those seeds could easily be carried out to sea and round in the South Pacific to Easter Island or to Australasia – or, if they were really hardy, back past Cape Horn and so to Gough.

We thrust inland where there were tracks. We soon found that the forest edges, especially where they had been damaged by fire, were the worst obstacles for they were barricaded by bamboo (*Chusquea quila* or *quila* in Spanish) which grew like a looping, barbless, wire entanglement. I once spent a hour attempting to work my way through about a hundred and fifty metres of it, and almost as long getting out defeated, easily able to understand Eric's story of a tattered skeleton found in New Zealand bush of similar density. But once you were through, the primary forests often had open glades free from underscrub and carpeted by leaf litter. They were scented forests, dominated by a great tree, *Eucryphia cordifolia*, with bunchy clumps of leaves and white flowers, growing together with tall laurels (*Laurelia*) and myrtles (*Amomyrtus*) one kind of which had striking whitish bark. Only a few flowers – the most beautiful the pendant red and white bells of a climber, the *coicopihue* – broke the greenery. But these were the forests of the low ridges where the soils were fairly dry. There were other kinds close to the shore, where there were great masses of spiny bromeliads, and in the wet hollows the low-growing *tepu* (*Tepualia stipularis*) formed a truly impenetrable tangle.

And the animals? Willy specialized in extracting the tiny creatures that lived in the leaf litter, doing so by hanging samples to dry in big cloth funnels, so that the animals would crawl and drop to a container below. Many of the finds had never been described by scientists. For example, out of about 175 species of tiny beetle belonging to the family Pselaphidae, over a hundred proved to be new. And we found many tiny, flattened plant-bugs called Peloridiidae – 'living fossils' that have changed little in millions of years, now known only in Southern Chile, New Zealand, Tasmania, the eastern Australian mountains and Lord Howe Island between Australia and New Zealand. The dragonflies with striking red patches on their wings belonged to a family with very similar distribution. We were looking at an assemblage of trees, herbs and insects that used to live in the temperate regions of the great southern continent of Gondwanaland that united South America, Africa, India, Australia, New Zealand and Antarctica around a hundred million years ago.

There were frogs in mossy places on the forest floor. Little frogs a couple of centimetres long, and with a variety of colours. Darwin's frog, *Rhinoderma darwini*, first collected during the voyage of HMS *Beagle*. There are not many pools for tadpoles in the forest, but the male frogs have got round this by carrying the eggs in their mouths. It sounds uncomfortable (and one wonders whether larder and nursery ever get mixed up) but it seems to work, for the species is common enough.

The nastiest animals in the forests were leeches – little black ones about a centimetre long. They sat among the vegetation until you jarred it as you walked by, and they then wormed their way through your clothes until they could clamp their tiny suckers in place and pierce a hole in you with little horny teeth. At the end of a day in the woods your boot tops were often encircled with a little rosette of them, engorged with your blood and ready to drop off. I took great pleasure in dropping my passengers into tubes of spirit.

And mammals? There were not many. The largest was a little reddish-brown hornless deer called *pudu* (in Latin, *Pudu pudu*), a dainty creature living solitary in the thickets and usually visible only as a wave of disturbed undergrowth as it plunged away from you. There was also a grey fox, and small nocturnal creatures including pouched marsupials in the tree tops (South and Central America are home to two families of marsupial, but Chiloé is about their southern limit). But the bird fauna made up for the mammalian deficiencies. Green parrots with bright red tails flashed about in the canopies, while green humming-birds with scarlet crests flitted about the flowering shrubs at the woodland edges, including *Berberis darwinii*, now so familiar in English gardens. And the woods were full of strange calls. There was a voice that sang notes on a musical scale, rising in pitch and intensity as it went. There was a voice that screamed and another that yapped repeatedly, with near-hysterical shrillness.

This last was the alarm call of the *hued-hued*, a black bird with a pale throat. Some of the others belonged to the *chucao*, smaller and red-breasted, with a stumpy tail it carries jauntily like a wren. Darwin said that it was 'held in superstitious fear by the Chilotes on account of its strange and varied cries.' He also had something to say about the jaunty tail of a related species, *Pteroptochus albicollis*, also called the *tapacolo* 'or cover your posterior, and well does the shameless little bird deserve the name, for it carries its tail more than erect, that is, inclined backwards towards the head.'

Some of the tracks in the forests may well be ancient, possibly dating back to pre-colonial times. We found one by chance north of Chepu, because George, working on the shore, suddenly found an old woman nearby cutting the leaves of giant *Gunnera*. She vanished equally suddenly – into a rock-cut trench that deepened to a cleft with walls three metres high and overarched by ferns and branches. It was narrow and wet underfoot, but widened occasionally into what appeared to be deliberately constructed passing places. Although this chasmous cleft was only about fifty metres long, the track was deeply incised all the way to the crest of one of the hills, and led down the other side to a clearing and small settlement. According to Alfonso Muñoz it was the way to 'the lost mines' where the Spaniards dug their gold and silver.

We met Chilotes on the tracks from time to time, going down to the beach for shellfish or to Chepu to visit Alfonso. The men wore broad-brimmed cloth hats, floppy at the edges, and were draped in ponchos or lighter cloaks, and on their feet they had cow's hide moccasins just like those once used on Tristan. The women went bareheaded, with black hair straggling to the shoulders. Their bodies, usually broadening to a sacklike shapelessness in middle age, were wrapped in dark cotton dresses and their feet were bare. Sometimes they would be leading a bullock, squelching ankle deep into the peaty ooze. Occasionally the beast would be dragging a heavy wooden sled, cut like a dug-out canoe from a single tree trunk; even more rarely they would be leading a pair of bullocks towing a wooden cart with great wheels cut as single discs of timber.

Chepu colonization was slow, wasteful, and quite clearly impoverishing the land. As in other pioneer areas, fire was used as the main way of clearing the ground, because it needed little labour. First patches of bush and underscrub were burned, and then remaining brushwood was piled around the big trees and lit, killing them and leaving them standing gauntly like the stumps on a first World War battlefield. Potatoes were grown in small, fenced plots (Chiloé is the place of origin of several varieties), but corn was a rarity in that wet climate. Grass seed was scattered to create some kind of pasture, but coarse strains like the universal Yorkshire fog predominated. Rushes sprouted freely, but the grazing was good enough for a few sheep or cattle. If they were too thin on the ground, shrubs – many with bright flowers – soon sprang up, and bamboo came looping in. The progressive lightening of the soils as fertility declined after clearance was evident. I do not know how far the process has gone now, but it was obvious forty years ago that the ancient and beautiful forests of Chiloé were being wasted to little benefit. I have read that a national park or nature reserve has now been established a little south of Chepu, but my guess is that the high forest will find its most secure refuge behind the barrier of the Cerros de Metalqui to the south, where steep ridges plunge abruptly to the Pacific.

George and I tried to reach those hills, following the coast and camping in an abandoned Chilote hut that we hoped was indeed 'a farm too far'. But it was clear that to explore the higher ground we would have to find another way. So, after a month at Chepu, our Air Force friends transferred us to Castro, capital of Chiloé, and after an overnight stay at the home of a most hospitable large farmer, we went on by bullock cart to the crest of the island in the Cordillera San Pedro.

In Castro, the Mayor complained about Darwin. 'He said some dreadful things about our town.'

November 30, 1834. We reached Castro, the ancient capital of Chiloé but now a most forlorn and deserted place. The streets and plaza were coated by fine green turf on which sheep were browsing. The Church, which stands in the middle, is entirely built of plank and has a picturesque and venerable appearance. The poverty of the place may be conceived from the fact that although containing some hundreds of inhabitants, one of our party was unable to purchase either a pound of sugar or an ordinary knife. No individual possessed either a watch or a clock; and an old man, who was supposed to have a good idea of time was employed to strike the church bell by guess . . .

November 6, 1958. The main plaza was well laid out with paved walks, flower beds and ornamental trees. The Church had a semi-baroque Spanish Colonial front, and its back portions were clad in corrugated iron rather than planks. There was bustling traffic that mingled bullock carts, 1925 or 1930 Ford cars, ancient buses with flapping panels and modern American cars and lorries. The railway from Ancud ended in a length of rusted rail on which an elderly locomotive lay in retired disintegration across the steps of a wine-shop. There were well-stocked shops at the harbour front, where neatly-dressed passers by looked down on families of fisher-folk squatting on the stones and cooking fish and shellfish on open fires.

It took twenty bullock carts to transport our gear up the long track to San Pedro. At one point we had to ford a swift river, the bullocks struggling in the current and ourselves perched precariously atop the loads (one cart dropped in a hole so that the animals had to swim). As we climbed in rain we came to new kinds of woodland dominated by the southern beeches, *Nothofagus*, which are the best known of all the southern temperate trees.

From the air we had glimpsed strange whitish expanses on the summit plateaux. Now we could see what they were. To Eric they were familiar – wet, tussocky grassland merging into the strange and distinctive carpet bogs typical of southern Chile, the Falklands, and southern New Zealand. Bogs made not of mosses, as in the northern hemisphere, but tight cushions of higher plants, including the genera *Donatia*, *Astelia*, *Gaimardia* and *Oreobolus*, all found in both Chile and New Zealand. Another Gondwanaland link. But the San Pedro plateau was not as pristine as we would have liked – for the uplands were littered with the debris of an abandoned sheep ranch and there were many signs that the forest had been burned to make more pasture. We set up our base in the largest and most weathertight of the abandoned hutments.

Damaged or not, the top of the Cordillera San Pedro was an exhilarating place. It looked out over the whole eastern plain of Chiloé and beyond it, across a broad gulf of sea, to the white-topped crest of the Andes marching along the far skyline. In the clear air we looked at nearly 500 kilometres of mountain, rising over the northern horizon to the shapely volcano of Osorno and sweeping past the peaks of Calbuco and Corcovado to sink into a cluster of ever fainter mountains away south. We confirmed Darwin's observation that the mountains, actually running straight from north to south, seemed to the eye to be bent in a semicircle. There was only one major difference between his view and ours. We saw the cone of Osorno against a cloudless sky where he saw it 'spouting out volumes of smoke'. Had we been eighteen months later the pictures would have coincided exactly.

We spent two rather uneventful weeks on the hills. There was one climatic surprise – a snowstorm, which at latitude 42 degrees south, a month before the longest day of the year, was a bit disconcerting. There was one rebellion. Willy could stand our food no longer.

'The food you have is all very well,' he said. 'But I am a Chilean, and for me red meat is essential. Give me a gun. I go to shoot a Pudu . . .'

My conservationist friends will shudder at this point. The Pudu is now a threatened species, with a declining population (though it was common enough then on the hills of Chiloé). But it did make a splendid *asado*.

And so we turned south. Back down the winding road. Back to Castro. Aboard the ship *Navarino* that plied regularly between Valparaiso and Punta Arenas on the Straits of Magellan. Off to far wilder country. Off to visit the Alacalufs.

When the next dawn came, *Navarino* was alone in a broad gulf of sea. Astern, Chiloé was swallowed up in low clouds and drizzle while ahead the first outliers of the Chonos Islands were dim in the murk.

Chiloé has long been looked on as the last outpost of semi-civilization in Chile. The Chonos are the first wild country beyond the frontier. They stretch southwards for over six hundred kilometres in a series of towering rocks, plateaux and hump-backed hills that in 1958 were still for the most part forested from the water's edge almost to the crests. Between them and the mainland there is a sheltered, navigable channel so that you do not have to brave the surge of the Pacific until you come to where a barrier of ice and glacial debris blocks the channel at the base of the Peninsula of Taitao. Here, at Laguna San Rafael, glaciers descend to sea level, calving icebergs into the lake and fiord – an astonishing thing at a latitude of only 47 degrees south, corresponding to that of central France in the northern hemisphere.

Barred by ice and land, you have to swing westwards around the peninsula and into the Golfo de Penas, the Gulf of Pains, a colder expanse of ocean, where Black-browed albatross and Cape pigeons glide over grey, turbulent, Subantarctic seas. Soon we saw our first penguins. As we came back into the shelter of a further inshore channel it was obvious we had crossed an ecological frontier. Rocky, ice-scoured hills almost bare of trees rose bleakly to a swirling cloud blanket. Rents in the cloud disclosed rounded summits, white under fresh snow. We nudged our way through the Angostura Inglesa – the English Narrows – zig-zagging through low knolls covered in dark thickets of southern beech. A single brilliant white bird – a male Kelp goose – stood on a jut of rock and watched us go by.

'I hope you will have a happy Christmas here among the Alacalufs,' said a fellow-passenger ironically.

'It's a splendid climate,' said another. 'There's nothing quite like it in the whole world. When it isn't raining it's snowing, and when it isn't doing that it's blowing a gale. I have been through the Channels dozens of times and never seen the sun yet!'

We slowed as we neared Puerto Edén. Eden by contrast, for here the walls of the narrow channels – the Canal Mecier to northwards and the deep, gloomy Paso del Abismo, passage of the abyss, to southward – are broken by the mouths of lateral fiords. The channel opens into a broad and sheltered bay dotted with low, wooded islands. Across the open vista some of the peaks tower up nobly. One of them, nameless like almost all the mountains of Wellington Island, lifted a shapely, triple-peaked, snow crest above forest and moorland. There was a gleam of sun, and Edén almost lived up to its name.

'Soon we shall see the Alacalufs,' said Maria, a tall, fair girl insulated against the cold by fur-lined boots and a fur coat, flashing a dazzling Hollywood smile. 'Has anyone told you about them?'

My affirmative was swept aside as a conversational necessity, and she gushed on.

'They are the ugliest people in the whole world. Also the most primitive. Darwin said they were the nearest thing there is to the Missing Link. They live in boats and dirty huts, never wash, eat nothing but *mariscos*, wear hardly any clothes and talk in gurgles and grunts like monkeys.'

The doctor joined in. 'They are violent and quite unteachable,' he said. 'The Government has tried several times to take Alacalufs to school in the north, but it has never worked.'

'And they are full of disease,' said a hefty, tweed-skirted Señora disapprovingly. 'Tuberculosis, chest infections and even worse'(she meant syphilis). 'They are dying off fast, and soon there will be none left.'

'And a very good thing too,' came the chorus.

The Alacaluf Indians are (or were) one of the three tribes of canoe people that ranged from Tierra del Fuego to Chiloé. Of the Chonos people in the north, nothing is known. The Alacalufs, in the main western archipelago, and the Yámana or Yahgans in Fuegia, were coastal nomads, living largely on sea food – shellfish, fish, seabirds, sea-otters and seals. When Europeans first described them, their boats were made of three wide bark strips, pierced at the edges with a bone awl, stitched with creeper and caulked with seal fat and soot. They cut and peeled the bark using sharp stones or knives trimmed from big shells ('Alacaluf' is said to mean 'people who use clam shells for knives'). But in the nineteenth century iron axes reached them and they began to make dug-out canoes – now further modified into rough clinker constructions by using crude planks to raise the freeboard of the dug-out keel. They used to carry fire in bundles of sedge straw, and when they came ashore they built beehive-shaped, skin-covered, branch huts with a central fire and smoke hole. A settlement just like this is featured in one of the illustrations to Captain Robert FitzRoy's account of the voyage of the *Beagle* and photographs we took over a century later show that little had changed. This life style was totally different from that of the other southern tribe – the Ona of Tierra del Fuego – who were a land-based people, living by hunting the Guanaco (a kind of wild llama) and other animals of the plains.

The Chonos tribe had perished by the time modern records began, but a

The Alacaluf encampment at Puerto Edén. The hut in the foreground is of traditional domed form with a frame of branches, covered by any available fabric.

century ago there were, at a guess, about five thousand Alacalufs, perhaps three thousand Yámana and four thousand Ona. In 1958 they had dwindled to around a hundred, thirty and ten. Indeed we learned later that there were probably no pure-blooded Ona remaining, and I think it likely that all three peoples have gone by now. The causes were conflict, murder and disease.

As we looked from *Navarino* across Edén bay we could see a cluster of buildings. The biggest, set on a terrace twenty metres above the water, was a large wooden house with yellowish walls and a red roof – said to have been built as a hotel for use by a seaplane service that was to have plied through the channels from Puerto Montt to Punta Arenas at the eastern end of the Straits of Magellan. It failed – not surprisingly, given the near-universal prevalence of low cloud and gales in this land of narrow channels and endless mountains. But the house was still maintained as an Air Force weather and radio station, and they *did* relieve the commanding officer in an ancient Catalina while we were there, as if to prove a point. We had been promised living and working space under its reassuringly solid roof.

By the shore was a ramshackle wooden hut and two beehive-shaped dwellings – the Alacaluf settlement. An Air Force dinghy and three Alacaluf canoes came out to the ship, the latter eager to barter sacks of mussels, coil-woven baskets and model boats in exchange for clothes and wine. In theory the latter was forbidden them, but something must have aided the singing that came rolling up the slope that evening.

We struggled ashore in the ship's boats which were laden with our stores and with Maria and other first-class passengers, cameras quivering with eagerness at the prospect of portraying an Alacaluf. The boat was so laden it grounded well clear of the jetty, and we had to improvise stepping stones using boxes and three vertebrae from a long-dead whale. Old Rosa Remchi, alleged to be eighty and looking nearer a hundred, emerging from the hut to answer a call of nature, found herself the focus of ten goggling eyes and five lenses. While the shutters clicked she stared back with the aloof condescension of a zoo animal, and then shambled back indoors, call postponed.

Up at the Air Force Station they had heard nothing about our coming, and for a moment it looked as if our tents might get a thorough testing, but Willy soon charmed everyone into agreement and we set up a laboratory and living arrangement much as at Chepu. As if to celebrate, the clouds dropped, the wind rose and it started to rain torrentially. It was a full day before we could go out and explore.

Across the bog behind the house there was a strip of beech woodland dominated by the Magellanic beech (*Nothofagus betuloides* known locally as 'coighue'), intermingled with a second beech, the 'coighue de Chiloé' (*N. nitida*) growing at its southernmost known location. With them were two coniferous trees, the 'ciprés' (*Pilgerodendron uviferum*) and a podocarp, the 'maniu' (*Podocarpus nubigena*), the latter with many close relatives in New Zealand. Finally there was that beautiful tree that Darwin always anglicises in his writings as 'the Winter's Bark' (*Drimys winteri*, the 'canelo'). There were tree ferns also – *Blechnum magellanicum*, a bigger version of the *Blechnum palmiforme* of Gough Island and Tristan. And in a clearing there was a dug-out canoe, abandoned because of a weak spot, only discovered late during its making.

We climbed up towards a rocky crest some 750 metres above the sea, leaving tree after tree behind, and encountering one further species, the Antarctic beech or 'nyere' (*Nothofagus antarctica*), which is unlike the others in being deciduous and forming thickets of high-level scrub on the edge of the open mountain. And as we surveyed the country we were struck by its relative treelessness. According to the vegetation maps all the lowlands should have been covered with 'dense evergreen Magellanic rain forest' like that Darwin had struggled through near the Straits. But here the forest was confined to the coasts and to gullies, hollows and the slopes around some upland lakes. Everywhere else there was soggy peatland covered by tawny grass and sedge and the greens and yellows of cushion plants. We concluded that this was a natural pattern and that except on well-drained slopes, the land was too wet for trees. Eric proposed the term 'Magellanic moorland', and it has stuck.

There were stunted trees among the snow even on our ridge crest at well over 600 metres, but it was thawing fast and the true permanent snowline clearly lay well over three hundred metres higher, where there were gleams of crevassed ice on the face of a shapely double peak that dropped in cliffs to a black, oval lake girdled with forest. Across the channel, on the mainland, the whale-backed crest of Monte Jervis rose some 1300 metres from the water, and on those rare moments when the clouds lifted you could see the gleam of glaciers descending from the real mountains – the Cordillera of the Southern Andes that here culminate in a great ice cap fringed by mountains over three thousand metres high. We saw these mountains distinctly only once, and even then the view was partly blocked by cloud.

We soon dropped into our usual routine. Out to collect – Bill, scrambling across country for rocks; George on the shore, examining all manner of marine creatures and occasionally bobbing about in the shallows in a dry suit, face-mask and flippers; Eric hunting plants and noting vegetation; Willy and I after land animals, and making notes on the wider ecology of the region. I also had a film camera, which yielded a passable record of the expedition but taught me that I lacked the skill and patience to make a natural history film that met the increasingly exacting standards of the time. Which was a pity, because the setting was magnificent, and there were plenty of photogenic birds by the shore. Among them were Kelp geese with white males and dark females, Grey-headed geese, Magellanic penguins, green parrots and even a few humming birds, incongruous beside fiords in which little icebergs sometimes floated. The most impressive common waterbird was the Steamer duck – so named because when approached it does not fly, but threshes the water with its wings, 'steaming' along the surface like a side-paddle ship.

As to the insects – dragonflies hawked over the boggy flats, horseflies nipped you if you loitered, and white and pink butterflies fluttered elusively through the glades. But much of the fauna sat under stones. Stone-turning was therefore quite rewarding. We found frogs, spiders, beetles, worms and much else. Willy – who was a specialist in weevils – came down elated from his first visit to the mountains because he had found twenty-one specimens of a species hitherto known only from one individual collected by Darwin in 1834. Not to be outdone, I collected 35 when I was next out. Willy gathered another 40. By the time the private race ended we had shown that the 'rarity' of Darwin's weevil, *Telurus dissimilis*, was a rarity of collectors, not of the animal itself. Indeed, Willy later described it as 'very common' and 'the best indicator species' of the Magellanic moorland zone. I suspect that collector-rarity will similarly account for the apparent scarceness of a hitherto undescribed frog I collected one day further south – and which the British Museum specialist declined to name from a single specimen.

We worked alone, as we had often done on Gough Island. Not ideal in untraversed and poorly mapped mountain country (our best maps were the 1:1 million scale sheets published by the American Geographical Society, supplemented by the invaluable air photographs given us by the Instituto Geográfico Militar), but inevitable as each of us had a different scientific mandate. Solitude put some constraint on our exploring. For example, one calm, sunny day I found an easy way onto the upper snow slopes of a fine peak north-west of Edén, but felt I could not go to the top because nobody would know where I was. Anyway, I was there to collect insects, not mountains.

We were out whenever it was not impossibly wet, windy and misty, but there were days when collecting had to stop – including one, not far short of the longest day, when heavy snow blanketed the vegetation right down to sea level. The pink, tubular blossom of 'copihue', *Embothrium coccineum*, jutted incongruously from white drifts.

Working in the Station we watched various comings and goings in the bay. One evening a canoe arrived, containing a man with broad shoulders and a wide hat, a woman, and about five dogs which clustered in the bow and yelled defiance at those already at the Alacaluf settlement.

'It's Panchote!'

Panchote Sotomayor, oldest of the Alacaluf men in the Edén group, was the first of several arrivals. Wilfredo Benevedias, station Medical Orderly, explained. 'The canoes come in every year, at about this time. They will then travel northwards as a group towards Isla San Pedro in the Golfo de Penas. The number we have here varies enormously. Only two men – Manuel and Chileno – are here always. The babies and young children go with everyone else. Often they are born in the boats. You see that boy?'

He pointed to a sturdy lad of about twelve, and went on:

'His Alacaluf name is Petayem, but he is registered as Carlos Mecier Los Canales because he was born in Mecier Canal. And that little Juliana has a deformed skull from a knock against the side of the boat when a baby. But not many babies die – they lose far more to tuberculosis when they are fifteen to twenty years old.'

The Alacaluf way of life is, in fact, highly adapted. They live in a land which is cool, but not impossibly cold. The soil yields little. But there are several edible plants – notably fungi that grow on tree-trunks, herbs including wild celery, and berries – among them the red southern

Two Alacaluf women and a child in a canoe among the southern channels.

'crowberry', *Empetrum rubrum*, which is also the only edible berry on Tristan. Animal life is scanty away from the coasts, and the only deer species, the Huemul, *Cervus chilensis*, is rare and shy. But things are different in the coastal zone. Here birds like Kelp geese, Grey-headed geese and Steamer duck give occasional feasts of meat and eggs, and penguins, Sea lions and Fur seals are doubtless killed when opportunity offers. Sea-otters, which bear valuable pelts, are now rare. The shores are also rich in 'everyday' food. Big edible mussels extend in an almost continuous band on rocky coasts, and sea urchins are common. Small fish abound and can be trapped on a falling tide behind barriers of close-set little branches stuck into the sediments of the shallow, silty bays. A nomadic life in a boat therefore fits the environment well.

Shelter is needed in this land of high wind-chill, and there are not many caves. The beehive-shaped huts are easy to make, for branches can be stripped from the woods almost anywhere, and tied into shape with grass or rush stems. Skins are the traditional roofing, carried from place to place in the boats (where they can double as cloaks), while thatch would work in case of need. Fire is also easily carried, smouldering, in grass bundles. And given a certain tolerance of cold (and the people have evolved a response which actually raises peripheral blood flow in a cool skin), going without clothes, apart from skin capes over the shoulders to cut out wind-chill, makes sense. For in that climate, clothes soon get soaked. But rain runs off a bare and greasy skin and if the sun shines its warmth is at once beneficial.

Panchote soon turned up in our kitchen. There were goodies there, and after all, we were curiosities too. He was a tough-looking character with a long, jutting jaw, a square, wrinkled face and a mop of black hair. He watched as I opened some crates.

'Aha,' said I, delighted at the appearance of a delicacy.

'Aha,' echoed Panchote.

I was reminded of something Darwin had written:

'They are excellent mimics; often as we coughed or yawned or made any odd motion, they immediately imitated us. They could repeat with perfect correctness each word in any sentence we addressed them, and they remembered such words for some time . . .'

We did not encourage such visits – lest, as Willy put it, 'Panchote comes in and eats all we have.' But on one occasion I played Father Christmas to the camp followers.

It was all George Hemmen's fault. 'You don't want to take that nasty tinned cheese,' he said. 'What I'll do is have three mature Cheshire cheeses packed for you – one crate for Chepu, one for Edén and one for the south. Enjoy Real English Cheese!'

The Chepu crate encountered a docker's pick at Valparaiso and was condemned. I opened the second at Edén on a warmish day in December, after it had spent six months in a polythene bag, three of them in a warm climate. The polythene was bloated and the cheese within looked as a biological specimen does when disaster has struck the preservative or the freezer. This was a case for exploration in the open air. Outside, I grasped a scalpel and made a median incision. There was a hissing noise and the front terrace became Cheeseland-on-High. There was a rustle and a patter, and about twenty Alacaluf dogs appeared, squatting in a circle with tongues hanging out. They got the top couple of centimetres of the cheese to squabble over. My investigation continued. The inner parts tasted . . . tolerable, though not as Cheshire should. I cut more of the rind off. One or two dogs began to look a little queasy. There can be no doubt that we found a new way of maturing cheese – ship through the tropics in a polythene bag. But I doubt if it would be a commercial success.

Early in December, Rosita Edén del Carmen fell ill. She had been a conspicuous figure during the first days of our visit, in a brilliant scarlet dress that flared against forest and shore. She had been in the group that rowed off to *Navarino*, and had visited another ship a few days afterwards. Soon after that, seven out of the twenty-five Alacaluf in the settlement went down with influenza, and Rosita's merged into pneumonia. She had a bad heart, a history of tuberculosis and was pregnant. She lay in the squalid and smoke-filled hut amid the other invalids, with the dogs wandering in and out and scratching – always scratching – on the floor. Neither we nor the station had the heart stimulant Wilfredo Benevedias wanted. Willy resumed his priest's garb and went to ease Rosita's passing. He came back, obviously impressed. 'They know how to pray,' he said. On 10 December the Sergeant came in and spoke to Willy.

'She is dead,' he announced. 'Have we any box suitable as a coffin?'

Rosita Edén is certainly the only one of her people to be rowed to her grave in a coffin with ROYAL SOCIETY stencilled on its lid. 'She is the first this year,' said the Sergeant. 'But when I was here five years ago I made seven crosses in twelve months.'

The history of all the indigenous peoples of the far south – in Tasmania and the Cape of South Africa as well as southernmost America – is full of darkness. The Ona hunters of Tierra del Fuego, and the Guanaco they depended on, were deliberately slaughtered by European settlers to make room for sheep. And in the western channels it was little better. Women were kidnapped and canoes were shot at if they approached ships to trade. Even the devout English captain of the *Beagle*, Robert FitzRoy, took two adult natives hostage in an attempt to persuade quite unrelated thieves to return a ship's boat, and purported to 'buy' two children to take to England to display, educate, and bring back as aids to a Christianizing mission. By the time the Swedish explorer Carl Skottsberg was there, in 1910, the reaction to an approaching ship was to mutter '*Christianos – malos*' (Christians – bad people) and get out of the way.

But diseases and missions (the two worked in a strange combination) may have been even more deadly. Like all the Amerindian tribes, the Fuegians had no resistance to infections from Europe. Measles, smallpox, chickenpox, diphtheria, influenza, scarlet fever, tuberculosis and syphilis spread like wildfire. William Denevan, in a fascinating analysis, has suggested that at the time of European contact in 1492 there may have been 80 million people in the two American continents – and 90 per cent died of disease within a century. The empty lands encountered by European colonists may have been cleared by a wave of pestilence. In the far south missions, appalled at the naked and ignorant savagery of the canoe tribes, gathered them in settlements, tried to teach them a more godly and righteous way of life, but inevitably helped infection to spread.

And all this was made easier by cultural barriers which meant that the skills and adaptations of the people were ignored. Witness Darwin:

We pulled alongside a canoe of six Fuegians. They were the most abject

and miserable creatures I anywhere beheld . . . They were naked, and
even one full-grown woman absolutely so. It was raining heavily and
the fresh water together with the spray trickled down her body. . .
These poor wretches were stunted in their growth, their hideous
faces bedaubed with white paint, their skins filthy and greasy, their
hair entangled, their voices discordant and their gestures violent.
Viewing such men one can hardly believe that they are fellow-
creatures and the inhabitants of the same world . . . Whenever it is low
water, winter or summer, night or day, they must rise to pick shell fish
from the rocks: the women must dive to collect sea-eggs, or sit
patiently in their canoes and with a baited hair-line without any hook,
jerk out little fish . . .

And so on. Most of the observation accurate, most of the interpretation
quite wrong. The same thing happened over language and customs. Darwin
described the Yámana language as 'scarcely deserving to be called articulate'.
Lucas Bridges wrote later, from much deeper knowledge, that 'we who
learned as children to speak Yahgan (Yámana) know that, within its own
limitations, it is infinitely richer and more expressive than English or
Spanish. My father's *Yahgan-English Dictionary* contains no fewer than 32,000
words and inflections, the number of which might have been greatly
increased without departing from common speech. The Yahgans had, at the
very least, five names for "snow". For "beach" they had even more,
depending on a variety of factors: the position of the beach in relation to the
speaker, the direction in which it faced, whether the speaker had land or
water between it and himself and so on . . .'

Some similar muddle must explain the oft-quoted 'cannibal' incident,
when Jemmy Button (one of the 'purchased' children, his 'price' a pearl
button) told Darwin that 'when pressed in winter by hunger they kill their
old women before they kill their dogs' explaining that 'doggies catch otters,
old women no.' Lucas Bridges was equally scathing about this comment.
'We who later passed many years of our lives in daily contact with these
people can find only one explanation for this shocking nonsense. We
suppose that when questioned, York Minster or Jemmy Button would not
trouble in the least to answer truthfully but would merely give the reply that
was expected or desired . . .' Indeed, Bridges thought they were probably
having Darwin on. For anybody who has had any real contact with the
Fuegians has been clear about one thing – they were *not* cannibals. Whether,
when pressed by winter, they ever abandoned old people who were too sick
to travel we cannot tell, but if they did it was probably done with dignity and
acceptance on both sides.

The Alacaluf in 1958 still had a habit of imprecise answer, probably designed to make the questioner happy.

'How many canoes are still away?' asked Willy one day.

The answer came back pat. 'Six.'

'And how many people in each?'

'Two-three.'

'Only two or three? Surely some have more.'

'Oh, yes. Four or five.'

'Then how many are there in most canoes? Some with families must have as many as five or six?'

'Of course. Five or six people in each canoe . . .'

We were high on Monte Jervis one fine day, when a black smoke column drifted down from the north. An ancient, grey-painted oil tanker and a tug passed slowly by.

'Ah,' said Willy. 'Those are our Antarctic ships – the tanker is the *Maipo*, and the tug the *Lientur*. The Chief said they would be here today.'

A helicopter buzzed across the bay. 'Messages to the Chief,' we said. The radio transmitter was broken and he had been waiting for weeks for news of a seaplane that would bring spares. We thought no more of it. But when we returned on a rare evening of glorious sunshine, with the mountains blue-black against a clear sky, Willy had grave news.

'The message was for us,' he said. 'A patrol ship, the *Micalvi*, will call for us in two days. Otherwise we have to stay until February.' We packed rapidly. And we had to deal with a sheep.

This was another result of Willy's addiction to *asados*. He had begged Capitan Garcia of the *Navarino* to bring us a lamb when he called on his northbound return from Punta Arenas. It was to be 'on the hoof', to be fed on the grassy sward until needed. It was duly sentenced to die next day. After breakfast Willy, a farmer's son, vanished behind the house with the lamb, an Alacaluf assistant, and a viciously sharp knife. That evening we made our *asado* in the open, still under cloudless skies. The station people and the Alacalufs mingled. The stocky, middle-aged man they called Chileno, the Chilean (because he had actually been to mainland Chile), was in happy mood. 'You are a Gringo,' he told Bill, Willy, Eric and me in turn. 'But' (turning to George) 'you are not.' Maybe the hefty red beard made the difference. As for himself, he was emphatic. '*No soy Indio*, I am not an Indian,' he affirmed, mouthing the last word with distaste. '*Soy Alacaluf*.'

After that there was a babel of mixed Spanish and Alacaluf as they sang songs. Chileno danced on the pathway, and when George joined in, the audience found the spectacle too much to bear in solemn silence. Three of them later tried to teach us words in Alacaluf. The only one I remember is 'yataghsta,' which Julio assured me meant 'goodnight'.

Micalvi came in next day. She was old and odd-looking, with square bows but a schooner's curving stern: a high fo'c'sle, a deep foredeck and a tall narrow funnel half obscured by chicken coops and rope. There were sheep on her foredeck and great piles of *ciprés* poles further aft. Her paint was a nominal Navy-grey, flecked with soot and rust. She carried no radar, but she *did* have a Kelvin deep sea sounding machine dated 1874. 'We got that last year,' said Captain Otto Niemann, 'from a destroyer they were breaking up.'

Otto was honest about her sailing capacities. 'We make eight knots with the current, six in calm water, and maybe two knots when the current is against us. The boiler is very old and if we try to go faster we might blow up. And we do not travel at night. I like to find a nice bay, anchor and fish. The Admiral has told me to help you, and if you want to go ashore for a day, just tell me. We go so slowly it won't make any difference.'

Clearly the ideal ship in which to potter through the South Chilean fiords.

'Oh, and don't worry if we hit a rock,' he went on. 'All the bottom of the hull is lined with water tanks. If we make a hole it will only go into a tank...'

We spent twelve days in *Micalvi*, plugging gently through the fiords and among the islands. Somewhere in the maze, we passed *Navarino* going north. Only later did we discover that she was carrying two more lambs and a case of champagne, sent by our agents in Punta Arenas to gladden our Christmas. We had visions of a very happy Puerto Edén with some very bubbly Alacalufs. As for us, Christmas saw us at Isla Guarello, an improbable island of bare white limestone where they quarried stone for use as flux in the northern blast furnaces of the Chilean National Steel Company. We botanised, and Eric found two ferns not previously known from Chile. We examined the quarry, dug like a crater into the heart of the hill. And we had one whale of a party. The culinary high point was a *curanto*.

This is a Chilote speciality, and a Chilote prepared it. He dug a hole in the ground and lined it with stones: he lit a fire on top and fed it until it became a mass of hot embers. They were raked out, and the hole filled with mutton, chickens, *mariscos* (especially the two kinds of mussel they call *cholga* and *choro*), potatoes and a kind of rough bread. The earth oven was covered over and left to cook, each element pervading the others so that the chicken tasted of mutton and of shellfish and the bread had the savour of them all. The New Zealanders felt at home, for the Maoris cook in a similar way. Like the coil-weave baskets the Alacaluf make, earth ovens are found throughout the Pacific, though what this means in terms of past human and cultural

Monte Burney and the southern Andes from a nameless hill just north of the Straits of Magellan.

links is not clear. After the *curanto* came much wine – and one of George and Eric's travelling companions was so fuddled that he scarcely woke up after falling from a third-tier bunk to the decking.

We crossed inlet after inlet, passing island after island – an immense, intricate mingling of land and sea. And one day we took Captain Niemann at his word and went ashore to climb a hill and look at the upland animals and plants. It was only a little hill, 810 metres high, but the air was brilliant, and it commanded an incredible view. To the north the southernmost active volcano in Chile, Monte Burney, reared its ice-capped 1750 metre cone, its flanks hidden under tumbled glaciers. Southwards, close to the Straits of Magellan, a broad icecap called the Campo Nevado rose above a tangle of rock ridges. Across the Straits was the long, serrated outline of Isla Desolación – named 'South Desolation' by Sir John Narborough because it was 'so desolate a land to behold'. At its far end, Cape Pilar abutted on the golden fume of the ocean. Here Magellan had sailed out into the uncharted western seas. Here Drake had encountered such a storm that:

> the winds were such as if the bowels of the earth had been set at libertie or as if all the clouds under Heaven had been called together to lay their force upon this one place.

Next day we headed eastwards through the Straits – still in weather of extraordinary brilliance so that every ice crest sparkled and every view was clear. Even the ice cap of Isla Santa Inés – a place so habitually obscured that the aerial survey of Chile failed to cover it and the western slopes were still labelled on the maps with INEXPLORADO in bold red letters – was in full view. 'I think that there is not in the world a more beautiful country or a better strait than this one,' wrote the Chevalier Antonio Pigafetta, Magellan's companion. We were obviously enjoying 'Magellan's weather'. We took advantage of it by noting how vegetation type succeeded vegetation type as we passed from very wet to less wet zones, and from the open, soggy Magellanic moorland to the more continuous woodland that covered the slopes around Cape Froward, southernmost point of the American mainland, with its towering white cross. And we looked south, as Darwin had, at island beyond island and mountain beyond mountain, appearing 'to lead beyond the confines of this world'.

So we came to Punta Arenas – Sandy Point. We stayed in the Hotel Cosmos – a charming, seedy, ramshackle wooden building where the telephones were of brass, and you had to crank a handle to make the bell at the other end ring. In the British Club we listened to the English vicar from Valparaiso giving a recital of Edward Lear on a Sunday evening. We sat in leather-covered armchairs to scan the *Spectator* and the *Illustrated London News*. We looked at a framed letter from the Royal Geographical Society, thanking the club for the gift of the sextant used on Shackleton's epic boat journey from Elephant Island to South Georgia. The broad staircase, the massive furniture, the moulded ceilings, the billiard tables – all seemed to have strayed from Pall Mall, and lingered as a strange cultural island.

The Club was there because Punta Arenas and the sheep country around it had long been settled by the British, who were a dominant influence in the *Sociedad Explotadora de Tierra del Fuego* – the Fireland Development Society. Scots shepherds brought their flocks to the meat freezers and their wool to the warehouses. British and Argentine commercial interests were dominant – the latter represented especially by the family of José de Menendez whose descendants were still prominent. We were invited to a picnic, where we met a number of them – including some very pretty girls.

Punta Arenas stands at that point on the Straits of Magellan where mountains give way to plains, and forests to scrub and grasslands. Darwin commented in 1834 on the dramatic change, from 'rounded mountains concealed by impervious forests which are drenched with the rain' to 'a clear and bright blue sky over the dry and sterile plains' all in a distance of under a hundred kilometres. The first European settlement to guard the Straits was established by Spain in 1583 and named San Felipe – and by 1586 almost all its 150 people had starved, winning the place its new name, Puerto Hambre, Port Famine. A new settlement was not built until 1843, when Captain John Williams (a Chilean of Bristol stock) claimed the district, built huts within a stockade, and re-named the site Fuerte Bulnes after the President who had sent him. Today's town stands about 25 kilometres to the north, on a more spacious site.

Punta, in 1959, gave the impression of a place that had seen better days. The waterfront was dominated by a long jetty thrust out into the Straits. From it, you looked past a scatter of anchored craft, including the hulk of a four-masted sailing ship, to where the great ice-peak of Monte Sarmiento, over two thousand metres high, glowed on the horizon like a distant thundercloud. The streets were laid out as a grid, but some were narrow and with poor, decrepit houses. Others were wide and prosperous, the broadest – like that in Santiago – dominated by a massive figure of the liberator of Chile, Bernardo O'Higgins. In the main square there was a fine statue of Magellan, with a Fuegian squatting at his feet, and gardens about him. We were told that if you touched the Fuegian's toe and ate berries of the straggly *Berberis buxifolia*, locally known as 'califate', you would come back to Patagonia. I did both, which may or may not explain why George and I were back in 1982 on our way to the Antarctic. The town was richer then, with new warehouses, new factories, an enlarged airport, and ski-runs on the forested slopes above. And the British Club was closed, with shuttered windows tilting into decrepitude.

We had a day on the grassy plains – the beginning of the pampa that rolls unbroken northwards to Buenos Aires. We admired improved pastures where the carrying capacity for cattle had been increased tenfold. But on the wilder lands we saw numerous Guanacos and a grey fox. Flamingos flew over and settled in brackish lagoons by the sea: there were Black-necked swans and the smaller white Coscoroba swan, abundant Pintail duck and huge numbers of Upland geese. There were also quite a lot of Rheas (the South American equivalent of an ostrich). I caused hilarity afterwards when recording the commentary for our film on the expedition:

And we saw Darwin's rhea strutting across a valley...

But, while we enjoyed this interlude in Punta, and the immensely generous hospitality (especially from the Huntley family), our work lay elsewhere and we were delighted when the FACh arranged a flight south to Puerto Williams on the Beagle Channel, early in January. We glimpsed the tangled glaciers of the Cordillera Darwin, the highest massif on Tierra del Fuego, which cascaded to the sea in aprons of ice that the rain had carved into crazy pinnacles. I was reminded of Eric Shipton's description of Patagonian glaciers – 'the nastiest, most impossible masses of broken ice you can find anywhere in the world.' Then came the Beagle – a long channel that runs between the main island of Tierra del Fuego and the archipelago to the south, in Darwin's words 'a most remarkable feature . . . about one hundred and twenty miles long with an average breadth of about two miles and . . . throughout the greater part, so perfectly straight that the view, bounded on each side by a line of mountains, gradually becomes indistinct in the long distance.' If the canals of Mars really existed, they might have looked like that.

In 1834 Darwin noted how the mountains 'rose in one unbroken sweep from the water's edge and were covered to the height of fourteen or fifteen hundred feet by the dusky forest. It was most curious to observe as far as the eye could range, how level and truly horizontal the line on the mountain side was, at which trees ceased to grow; it precisely resembled the high water mark of drift-weed on a beach.' It still did over a hundred years later, but swathes of coarse grassland now swept upwards from the shore, where axe and fire had done their work.

Puerto Williams, on the north shore of Isla Navarino, was a naval base; a cluster of little wooden bungalows painted diverse colours, set out on a low hilltop above a square-set bay barred by a long spit. We were welcomed and accommodated in the hospital, with an empty house to use as laboratory, and we gained further saving in time by being allowed to eat, at a very cheap rate, in the mess used by unmarried officers. We called on the Commandant, Capitán de Fregata Ramón Aragay, in his neat house surrounded by a flowery garden which two *conscriptos* were weeding. Two bulls and three cows stared longingly over the fence.

We were there a month. We explored the seaways with the Navy, noting that there was still an abundance of whales in the channel, as there had been in the time of the *Beagle*. There were Sea lions, too, roaring from little rocky islets. I was, to my annoyance, laid low by a touch of flu when George, Eric, Willy, Bill and a Swiss geologist, Hans Katz, who had teamed up with us, went in the tug *Leucoton* to Cape Horn island and its neighbours. And I missed their near-involvement in a Diplomatic Incident.

It was all about Snipe Islet – Islote Snipé – or rather, the bigger contention of which it was the bone. A frontier dispute between Chile and Argentina. Both claimed Snipe and three larger islands near it, the whole argument depending on how you interpreted the decree that Chile shall have no territory on the Atlantic, nor Argentina on the Pacific, and weighed that against the contradictory statement that the frontier shall run across Tierra del Fuego from north to south 'until it touches the Beagle Channel and proceeds from there eastwards along the channel leaving the lands which lie to the north to Argentina and the south to Chile.'

Chile claimed Snipe because it lies south of the Beagle. Argentina claimed it because it lies on the Atlantic side of Cape Horn, and east of the deep-water channel that curves around Navarino Island. The debate has rumbled on for decades, with a British adjudication in the 1960s, and a Papal one after that. When we were there matters had moved to Direct Action. A Chilean navigation beacon on Snipe Island was removed after an Argentine objection, but then replaced on a larger scale. Argentina sent a destroyer which removed the offending installation and landed a party of sailors, who ate their way happily through the Chilean sheep that been grazing the island. There were protests and counter-accusations. Two Argentine cruisers began to patrol the Beagle Channel from their base in Ushuaia. The Chileans loaded some launches with mines, planning to give the cruisers an interesting time, and concentrated their fleet in the islands behind Cape Horn. Artillery experts appeared, and studied how to make Puerto Williams more defensible. In the end things were patched over, but while we were there sensitivity remained high. And we nearly got caught up in it.

It all happened on that cruise in *Leucoton*. I remember telling the British Ambassador about it when we were back in Santiago. 'We nearly caused you a headache,' I said.

'How?'

'Well, four of our party went for a cruise in *Leucoton*, and landed on Snipe Island.'

He sat up, sharply.

'The Chileans put up a monstrous great notice board recording the visit, with VIVA CHILE on the back. Everybody signed it – and they passed the pencil across so that our people could show friendly solidarity...'

'My God!' he exploded. 'They didn't, did they...?'

No, they didn't. Fortunately, for a few weeks later the board was removed, and all the names were included in a formal note of protest. The Royal Society would not have been amused...

Puerto Williams was also on the border of another disputed frontier – the Antarctic, where Chilean 'Tierra O'Higgins' overlapped with the Argentine 'Tierra San Martin' and the British 'Graham Land'. The three claimant nations had discreetly separated bases around the magnificent natural harbour formed by the flooded central caldera of a big volcano, Deception Island. The Chileans decided to cement their claim and raise public interest by taking tourists there, and the very first party – perhaps the very first of all Antarctic tourists – arrived at Williams while we were there. They were clearly a bit apprehensive, and they were not calmed by the sight of the frigate *Iquique* which had just docked with ice damaged bows that looked as if some giant had laid about them with a Herculean club. They were a bit calmer after a tremendous *asado* at which six sheep were eaten and uncounted flagons of wine consumed. Next day they departed. Ten days later they were back having crawled into Deception in fog. According to one of them, they had been seasick for three days, fog-bound for three more, and ashore for a few hours. 'Wonderful party,' he said. 'Wonderful experience. And I never want to do it again!'

My flu soon departed, and on 14 January (my 28th birthday) I went onto the uplands of Navarino for the first time. The track crossed a series of low ridges of glacial moraine with peat bogs between – and on this dry side of the island they were moss bogs with *Sphagnum*, not carpet bogs. The forests beyond were of deciduous beech, *Nothofagus pumilio* with a little *N. antarctica*. The interior was a tangle of leaning and upright trees, but with only sparse undergrowth; you could walk almost anywhere, as you can in an English beechwood. It was all quite different from the sodden, ferny tangles of the west.

Above the forest I came to open heathland picked out with great swelling grey-green cushions of the Bog-balsam, *Bolax gummifera*, a plant long famous in the Falklands. There was a lot of red-berried *Empetrum* there as well, growing just as it does on Gough Island and Tristan. I looked south to a range of jagged rock towers – Los Dientes de Navarino (the Teeth of Navarino), rising to about 1100 metres. As I scanned them with binoculars a long, laughing cry echoed across the forests. Guanacos. Five of them, grazing on a tongue of grassland. I stalked closer, admiring their ruddy-brown backs paling on the flanks to the cream of the underbelly: vivid splashes of colour in the sunlight. From time to time one would raise its tall neck and gaze around, oval ears cocked and black muzzle twitching. I brought a ciné-camera to bear, it whirred, and one noticed me.

'They are generally wild and extremely wary,' wrote Darwin. But, he explained, if you meet a group at close quarters 'they will generally stand motionless and gaze intently; then perhaps move on a few yards, turn round and look again . . . That they are curious is certain; for if a person lies on the ground and plays strange antics such as throwing up his feet in the air, they will always approach by degrees to reconnoitre him.'

They certainly reconnoitred me, clearly finding a camera on a shiny tripod a great novelty. Once I tried the upside-down trick, bemusing an old male that spent some ten minutes circling while George, for whom I was waiting, tried to work out what on earth I was up to.

The guanaco were at the heart of the culture of the Ona of Tierra del Fuego – a strikingly tall, handsome people like the race of giants (Patagones

= 'big feet') for whom Magellan named Patagonia. Guanaco provided skin capes, caps and water bags, guanaco leather made girdles, guanaco sinews were used as bowstrings and guanaco skins covered their tents (which were made of straight poles and pointed-topped, like a North American tepee rather than beehive-shaped like the Alacaluf shelters).

The hunting was their undoing. For Guanaco were perceived by sheep farmers as competitors and were shot. On their side, the Ona saw the 'white guanaco' that invaded their ancestral hunting grounds as a most acceptable alternative quarry. The *Daily News* is said to have reported in 1872 that Tierra del Fuego was ideal sheep country 'subject only to the single inconvenience of the manifest necessity of exterminating the Fuegians.' Some ranchers employed professional Indian hunters who were paid a bounty of £1 per head for men, women or children. A man named MacLennan, who lived at Bahia Inutil (Useless Bay), is said to have handed out £412 in one year. I have seen ciné-film of the last of these hunters who was alive in retirement in the Falklands as late as the 1940s. A gold rush in 1880 filled Tierra del Fuego with wandering bands of armed and unscrupulous prospectors, and this was cause of further slaughter. By 1900 the Ona population had fallen from about 3500 to 700, and despite some enlightened efforts by people like the Bridges family at Harberton on the south coast of Tierra del Fuego, by 1958 there were virtually none left. We met only one, a stockhand on the farm west of Puerto Williams, and he was said to be only half-Ona.

On the uplands there were many birds – little grey-headed Tyrant flycatchers, a Seed-snipe (which appears to fill the same ecological niche as the northern ptarmigan), and most striking of all, the great Andean condor. I found you could attract Condors rather like you could Guanacos – at least, one day while I was lying face-down looking for insects under stones, I heard a noise of the wind creaking through feathers, and there was one about ten metres up, clearly wondering whether I was yet moribund enough to eat. And there were some unfortunate introductions – we dug out a burrow which proved to contain a musk-rat, introduced to Argentine Tierra del Fuego for its fur and very likely to become a troublesome pest. And we heard later of a zany plan to release reindeer on Navarino – a recipe for disaster if they multiply and behave as they have done on South Georgia.

We ended our time in Chile by exploring the way south across Navarino, climbing close under the end of the Dientes and camping high up near a gap that separated them from an unmapped ridge that ran southwards. On this trip, Bill Watters found sparse fossils of a ribbed mussel called *Inoceramus* that dated the muddy shales of the Yahgan series to the Cretaceous period. We got a lift round the island in a Naval launch, passing Wulaia (called

Woollya by Darwin) where Captain FitzRoy established an ill-fated Christian mission, and stayed for a few days on Isla Bertrand, at the southernmost farm in the world, where Alfredo Grandi struggled to make a living, rarely raising more than 60 lambs per 100 ewes and sometimes half that number. We climbed the other side of the unmapped ridge, noting how the peat of the carpet bogs had slumped down a steep slope to form a series of steps, each crowned with a pool. I puzzled why it was that despite the universal peat blanket of western Patagonia there was no open gully erosion such as dissects the peat moors of the English Pennines. On Isla Bertrand I think I found the answer – for where there were sheep, there were open, eroding channels.

From the top of the ridge we looked out over Isla Bertrand to the wrinkled blue silhouette of the Wollaston Islands and the Cape Horn group, with nothing beyond them but the turbulent seas of the Drake Passage and Antarctica. It was a clear, cold, rain-washed landscape at the uttermost end of the Earth.

CHAPTER FOUR

The True South

Back in Britain activity was intense. The Royal Society Committee needed briefing. Specimens needed sorting and distributing to specialists. Reports needed writing and film needed editing. An exhibit had to be prepared for the Society's Soirée. It was decided that our findings – inevitably preliminary as there was so much evaluation to do – would be reported to a special Discussion Meeting on 'the Biology of the Southern Cold Temperate Zone', and this brought all the members of the Expedition together in London in December 1959. The tempo was more feverish because the three hundredth anniversary of the Royal Society's foundation by King Charles II was approaching.

The year 1959 was important for me for two reasons. First, it transformed me from a local University Lecturer into someone with contacts in the national corridors of science. Second, I met Ruth. She was one of the only two women I have ever wanted to marry. She was a naturalist and wild-life artist. We spent days looking at plants and buildings in and around Norwich, where she lived and worked. She came with me to some of the Royal Society tercentenary events. She visited Blackpool. But it did not work out – and she has been happily married to someone else for nearly forty years. So have I. But I will always be grateful to her for building my confidence, for showing me many beautiful places, and for a lot of happiness.

The Expedition transformed Willy's personal life too. He was invited to New Zealand, to work in the Dominion Museum at Wellington. This gave him new opportunities for research on his beloved weevils. There was a girl there named Beverley. She was also a weevil enthusiast. They spent a lot of time comparing specimens and arguing about the merits of two rival systems of classification. The next thing we knew was that Willy was dispensed from his priestly Orders and that they were getting married. I do not know whether any of their three children has inherited an interest in weevils . . .

The Discussion Meeting may well have been the first occasion since the days of Darwin and Hooker when what Carl Pantin called 'the biological history of the southern hemisphere round the pole' was thoroughly discussed. It brought together many distinguished explorers. Carl Skottsberg, then well into his eighties, recalled how he had gone to the Antarctic with the Swedish Expedition led by Nordenskjöld in 1900 and had discovered fossil plants belonging to genera now living in South America and New Zealand.

'When we came back, in 1906,' said Skottsberg, 'I went to see Sir Joseph Hooker, and told him what we had found. He was pleased.'

That simple comment bridged 115 years of Antarctic botany.

But what did the Royal Society Expedition to Southern Chile achieve? First, it showed that a small party could indeed move relatively easily in places like Southern Chile – if, like us, it had the generous support of people along the route. Second, it suggested that the original notion of an island-hopping traverse of the tropical and sub-tropical South Pacific would be unlikely to shed much light on biological relationships between the southern continents.

This was because it seemed clear that the similarities between the floras and faunas of southern Chile and New Zealand were not the result of a simple trans-Pacific link. The distinctive forest trees and carpet-bog plants, and most of the other plants and invertebrates associated with them, occurred wherever there were continental areas with a temperate climate in the southern hemisphere. New Zealand, southern Chile, Tasmania and adjacent south-eastern Australia all had this kind of flora. Fossils showed it once grew in part of Antarctica. But while the islands scattered around the southern temperate zone also had floras and faunas with many related species, these did not include the forest and carpet-bog plants or their associated insects. And there were anomalies. For example, Kerguelen, in the middle of the South Indian Ocean, had some sedimentary rocks, including coals, with fossils of conifers and their pollen, and even though the islands are now impoverished (probably as a result of glaciation), they still have some very distinctive and probably ancient plant species including the famous 'Kerguelen cabbage', *Pringlea antiscorbutica* and some equally peculiar invertebrates.

In the late 1950s, theories of continental drift were still regarded as speculative (there was only one mention, in the whole Discussion Meeting, of new evidence from the magnetism of ancient rocks that would shortly bring these theories back into credence). We now believe that many of the relationships date back over 60 million years, to when South America, Africa, India, Antarctica, Australia and New Zealand were all joined in the supercontinent of Gondwanaland. Kerguelen may also be a continental fragment. Today's southern mainland assemblages survived as the fragments slowly drifted apart, where the climate remained suitable – but disappeared where the land became too tropical or arid (India, Africa, most of Australia) or too icy (Antarctica and also Kerguelen). The volcanic islands are all younger than the mainlands, forming on the oceanic ridges that marked Gondwana's fissure-lines. Their impoverished, but evidently related, floras and faunas fit the hypothesis that they have come from the temperate mainlands by trans-ocean dispersal.

Many people no doubt see such things as remote in space and time from the human problems of the modern world. In his introduction, Carl Pantin argued that they were not. 'Conditions are changing too fast for us to predict our biological future,' he said, 'and vital information about the present and past condition of living things is vanishing; yet it is upon just such information that our prediction of our own future must be based.'

He went on to make a diagnosis of the world environmental situation that would have done credit to an environmentalist twenty years later – but passed almost unnoticed at the time:

> It is the speed and character of the change in world ecology which makes our problem urgent ... Biological systems depend on the interaction of a multitude of different factors, and a small change in any one of those may cause an almost cataclysmic change in configuration, as with the turn of a kaleidoscope. What will follow from the general destruction of our forests, from the erosion of soil which follows agriculture, from the effects of the widespread use of insecticides, from the increase of the products of nuclear fission in the atmosphere and in the sea, and now we may even perhaps ask what will follow the arrival of the first cargo of bacteria and of men upon another planet? We are attempting to control nature and the immediate consequence is a staggering increase in the rate of change of the natural world, in directions we cannot predict.

The Expedition and Discussion clearly convinced the Royal Society that more should be done to unravel the patterns and relationships of life at the bottom end of the world. It seemed clear that the circumpolar region had to be thought of as a whole. And there were gaps and anomalies, especially around the French possessions of Kerguelen and the Crozet Islands in the south Indian Ocean. It was suggested that a seaborne party should circumnavigate the globe, and look especially at the ecology of these neglected regions. I was invited to plan this Expedition, moving from Durham to a base at the Scott Polar Research Institute in Cambridge. By chance, Lewis Davies, whose place I had filled at Durham, wanted to come back from Canada, so we swapped again! Gordon Robin, Director of the SPRI, was most welcoming: he wanted a biologist as one of his two Assistant Directors of Research. So in October 1960 I was back in Cambridge, living in a flat on the corner of the Market Square and busily preparing expedition plans.

Despite the forceful persuasion of Lord Fleck, former head of ICI and Treasurer of the Royal Society, the Government refused the grant that would have made the new expedition possible (by another of those odd coincidences, it was Lewis Davies of Durham that eventually got to the Crozet Islands and discovered an endemic midge with South American and Australasian relationships). So in the summer of 1961 I found myself at something of a loose end. It was clear that Ruth and I were not going to get married. My Chilean material was safely deposited at the Natural History Museum. There was no immediate prospect of new fieldwork in the Subantarctic. What to do?

Every year FIDS – the Falkland Islands Dependencies Survey (or F***ing Idiots Down South as the Falkland Islanders interpreted the acronym) – held its briefing conference for new recruits at the Scott Polar. The 1961 intake included Peter Tilbrook, who had been one of my students at Durham, and Barry Heywood from Birmingham. They were supposed to be starting a new biology programme based on Signy Island in the South Orkney group. Jim Cragg had reconnoitred this site two years previously but his tour had been cut short when the RRS (Royal Research Ship) *Shackleton* in which he had been travelling hit a lump of ice, opened a ten-foot gash in the forehold, and nearly sank. Now action was beginning, although not steered from Durham. I was told that Jim's direct manner had upset the Governor of the Falkland Islands who was still nominally in command of all British Antarctic operations.

I was misinformed. The truth – which I only learned thirty years afterwards – was more surprising. According to Bill Sloman, for many years the Personnel Officer of FIDS and then of the British Antarctic Survey, it all went back to the time when Jim Cragg applied for a job at the University of Melbourne in Australia. Those were the days of anti-Communist paranoia, and applicants were required to answer the McCarthy Test: 'Are you, or have you ever been, a member of the Communist Party?' Jim had not, but he thought the question improper and refused to answer it. He did not get the job. But the Vice Chancellor of the University of Melbourne at that time, Sir Raymond Priestley, who had served in the Antarctic with both Scott and Shackleton, had become Chairman of the FIDS Scientific Bureau in 1959, when Jim's name came forward as the prospective biological mentor of the Survey. Bill Sloman told me that Sir Raymond blocked the appointment. I remain surprised, because he always struck me as a wise and tolerant man. But we all have our hang-ups. His, in my view, did British Antarctic science a grave disservice. The role passed to Professor (later Sir) Eric Smith, Professor of Zoology at Queen Mary College, London. Eric was a charming, distinguished, marine biologist. But he did not have Jim Cragg's verve. It was clear that Peter Tilbrook and Barry Heywood were missing the kind of close guidance and back-up that Jim would have given them.

An idea took shape in three minds almost at once. I went to find Sir Vivian Fuchs, Director of FIDS, who was presiding over the conference. I knew him by reputation, of course, as the leader of the Commonwealth Transantarctic Expedition, the first crossing of the continent from the Weddell to the Ross Sea. I knew him slightly personally, because Father had taught him chemistry at Brighton College and they had kept in touch.

In an hour or so, he, Gordon Robin and I had agreed that I would indeed go south for a summer season to help Peter and Barry get started, to advise on the biological research potential of Signy Island, and to help plan a new laboratory. Two months later I was in Montevideo, boarding the RRS *John Biscoe*. So began six years involvement with Antarctic research.

'Monte' was the last big seaport the FIDS ships used going south. It took them five weeks to get there, chugging slowly from Southampton. Five invaluable weeks at close quarters, to 'shake down' the temperaments of the new hands and let them imbibe knowledge from old stagers going back for another tour of duty. Five weeks to reveal any character defects. Sometimes problems were discovered in the nick of time, as with someone I will call Mike. He was a tough builder, recruited to help construct an aircraft hangar. He was charming and easy to get on with – when sober. He became violent when drunk, and he got drunk easily. One night he picked a quarrel and chased his opponent down the corridor between the ship's cabins, swinging an ice-axe. The quarry made it to his cabin and slammed the bolt – and the ice pick smashed through the panelling. Mike, quickly restrained, was soon on his way home.

There were other character tests in Montevideo, whose sleazy waterfront had many traps for sailors. The doctors made no bones about it at the briefing conference. 'Any woman you can sleep with in Monte will have VD!' they thundered. But young men have strong urges, especially after five weeks at sea. As a second line of defence, condoms were on free issue. It was only a partial solution, and there were a few embarrassing medical discussions on the radio between bases with doctors and those without, as late doses presented themselves weeks afterwards.

Putting out from Monte, the Southern Ocean takes hold of you and on my second visit in 1963 I witnessed a Darwinian Episode. The hot, dry wind they call a *pampero* was blowing off the land, and the waters of the River Plate were alive with dragonflies and butterflies, the latter fluttering like helpless scraps of paper and seeming always about to sink into a wave crest but never quite doing so. Darwin noted the same phenomenon in 1833: 'Several times when the ship has been some miles off the Plate . . . we have been surrounded by insects. One evening . . . vast numbers of butterflies, in bands or flocks of countless myriads, extended as far as the eye could range.' It was easy to see how the big orange-and-black Brazilian moth I had caught at lights on Gough had got there. A dragonfly was still alive in my cabin when we reached Port Stanley, four days later.

The Falkland Islands are not a dramatic landfall. They heave over the rim of ocean as a long undulation, jutting occasionally into sharper points of rock. They are a land of rolling hills, rocky ridges, immense peaty moorlands, and racing clouds. Windy, always windy. The coasts are a maze of inlets and islands, and where shielded from grazing they are green with tall tussocks of the same grass, *Paradiochloa flabellata*, that dominates the coastal slopes of Gough. The tussock coasts are alive with several kinds of penguins, petrels and Sea lions. As you come into harbour, Wandering and Black-browed albatrosses, Giant petrels, Cape pigeons, slate-grey prions, heavy-bodied Brown skuas and dainty swallow-like white-rumped Wilson's petrels are all about you. Steamer duck paddle desperately out of your way, while on shore, Kelp geese – the same species as in Chile, with white males and grey females – are much in evidence. And in those days, as you slowed to pass through the outer approaches to Stanley, you might glimpse Sparrow Cove where the *Great Britain* lay beached, her hull cracked and her masts mere stumps, awaiting rescue to Bristol.

I was rather alarmed as we approached Stanley in 1961. A telegram was handed over.

HOPEFUL YOU WILL STAY WITH US ON ARRIVAL it read. I looked at the foot of the page. Signed GOVERNOR.

'I hope you've got your dinner jacket!' said 'Fuzz' the Radio Operator.

'Essential uniform for senior visitors to Stanley,' echoed the Chief Officer, Tom Woodfield. 'Prof Cragg from Durham upset the Guv because he didn't bring his, and said he'd sooner stay aboard ship and get on with some useful work.'

I had been discussing just that with Peter and Barry, but knew when duty called. Sir Edwin Arrowsmith's Official Vehicle – a black London taxi – was waiting for me as we docked.

'I use it because it's the only car I can get into when wearing my plumed hat,' he explained. 'Of course I could have a Rolls but there's no sense in that – the roads are only good enough for a car for a few miles from the Residence to a bit beyond the Cathedral, and if you go into the Camp you need a Land Rover, or even better, a horse.'

I was fitted out in Sir Edwin's slenderest spare dinner jacket, and with a little tacking and pinning the trousers stayed up. 'You'll have plenty of time to do some biology,' he went on. 'Bunny wants *Biscoe* to go straight down to

Deception Island, so you will have to wait for *Protector* and she won't be here for ten days. I'd like you to do a job for me. I'm keen on fishing, and we've got some good trout established – introduced from Scotland. But they're all very small, except by the sea. I don't think they've much to eat in the streams. Would you have a look and see what the little beggars are feeding on?'

Stanley Harbour is almost totally land-locked, but the approach, though narrow, is deep. This was what attracted Sir James Clark Ross when he established the settlement on its present site in 1843. 'Vessels of large size,' he wrote, 'may pass through the narrows into the inner harbour in any wind ... There is sufficient depth of water for a first-rate, and ample room for twenty sail of the line.' In 1961 there was still one four-masted, iron built, sailing ship swinging at anchor, serving as a store for coal or wool. Many derelict vessels lay by the shore, one of them serving as the termination of a jetty. Some are historic, including the last vessel known to survive from the California Gold Rush of 1849. And they are in Stanley for the same reason that their counterparts lie at Punta Arenas – these ports are the first refuges a ship can find after rounding Cape Horn eastbound. Many a vessel, strained beyond safe onward voyage, put into one or the other to be written off by the local Lloyds agent, their cargoes transshipped and their hulls sold as hulks or to be broken up for timber.

Port Stanley looked rather like Punta Arenas, and both look rather Nordic. Many houses are single-storey, wooden buildings, painted white, cream or pink and with red or green corrugated roofs. The Government House of 1961, though bigger, was a white-painted, green-roofed variant on the same theme. Only a few structures were more solidly built. They included Jubilee Villas – yellow brick houses with bay windows – and the Cathedral, which had a churchyard gate fashioned of the jawbones of two Blue whales. Strange (but how human!) to approach a monument to the Creator's love through something built from humanity's devastation of the largest creature ever to have lived on Earth ...

From Government House you looked across the harbour to a slope of moorland with historic ships' names picked out in white stones. BEAGLE ... SPARROW ... DARWIN. I was told that some time later, the Navy, with typical enthusiasm, added PROTECTOR. The lads from *Shackleton* and *Biscoe* watched, and struck back – they slipped across one night and turfed over all the stones except the three that spelled ROT. The teasing rivalry was typical.

We had two weeks on the Falklands. We met Ian Strange, who was running an experimental mink farm for the Falkland Islands Company, but being a keen naturalist, was taking double precautions to ensure that none escaped. We met Robin Woods, island ornithologist. We went into the open

Port Stanley, Falkland Islands, in 1961. Government House is the nearest building, on the right.

country – 'the Camp' – walking to the rocky crest of Mount William, across carpet bogs very like those of southern Chile, spreading amid heathlands very like those on top of Navarino. We looked across great stone-runs: fields of rough boulders that may have been spread across the landscape in ice age times, when there were certainly glaciers on the highest of the island hills. Several Tristan and Gough plants were also conspicuous – and one of the birds brought me back to a real island puzzle.

It was a little finch with a blueish head, green body and black throat, with the Latin name *Melanodera*. It is clearly closely related to *Rowettia*, the Gough Island finch, which looks like a paled-down, greenish, version of the Falklands adult male. But here comes a difference. The Gough Island adult males and females are almost identical, but the females of the Falkland *Melanodera* are brownish with a speckled breast – a plumage typical of immature Gough Island birds. There are behavioural differences, too, for while both are birds of the hills and shore, on Gough we had noted *Rowettia* taking both insect food and seeds, whereas the authoritative book on Falkland birds says that *Melanodera* is a seed eater. Michael Swales, who has used the structure of the feather barbs as an indication of relationships, is clear that both species, together with a related *Melanodera* that does not now breed in the Falklands, come from a common ancestor that is now extinct.

One thing I do believe is that the successful colonist of Gough had a broad food spectrum, for it must inevitably have found different things to eat there and a picksome feeder would have been at a disadvantage.

The natural history of the Falklands is very like that of Fuegia, but with important things left out. Trees are surprising by their absence. The biggest native Falkland bush is a *Hebe* (*H. elliptica*), growing in a few places along the coasts. There seems no good climatic reason for the islands' treelessness, for the rainfall and temperature are certainly within the tolerance of the hardier southern beeches, and there are places with quite enough shelter for scrub forest. Maybe trees simply failed to recolonize the islands after the ice age – but in that case why have introductions failed? Sir James Clark Ross (advised, no doubt, by his botanist Joseph Hooker) brought about 800 Magellanic and Antarctic beech from Hermite Island near Cape Horn, which is every bit as cool and windy (though wetter), to the old capital of the islands at Port Louis, without success. Yet today a variety of trees and shrubs grow well enough in sheltered places in and around Stanley.

In Darwin and Hooker's time, the coasts of the Falklands were dominated by tussock grass which formed a band up to half a mile wide and completely covered all the smaller offshore islands. It flourished because there were no grazing mammals – another gap in the wildlife spectrum, and a parallel with oceanic islands like Tristan and Gough. Guanacos never made it across, even when sea levels were lower during the last ice age, and the only mammal certainly native to the islands (apart from seals) was a large fox (the 'Warrah' or Falkland wolf). Darwin 'had reason to suspect that there is a field mouse', but no specimens have confirmed his suspicion. The Warrah is an ecological puzzle for there are no small mammals for it to live on. Did it subsist on insects, or ground-nesting birds? Darwin's account implies it may have scavenged for carrion, for example on seal breeding beaches. We will never know for sure, because it has been extinct since around 1875.

As on other islands, once humans arrived all this changed. Cattle and horses, introduced around 1764, were followed by rabbits, sheep and pigs. By the time the *Beagle* called, wild cattle were everywhere and had become a menace. In 1842, Lieutenant Governor Moody estimated that there were 30,000 head of them in the archipelago, along with 3,000 wild horses. They made tracks for the tussock as the sweetest grazing, and soon all but destroyed it: once the cattle and wild horses had been killed off (there are a few wild cattle still in the highest hills), the sheep (introduced in the 1850s) completed the job. Today the tussock is only found on outlying islands with little or no grazing.

Several of these islands are now nature reserves. Peter Tilbrook and I spent three days on one of them, Kidney Island. The tussock was immense –

far bigger than the same species achieves on Gough. I took a photograph of Peter, dwarfed by two metres of tussock base and a further metre-plus of waving crown, and realized why at least one early navigator mistook this vegetation for low-growing woodland. There was wild celery and small ferns like those on Gough, along with quite a few introduced European weeds. We counted around 150 Sea lions (*Otaria byronia*) and 15 young Elephant seals. The big Sea lion bulls are much bigger than a male Fur seal, and their deep-throated roars echo among the tussock. You can meet them anywhere: one took up residence in the porch of the little hut we were sleeping in, which would have been a bit of a nuisance had we wanted to go out in the night. I gave Peter the chance of some comic film when, coming round a corner in the grass, I heard a loud braying yell, and was on top of a tussock feeling silly when I realized that the cry was that of a Magellanic penguin, in its burrow among the grass roots!

Kidney also had lots of Rockhopper penguins, many other seabirds and a rich land-bird fauna. But for me the insects were especially interesting. Not surprisingly, given the proximity of the South American mainland, they were much more diverse than on Gough despite the similarity of the tussock-grass habitat. Among other things, I collected a series of small moths which proved to belong to two species, both flightless, both new to science. One was the first South American record of a genus previously known from New Zealand and Tasmania. The other was a new species of a genus previously believed endemic to Campbell Island, south of New Zealand. Somebody could still find a lot of new species in the Falklands, and in doing so alter our notions of Subantarctic biogeography.

We did not forget Sir Edwin's trout. The answer seemed fairly clear. The streams that swirled across the open Camp did have food for fish, but not much of it. There were a few stonefly and midge larvae, small crustaceans and worms, together with leeches and flatworms. Most of them were hidden among mosses or under stones, sheltered from the turbulent currents. But down by the sea, where the streams were broader and slower-flowing, there was a much richer fauna. When we opened up trout the Governor had caught, they fitted these findings – the little specimens from up-river being largely full of midges, stoneflies and land insects that had been swept downstream, while the bigger fish from near tidal limits were crammed with estuarine crustaceans and small cockle-shells.

All this made us think about the natural resources of the islands. In the early 1960s the two thousand inhabitants lived largely off sheep ranching. The Falkland Islands Company collected and shipped the wool and imported essential stores for sale in the island shops. Various efforts had been made to diversify the economy. There were plenty of sheep – they called mutton 'the three hundred and sixty-five' in Stanley – so why not a meat freezer like that at Punta Arenas? Maybe the meat was not of sufficient quality: anyway the venture went bust. The mink farm (thankfully) also did not pay and was closed down. Ian Strange, well aware that escaped mink have proved a menace to wild life in many other places, including both Britain and Iceland, took care to destroy all the animals. The sea was the obvious unexploited wealth, but at that time there was little interest in it. At one meeting I attended after returning home, representatives of the British deep-sea fishing industry argued that the islands were too far away; that British fishermen had to come home to their families every month; and that the unfamiliar southern fish would be rejected by northern palates! It took Lord Shackleton's report, years later, and the war of 1982 to stimulate the fishery from which the islands now derive large royalties – but virtually none of that fishery is British.

In the early 1960s it would have stretched the imagination to think that these empty, treeless, moors and this friendly little backwater called Stanley would become a war zone. Yet disputes over sovereignty had been rumbling on for centuries. Nobody is really sure who discovered the islands in the first place. It may have been Amerigo Vespucci of Spain, in 1501. It may have been John Davis, in 1592. Sir Richard Hawkins claimed them soon afterwards and gave them the strange name of Hawkins' Maidenland (the maiden being Queen Elizabeth I). In 1688 somebody renamed them in honour of Samuel Pepys; a Dutchman named them the Sebaldinas and Frenchmen variously dubbed them 'Îles d'Anican', 'Îles Neuves de Saint Louis' and 'Belgie Australe'. The name 'Falkland Islands' was conferred by a buccaneer, John Strong (who some say was making an innocent voyage of exploration 'to whitewash his former bad record'): Lord Falkland was his Patron. Breton fishermen from St Malo began to visit frequently in the eighteenth century, and nicknamed the group 'Îles Malouines' – hence the current Spanish 'Islas Malvinas'.

The history of settlement is another muddle. In 1764 a French expedition under Bougainville set up a colony of so-called Arcadians, suggesting (by some weird exercise of the imagination) that these new lands would compensate for the loss of Canada. Spain, disliking trespass in her traditional sphere of empire, bought the French out for £30,000. But at the same time, an Englishman, Commodore Byron (ancestor of the poet and com-memorated in the Latin name of the Sea lion *Otaria byronia*), established a British colony. For several years French and British lived in mutual ignorance in different localities – until two very surprised commanding officers chanced to meet at sea. The British hung on when Spain bought France out – until the Governor of the Spanish Colony in Buenos Aires removed them by force in 1770. This led Whitehall – always better at responding when disaster has struck than at spending money on preventing it – to send a naval expedition (shades of 1982!). Captain Hunt (yes, the commanding officers of the British Colony were named Hunt, both in 1770 and 1982) had no sooner reached London than 'a powerful fleet was assembled, well manned and well stored . . .' and the Spanish were forced to repudiate the actions of their Man in Buenos Aires.

Samuel Johnson used the occasion for a rumbustious tract. 'We have, by obtaining a disavowal of Buccarelli's expedition and a restitution of our settlement, maintained the honour of the crown and the superiority of our influence,' he wrote. 'But beyond this, what have we gained? What but a bleak and gloomy solitude, an island thrown aside from human use, stormy in winter and barren in summer; an island which not the southern savages have dignified with habitation; where a garrison must be kept in a state that contemplates with envy the exiles of Siberia; of which the expense will be perpetual and the use only occasional; and which, if fortune smile upon our labours, may become a nest of smugglers in peace and in war the refuge of future buccaniers.'

I copied this paragraph to Sir Robert Armstrong, Secretary of the Cabinet, in 1982 suggesting that the Treasury might find sentiments to approve of. He responded – opera buff that he was – praising the cadences of the language. But he did not think it prudent to circulate it to Margaret Thatcher's Cabinet. Nor, I am sure, did he remind them of what had happened after the success of the Task Force in 1770. For Britain evacuated its settlement in 1820, and Argentina then set up a post that remained unchallenged for thirteen years. In 1833 the British had to send another gunboat to remove them and establish the British settlement that has been continuous since then. A settlement whose people, like those of Tristan, are immensely loyal to Britain and – as they showed when war came – have no wish to change their status.

Yet to many people around the world, these little outlying vestiges of European imperial sovereignty – French and Dutch as well as British – are an anomaly, and to some they are an offence. In the post-Colonial era many voices, in the United Nations and elsewhere, question why patches of land and tiny groups of people in the Gulf of St Lawrence, the Caribbean, the Indian Ocean, the Pacific or the South Atlantic should be ruled from Europe. The problem is that the remaining British overseas territories are all too small for independence, and have no wish to be amalgamated with their larger neighbours. In the 1940s, Britain transferred the uninhabited Marion and Prince Edward Islands to South Africa, and some thought that Tristan and St Helena should go the same way – but apartheid put paid to that, since their people are ethnically mixed. I doubt very much whether the question will be posed again.

In the 1960s, diplomats were trying hard to resolve the long-standing dispute between Argentina and Britain over the future of the Falklands. Some hoped that the Falklanders would accept change of status if they got to know more about Argentina. It was pointed out that there were many thousands of Argentine citizens of British origin, who have retained language, cultural identity and links with the UK. I myself have a considerable number of third and fourth cousins among them. An air service was introduced, and visits in both directions encouraged. It was a long-term strategy of convergence, and with patience on both sides it might have led in due course to a transfer of sovereignty with preservation of the Falklanders' rights to land, local self-government, and dual nationality. The war of 1982 threw all such ideas into limbo, and brought a new military airport, a vastly strengthened British military presence, and a hardening of hostility towards Argentina. None the less, I suspect that the story is not ended yet.

But our visit did end when Peter and I got back from Kidney Island. HMS *Protector* was lying in the inner harbour, her 4000 ton bulk dwarfing the other vessels. There were parties ashore and at Government House. Two days later, Peter, Barry and I left for Signy Island.

The Antarctic summer is short. From around April until November even the northernmost bases in the South Shetland and South Orkney Islands are surrounded by drifting sea-ice – the 'pack' – and further south in Halley Bay or Marguerite Bay the sea is closed by ice for all but a brief spell around January to March. FIDS, and its successor in title the British Antarctic Survey, have never had an icebreaker such as allows the United States to plough scornfully through all except the heaviest ice. The RRS *John Biscoe* and the smaller *Shackleton*, of only 1600 and 1350 tons respectively, had ice-strengthened hulls, but could only push through fairly light and open floes. They had to go where and when ice, wind and weather let them. Managing the complex logistics of resupplying half a dozen stations scattered over a wide area was a tricky business. So the help from the Royal Navy, in the shape of *Protector*, a converted netlayer, was greatly appreciated – especially since, although she could not enter even light pack, she carried two helicopters. They were invaluable aids to field research.

We put out from Stanley into worsening weather. Before long a rating came into my cabin to fasten the deadlight – the solid, heavy metal plate that screws behind the glass of the porthole and reinforces it against the pounding of the sea. 'They say it's going to be dirty,' he said. 'It usually is around here.'

Protector's bridge had an old-style wooden chair – almost a throne – from

which the Captain ruled all he surveyed. It was over 12 metres above the
water line. As we came clear of the Falklands, Captain Robin Graham found
himself looking up to the foaming crests of those great, grey Cape Horn
swells. It was a magnificent sight – but I felt happier lying down ... When it
calmed, we found ourselves looking at stark towers of black and yellow rock,
capped and streaked with snow, rising three hundred metres or more from a
heaving ocean scattered with icebergs – flat-topped, tabular, icebergs calved
off from the great floating ice shelves that surround so much of the
Antarctic continent. The black and white landscape of the South Orkney
Islands showed vaguely through mist. We were approaching the Antarctic in
one of its bleaker moods, and the mood was not lightened by the fact that
our first action was to attend a funeral service for Roger Filer, killed by a cliff
fall while studying Sheathbills, those strange little white pigeon-like birds
that scavenge on the shores and around penguin colonies.

Roger was buried under a long cairn, built by his comrades – Russ
Thompson, Ron Pinder, Derek Clarke, Neville Jones and Brian Westlake.
Few people on earth have a more beautiful burial place. It lies on a low,
rocky headland looking out over the sea to a wonderful panorama of snow-
clad mountains. His five friends and the Chaplain stood nearest: we, the
new arrivals further back, for we were really intruders in the grief of a tight-
knit little group. The new arrivals: Peter Tilbrook (by then designated as the
new Base Leader, and nicknamed 'Pete BL' to distinguish him from Pete
Hobbs, the new Radio Operator), Barry Heywood, John Chambers, Terry
Mason, Fred Topliffe, and myself as summer visitor. And pilots, officers and
ship's photographer.

Afterwards the helicopter buzzed the ship's party back and we, the shore
party, walked overland to the base. Over little rocky hills, where skuas dived
screaming in defence of their breeding territories. Up a broad snowfield,
dwindling as spring began to thaw its edges. Over patches of rust-red moss,
and across outcrops tufted with grey and black lichen. Down a steep gully,
known locally as 'the stone chute'. And so to a low, black, wooden hut
flanked by two smaller huts – a boatshed and a loo – the functions of the
latter disguised by the word TEAS painted in big white letters on its side.
Somebody had set a piece of old waterpipe upright beside it, to hold a pole
bearing a tartan flag as indication of occupation. Beyond the black hut, on
the bare slopes beyond, about twenty husky dogs, chained in two long spans,
howled a welcome.

The hut was six years old, stout and homely (if a bit basic). The kitchen
and store room were at one end: next came sitting room, Base Leader's
Office and bunkroom; and then radio shack, meteorologist's office,
bathroom, generator room and fuel store. A corridor formed a central axis

from end to end. And nearby there were reminders of the original occupants of the site – the Norwegian whalers who had built a small shore station here in the 1920s. They were commemorated in the name 'TONSBERG HOUSE' over one door of the modern hut. There was a timber apron – the 'plan' onto which whales were once winched to be cut up. There was a boiler, to render the blubber down and extract the rich oil. There was a wrecked barge, once used to ferry fresh water from a stream across the bay. All rusty and derelict and a bit depressing, so one fine day I whiled away a few hours by giving the old boiler a coat of paint – depicting an Elephant seal and a bathing 'beauty' (not as shapely in execution as desire) looking at one another under a palm tree. The base made vulgar comments.

The Navy took one look at the little Base jetty and disapproved. 'Much too small,' they said. 'We have a splendid team of divers, we'll look at the foundations for an extension.' Led by a cheery Lieutenant Commander, Malcolm Burley, the 'splendid team' clad in black neoprene dry suits, flippers, facemasks and aqualungs, immersed themselves in fully a metre and a half of water and examined the ground. As they dived the tide fell. 'Yes,' said Malcolm, 'there's no problem about extending it. All you need is enough stones – lots around here – old oil drums, cement and timber.' The old hands nodded. The fact was that they had extended it most seasons – only to find that once they got into the deeper water, nothing they could build would withstand the pounding of lumps of ice five or six metres across, driven in by the wind. And every winter, unless the structure was dismantled, the sea froze about it and, when the winter ended, took it away as so many fragments in an ice floe. But everyone enjoyed the visit. Soon afterwards, *Protector* departed, leaving us to start work.

We had two tasks. To make a biological laboratory, and to look at field sites. The first was the more difficult. For the old hut was pretty full of people, and FIDS were not used to the kind of finicky laboratory-based science we were proposing. They thought of biology in terms of bucket mammalogy where someone armed with a big knife carved his way into the inside of a seal, dragging polythene bags and labels after him, and ended up with a bagged and tagged pile of bits amid the bloodied snow. Base Leader Russ Thompson conveyed the mentality perfectly in a report on the design of a biology lab: 'As the biologists will be working with the bulky Elephant seal, it is essential that the doors to the laboratory should be at least six feet wide . . .' When he heard I was coming, he soon had me sorted out. 'The Prof can look after the cement mixer.' He was a bit shattered to find that the biggest beasts Peter and Barry would be studying were about a centimetre and a half long.

There was no problem in fitting out two small rooms with benches and

Antarctic research centre. Martin Holdgate looks across the hills, lakes and eastern shores of Signy Island.

shelving. Power was the difficulty. Like most small FIDS stations, Signy had been used mainly to collect and transmit weather information. This meant observations every three hours round the clock – but the data were transmitted only twice a day, at the morning and evening 'skeds'. The generators were therefore only started up for these periods. Batteries were used if anyone wanted artificial light after daylight failed. The total power supply came from two tiny Enfield generators delivering 8.5 kilowatts each.

But Peter Tilbrook's insect extractors needed to run all night, and Barry Heywood needed an aquarium aerated by a pump that never stopped. We had said all this in London. Yes, they said – 24 hour power – no problem. But it seemed different in Stanley, and more so on base where there were worries over the fire hazard of generators running unattended all night (fire is the greatest danger on Antarctic stations, and for this reason they all have an emergency store with tents, food and equipment some way from the main hut). Action was none the less swift. *Shackleton* brought two builders and a third generator as a stand-by, the boathouse was swiftly converted to house all three machines, and soon a steady chugging indicated that science could commence.

That incident was symbolic. British Antarctic science was in transition, and this was to affect the goals, style and leadership of FIDS.

The Survey originated as a way of upholding British territorial claims to the Antarctic Peninsula – the long pan-handle of mountain that juts from Antarctica towards South America. We call the region Graham Land, but Argentina and Chile, which claim overlapping slices of it, know it as Tierra San Martin and Tierra O'Higgins after their respective founders. During the 1939-45 war Argentina began to reinforce her claims with a military presence, and the British Government responded by sending a naval mission, code-named Operation Tabarin, to set up manned stations. This operation, with the advent of peace, became the Falkland Islands Dependencies Survey.

And the name implied the work. It was to survey the dependencies of the Falkland Islands. There were over a dozen bases, because that was the way to fly many flags and explore a lot of territory. The emphasis was on weather observation, mapping and geological survey (the last, perhaps, with mineral resource prospecting somewhere at the back of the official mind). Most of the fieldwork was done by young men straight from university or recruited from the Services or crafts. The bases were supplied by sea, and overland fieldwork included many remarkable long-distance sledging journeys, using teams of well-trained dogs.

The same ethos was apparent in 1961. It was still an all-male operation, and its members came from all walks of life, and all backgrounds. There were mechanics and holders of University doctorates. There were expert climbers and small boat sailors alongside carpenters and scientists. There was only a skeleton of permanent staff, headed by the Director, Sir Vivian Fuchs. Scientific supervision was arranged through links with Universities or professional institutions. Geology, under Dr Ray Adie, was based at Birmingham, where Dr Stanley Greene led a small botanical group; zoology was supervised by Professor Smith at Queen Mary College; human physiology by Dr Otto Edholm at the Medical Research Council; meteorology through the Met Office and so on. The field staff went to the Antarctic because they wanted the adventure: pay was meagre and a tour of duty usually meant two and a half years in the south without a break. And FIDS prided itself on its community spirit and on maintaining the tradition of British antarcticism in which people turned their hands to many tasks.

Signy in 1961 fitted the model. The base was a relatively unspecialized place. The 'new hands' included two full-time biologists (Peter and Barry), three meteorologists (Fred Topliffe, Terry Mason and John Chambers), and a Radio Operator (Pete Hobbs). But people were encouraged to do sideline projects as well as their main job. The retiring Radio Operator, Ron Pinder, was studying Cape pigeons which bred in a little gully a few hundred metres away from the Base – and as soon as his relief was installed he switched to doing that full-time. Nev Jones, relieved of meteorological duties, took over where Roger Filer had left off, and worked on the Sheathbills at Gourlay Point. John Chambers stuck masses of temperature-recording equipment into the soil and set out to do a double job – met. and soil physics.

Everyone took turns with base chores. There was no cook – so everyone did a day in rotation. There was no running water – so when the tanks from which the cook filled the big copper that the kitchen Aga heated got low, everyone would rally round to collect lumps of clear glacier ice from the shore. The builders needed hands to help hump heavy objects: people downed tools. The row of full tins outside the loo made a boat-load, and the sea was calm? Volunteers, please, to dump them well out in the bay. A young Elephant seal hauled out nearby? Whoever saw it took a .303 rifle and went out and shot it for dog food – for each husky needed 3 kilos of raw seal every second day, and a bucket of clean snow every day. The dogs also got quite skilled at supplementing their diet with penguins. The technique was to keep well back and excite the birds' curiosity until they had wandered well within chain-length: as Apsley Cherry Garrard wrote of the same happenings on Scott's expedition in 1910, 'there was then a pounce, a snap, and the incident was closed . . .'

The huskies were one of the pleasures of Base, though to be frank they were not of much real use for sledging (there were a few exploratory runs in winter when the sea ice allowed crossing to Coronation Island, and they served as a kind of strategic reserve for bases further south). But they were great companions. They sound like wolves, and they fight viciously with one another until they have sorted out their 'pecking order', but with people they are the sloppiest of animals. Garth, largest and sloppiest of all, weighed around 60 kilos and could easily rear and put his paws on your shoulder while he licked your nose. If you took a dog for a walk on a harness, with a sledging trace as lead, you could easily be pulled over if it bounded forward at the sight of a friendly human, a tasty penguin, or a rival demanding a scrap. But these were days of increasing concern over conservation, and it was concluded that we simply could not justify killing seals to feed animals of no importance for sledging. Moreover, motor sledges were taking over. In 1963, a vet came down to Signy and destroyed the remaining dogs, at the same time making a detailed study of the arthritis that plagued them even when relatively young.

Very few 'retired' dogs left the Antarctic. But there were exceptions.

'You know, the Director took Darkie, his old leader, and two other huskies back to Cambridge,' said Ron Pinder. 'Did you hear about the trouble he got into?'

He needed no prompting. 'They needed exercise, and a husky wants to pull. But the Boss had no sledge, and when is there snow in Cambridge? So he hitched them to the towbar of his car, and crawled along the road at just the right speed for tight traces. Lots of dear old ladies complained to the RSPCA about "that horrid man in that big car, being towed by those poor doggies".'

I once asked Joyce Fuchs about this story, and she denied it. She said that *she* was the beneficiary of husky power, on her bicycle, and that her proudest moment came when her cries of 'irra, irra' were rewarded by a neat wheel around a Cambridge policeman!

People argued sometimes that the way everyone helped with everything on Base was terribly inefficient. They asserted that we should have a cook who cooked (we did in 1963), builders who built, and scientists who researched. The old hands argued the opposite. I remember Ron Pinder, feet propped on top of the old coke stove in the living room, mug of hooch in hand, lecturing me on the merits of the simple life and the perils of excessive 'ologising. He was right that something valuable would be lost if people ceased to be part of a versatile community. There had to be a balance. I think that as science slowly strengthened, Bill Sloman the Personnel Officer, probably at Bunny Fuchs' insistence, took immense pains to see that even the most highly qualified scientist was an all-rounder. Nobody can afford to be a narrow specialist in the Antarctic. The successful person is one who makes a full contribution to the normal demands of life and finds time for science as well. But as the 1950s and 1960s went by, there were good reasons why science had to become dominant.

The International Geophysical Year of 1957-58 had seen a massive international research effort in Antarctica, with the United States established at the South Pole and the USSR at the 'pole of inaccessibility' – the spot on the immense central icecap that was remotest from the sea. Britain – represented by the Royal Society – had established a scientific station at Halley Bay on the coast of the Weddell Sea, and Bunny Fuchs' Transantarctic Expedition had crossed the continent, making echo-soundings of ice thickness as they went. It was obvious, first, that Antarctica was an important place for research and second, that international co-operation was essential if the most was to be made of the cost and effort involved.

Science paved the way for peace. In 1959 the Antarctic Treaty was signed in Washington DC. One of its chief architects was Dr Brian Roberts, himself a polar biologist, who worked part-time in the Scott Polar Research Institute and part-time as the Head of the Polar Regions section of the Foreign Office. The Treaty set territorial claims aside for fifty years, banned military activities in Antarctica, and opened the whole continent for peaceful scientific endeavour.

The result was a challenge to British Antarctic policy, and to FIDS. For it was evident that there was little point in maintaining an expensive presence just to support 'frozen' territorial claims. If the Survey was to continue – and there were voices in the Treasury even then, arguing that the money could be better spent – it had to be justified by science. The Royal Society, through its British National Committee on Antarctic Research, played an increasingly important role as guarantor of research quality, and hence justifier of public funding. It endorsed Bunny Fuchs' case for a strong scientific programme, and biology was chosen as one of the sciences to be strengthened. I was not fully aware of it at the time, but the work we did on Signy Island in the southern summer of 1961-62 was therefore part of a scientific revolution in FIDS.

The scientific revolution was accompanied by an administrative one, for all the territory Britain claimed south of latitude 60 degrees South – the northern boundary of the Treaty area – was split off from the Falkland Islands Dependencies as a new entity, British Antarctic Territory. This supposedly separated sovereignty issues in the far south, calmed by the Treaty, from those that remained turbulent around the Falklands and South Georgia. The Treaty entered into force in 1961, and on 1 January 1962 FIDS became BAS, the British Antarctic Survey. We had quite a party at Signy to celebrate.

Signy Island is both compact and diverse – a rugged little world of bluffs and cliffed coasts, hollows and lakelets, snowfields and tiny glaciers. It is only eight kilometres long, five wide and just over 300 metres high. But it lies very close to the southern shores of the largest island in the South Orkney Group, Coronation Island, with its long ice plateau, rising to the graceful 1200-metre ice-summit of Mount Nivea and falling beyond into a spine of peaks. In warm summer weather the air vibrates with the rumble of distant avalanches.

In summer on Signy much of the lower ground is snow-free, and a vegetation of lichen and moss forms intricate patterns on knolls and slopes. We had come expecting a barren place, littered with glacial debris, and with plant life mainly represented by crusts and tufts of lichen. Instead, there were areas where continuous mats and carpets of moss covered half the ground, and liverworts, more delicate than mosses, were common in the wetter places. There were even little toadstools dotting some moist slopes, and patches of the only two higher plants native to the Antarctic, a grass (*Deschampsia antarctica*) and a green cushion-forming relative of the pink family, *Colobanthus crassifolius*.

Signy is in a latitude that corresponds to Shetland in the northern hemisphere, so the midsummer sun is above the horizon for most of the 24 hours and in December and January it is never dark. On those nights when talk went on late in the hut, you would come out at around 2 a.m. for a final pee, to see the new day blazing orange on the peaks of Coronation Island. That sun was the secret of life on land. We soon found that on a clear day, even if the temperature hovered about freezing point in the meteorologists' screens, it could rise to 10 or even 15 degrees Celsius in the moss mats. The two Antarctic flowering plants seemed to cluster in radiation traps, facing north towards the sun.

We needed a vegetation map and some kind of classification of soil and vegetation if Pete Tilbrook was to have a frame of reference for his sampling of soil animals. I took this job on, backed up by Handbooks of British Mosses and Liverworts, knowing that Stanley Greene, our moss expert in Birmingham University, would sort out the real species afterwards if I was consistent enough at discriminating between them and labelling them in the field. It was a splendid job, for it allowed me to roam all over the island, and I soon found that there were indeed distinctive kinds of vegetation in different situations. Exposed rocky crests were dominated by grey, branching *Usnea* lichens and a dark, low-growing moss named *Andraea*. Wetter slopes and ravines were carpeted by pale green *Brachythecium* and *Drepanocladus* mosses. On the drier slopes great mats of moss (including an old familiar friend, *Polytrichum alpestre*) had in places built up banks of frozen peat over a metre thick. That peat had the consistency of hard plastic, and I broke two ice axes chopping out samples we could date using radiocarbon ratios – finding that the oldest were nearly 2000 years old (later they found banks that went back twice as far). And soil and plants were different again on scattered serpentine marble outcrops, in places where bird droppings contributed excessive fertilizer, or where wallowing seals stirred everything into mud.

Pete Tilbrook set up insect extractors, heated by light bulbs to warm and dry cores of soil from above and so drive insects down the gradient to collecting tubes beneath. It was the same system that Willy Kuschel had used in Chile, but more exact, allowing the numbers present in each sample to be assessed. He found that the commonest animals were a little blue-black springtail a few millimetres long and various blackish and reddish mites. Meanwhile Barry Heywood went on a quick survey of the island lakes. There were about a dozen of these, ice-free in summer but covered with over a metre of ice in winter, through which he would have to chip his way laboriously using a hammer and cold chisel, keeping his sampling hole accessible by pitching a tent over it. In the lakes were a diversity of little shrimplets and water fleas, sustained by green algae and moss that formed a felt on the lake bottom.

Signy offered rich opportunities for other studies, too. It was a fine place

Adélie penguins on Gourlay Peninsula, Signy Island, with the mountains of Coronation Island in the distance.

for birds – many of which had been observed, counted and leg-banded by previous FIDS. There were four kinds of penguin – the trim, black and white Adélies, which, with the Emperor, breed as far south as penguins go; the dapper Chinstraps, with their thin helmet-strap of black across their white chins; the charming Gentoos, with their bright orange feet and bills and white head-patches; and just a few Macaronis, with dark yellow head tassels – southern relatives of the Rockhoppers so common on Gough and the Falklands. We were too far south for albatrosses, but there were big colonies of Giant petrels – in both the common dark phase and one with near-white plumage. There were abundant Cape pigeons, lovely all-white, black-billed, Snow petrels, burrowing Dove prions (we had to exile 'Ginge' the Base cat to the Falklands as he caught and ate too many), and little Storm petrels – both Wilson's and the rarer Black-bellied species. There had been a long-standing programme to put leg-bands on young Giant petrels and recoveries had shown that once fledged and departed to sea they ranged around the globe. Some had been recovered in Australia within a few months of leaving the nest. Yet after five or six years, when the time came to return as breeding adults, somehow these wanderers found Signy again just as Greater shearwaters find Nightingale or Gough Island, and penguins find their old colonies after roaming at sea for many months.

We did a little direct research on homing birds when I left Signy in 1962, again aboard HMS *Protector*. Nev Jones wondered whether the Sheathbills he was working on could find their way back to their nests. He was dubious because these are the nearest approach to land birds in the region, scavenging on shores and around penguin colonies, and appearing, with their dumpy bodies and only partly webbed feet, to be ill adapted to ocean life. So I took two breeding birds up to Stanley and released them as we neared land. The Navy entered into the spirit of the thing, with an entry in the Order of the Day:

'0930 – fly off Sheathbills.'

I explained that, unlike helicopters, Sheathbills did not require the vessel to come head to wind. At the due time, feeling distinctly ridiculous under the watching eyes of half a dozen sailors, I humped the two wooden boxes onto the flight deck, checked that the occupants seemed fit for duty, and opened up. For a while they scurried about, exercising their limbs, and then they were off – one, clearly strongly 'motivated' (as Americans would put it) circling the ship, while the other fluttered more weakly in the direction of the Falklands. The determined character took five days to get back to Signy, home and offspring.

Then there were seals. Signy was on the southern edge of the breeding range of the Elephant seal, whose tiny colony had been studied many years earlier by Dick Laws, later to succeed Bunny Fuchs as Director of BAS. There were abundant Weddell seals on the shores. And in the summer, an increasing number of young male Fur seals were arriving to moult – an overspill from the resurgent colony of South Georgia. Seabirds and seals all depended on the productivity of the sea, which was itself a further field for research. The island shores seemed barren because in winter they are scoured by ice, eliminating the zones of seaweed, barnacles and mussels familiar in temperate regions. But in crevices and below ice-depth there was clearly abundant marine life. American work in the Ross Sea had shown that scuba diving techniques could be used in the Antarctic, and they would allow detailed observation of the communities and species that lived below ice- and tide-zones.

All this led me to conclude, quite early in 1962, that Jim Cragg had been right. Signy Island was a good place for ecological research. The plan I proposed to Bunny Fuchs and Eric Smith was, in fact, modelled on that used by Jim's Department at Durham to dissect the ecosystem of the North Pennines, on Moor House National Nature Reserve. But I wanted to go wider and examine the interactions between the ecosystems of land, freshwater and sea. This was pioneering work at the time, when next to no research had been done on these ecosystems, and their place within the

Antarctic system as a whole. It would mean expanding the programme to encompass more soil science, more botany, and more marine biology – and also more work on the birds, and how they variously used the marine life. Bunny Fuchs approved the plan and agreed that BAS should commission a new laboratory and a larger base hut which would have space for visiting senior scientists in summer.

He also asked me to transfer from the Scott Polar Research Institute to become Chief Biologist of BAS. It wasn't an entirely easy transition. My Antarctic credentials were slender by comparison with people like Ray Adie, the chief geologist, who had a distinguished field exploration record, or Joe Farman, our atmospheric physicist, discoverer of the 'ozone hole', or, of course, Bunny Fuchs himself. And it was not helped by a certain lack of structure in BAS biology, or by a vast difference in style between Bunny and myself.

We – the British Antarctic Survey Biological Unit – were to be based at Queen Mary College in the Mile End Road, where Eric Smith was Professor of Zoology. The site was cramped, and our accommodation was an old and crumbling terrace house in Bancroft Road. It was renovated during the northern winter of 1962/63 so that it could come into full use when Peter Tilbrook and Barry Heywood returned from the Antarctic in 1964. Later on, someone – I forget who – also annexed the empty house next door, which was even more derelict and shored up with baulks of timber. It made an ideal store, especially for the smellier specimens, and the reek of formalin discouraged the dossers who had been using a back room.

But this was only one fragment of a scattered BAS home team. Headquarters was in Gillingham Street, behind Victoria Station. Ray Adie and the geologists were based in Birmingham, where our botanical specialists, Dr Stanley Greene and his wife Dorothy, were also located. Stanley – known as 'Mossy' to some, and adorned with a bushy botanical beard – was an outstanding expert on Antarctic plants, which he had studied on South Georgia, and he seized my Signy notes and specimens enthusiastically. But it was never wholly clear who worked for who. Bunny assured me that I was 'the biological Adie', but his own history of FIDS and BAS, *Of Ice and Men*, makes it clear that he saw Stanley Greene and me heading independent teams. Fortunately, Stanley and I got on well, visiting one another's homes and planning the development of BAS biology together. But there were tensions when I wanted field botanists to build on my 1962 vegetation survey. The Birmingham Department was contented enough when we recruited Royce Longton, one of their Research Students, in 1963, but became more difficult when I invited Dr Charles Gimingham, a first class plant ecologist from Aberdeen, to go south for a summer, and engaged one of his students, Ron Lewis Smith, to continue the work.

The northern summer of 1962 was a busy time. The first international symposium on Antarctic Biology was held in Paris, and I was able to present ideas about the main ecological regions and vegetation types in what I termed 'the Maritime Antarctic' – the oceanic fringes of the Antarctic Peninsula that FIDS called 'the banana belt'. The symposium was organized by the Biology Working Group of SCAR, the Scientific Committee on Antarctic Research, of which Gordon Robin of the SPRI was long-time Secretary. SCAR was the focus for international Antarctic scientists and it worked because it wasn't just another committee. Those attending it were leaders in Antarctic science, and knew the practicalities of life there. The various scientific Working Groups were made up of people at the frozen forefront of their 'ologies. I was for five years Secretary/Chairman of the Biology Working Group, which convened expert meetings, created networks for information exchange, discussed research priorities and put an international boost behind colleagues who wouldn't have got much of a lick at the financial gravy without it.

One early task was conservation, and Dr Brian Roberts of the SPRI and Foreign Office was its driving force. Brian was a remarkable man – rightly described as a 'polar pundit' in the volume of appreciation published after his death. An ornithologist who had done pioneer work in South Georgia, a diplomat and a scholar with immense knowledge of polar history. A curious combination of the highest, almost pedantic, intellectual standards and unrivalled skills as a 'fixer' of international agreements. An intensely emotional man, who could weep in frustration if crossed, and who could yet be relaxed, warm and generous even with those who opposed him.

Brian had decided in 1960 (or thereabouts):

'We need a set of conservation laws in Antarctica. You draft them, and I'll get them agreed.'

So I looked at the conservation laws of all the countries working in Antarctica, and especially those claiming territory (because the international measure must not conflict with their domestic rules). Brian and I decided on our objectives. No birds or mammals should be killed or collected without a permit, except in an emergency, or to provide indispensable food for men or dogs. Some should have absolute protection, like the Ross seal and the Fur seals that were still recovering from past devastation. Science should be the main justification for killing or collecting anything, and areas of especial ecological interest and habitats of key species should receive special protection. Those were the foundations of the Agreed Measures for the Conservation of Antarctic Fauna and Flora, accepted by the Treaty Parties in 1964.

Conservation was the cause of my only real row with Bunny Fuchs. Sometime in 1963 I learned that our staff aboard *Kista Dan*, heading to relieve the main BAS geophysical research station at Halley Bay, had shot two Ross seals and chopped them up for dog food. The Ross seal is the rarest and least known Antarctic seal, and Brian Roberts and I had proposed it for special protection under the Agreed Measures. I felt annoyed and let down by BAS's disregard for the conservation measures the UK was working so hard to establish. I thought that the animals should not have been shot at all, but that if a mistake had been made, the bodies should be the preserve of science. But the letter I wrote to Bunny was tactless. He responded firmly. 'When you know me better,' he wrote, 'you will know that I do not like being ticked off . . .'

In a way, the disagreement was between old-style and new-style BAS. Although he was a scientist himself, Bunny was first and foremost a personal leader. He was wonderful in the field, and achieved close ties of mutual loyalty with his men. He had been the ideal head of FIDS during its period of travel, mapping and geological survey. But the approach was rather paternalistic – 'Poppa and the Boys' as Nigel Bonner, Seal Biologist at South Georgia, put it. Although he supported the new, and more academic, research programme, I am sure Bunny still looked back with nostalgia on the era of great journeys. We were very different people – but we retained personal regard none the less. I well recall meeting him at Cambridge Station in the spring of 1995 – a little stooped, but with bright blue eyes still sparkling under bushy brows. 'Eleanor and I have just had a splendid trip south,' he enthused. 'I celebrated my 87th birthday at Scott Base. Wonderful to see the ice again . . .'

Whatever our differences, nobody could have been more supportive of the plans for expanding BAS biology. That meant planning the new Base on Signy. Somebody – I think it was Derek Gipps, the stores and equipment officer – saw a picture in a newspaper of a new telephone exchange built by the plastics company Bakelite at their Birmingham headquarters. It was made of sections of resin reinforced by fibreglass, with a central insulating layer of phenolic foam. It was said to be light in weight, strong, and never to need painting. It seemed to have polar possibilities. So we went to look at it.

I parked my nondescript Ford Anglia in the drive of the Fuchs home in Cambridge early one morning. The 'Bunnywaggon' – his E type Jaguar – stood ready. He appeared bearing two sledging anoraks. 'Better put one on,' he said. 'I always drive with the hood down, and it can be chilly on the M1.'

It was, when we began to eat up the miles at a steady 125 m.p.h. (this was before the days of speed limits). 'She can tend to drift at over 130,' he commented. We were early. But we did commission the Plastic Palace, carefully designed to have laboratories for eight scientists on the ground floor and new living accommodation for twenty people upstairs. It was to be a bright, cheerful, yellow colour, to gladden the heart (or at least guide the footsteps) of the returning Fid.

Midsummer 1963 got me a new name. It happened like this. BAS staff in England were gathered at a BBC studio to record our messages to those on Base preparing to celebrate their shortest day. The BBC laid on this special southern Midwinter programme every year. For us, in a bright English June of sunlight and scudding clouds it was an excuse for a party (the Beeb were quite generous with their gin). I think we enjoyed it far more than 'the lads' did – though no doubt they would be well into the Base hooch by the time the recording came through.

The system was simple. We lined up to deliver our messages, and the producer shooed us away when she thought we had rattled on enough or were using language too crude for Auntie (who was still quite prissy in 1963). 'Clem' Clements, the Storekeeper from Port Stanley, home to order supplies, was into his third blue joke, and getting near to Auntie's knuckle. Auntie intervened, with a delicate tap on the shoulder. Clem looked round, saw me, and muttered:

'Sorry, you fellows, I've got to go. All the best. I'm handing over to Doctor Holdforth.'

The *mot juste* has stuck in our family. Indeed, my first title for this book was *Holding Forth*.

In the southern summer of 1963/64 I went back to Signy to watch the Plastic Palace go up.

It wasn't such fun as in 1961-62. For an obvious reason. I had got married in April 1963. Elizabeth (or Lizzie, as she was generally known in the family) was the young and very lovely widow of Hartmut Weil, one of my uncle Nick's closest friends. She was the girl who had made me dance in the kitchen years earlier. We had met occasionally over the years, but only got to know one another properly during the second half of 1962. Now I was leaving her, and my new stepson Robert, in a little cottage in Hertfordshire, grappling with a new environment and new school, painting walls, and putting up with a mouse invasion of Gough Island proportions. I received vivid descriptions of mice playing helter skelter inside the lath and plaster walls, of mice swinging in the teacups, of mice being kept at bay with plugs of patent steel wool and cement mixture . . . I almost felt I should send her a skua.

But I was paid to run BAS biology and that meant going south for five

months. I suppose Lizzie accepted it as part of the package – anyway she was
marvellously uncomplaining. It was just that, for me, life had less zest than
in the previous season, and dangerous moments seemed less responsible. I
think I concluded quite early on that this life would have to change.

It was enjoyable, none the less. We went to Signy in *John Biscoe* but on our
way we spent several days in heavy pack off the west of the South Shetland
Islands. It was a wonderful sight, with dazzling floes spreading to where
mountainous islands jutted against a clear sky. But it was frustrating, and for
the captain a touch concern-making. For several icebergs floated not far off,
and they and the pack were moving in different directions. This happens
because the pack – whose floes are only two or three metres thick – moves
largely with the wind, whereas bergs, jutting several hundred metres into
the sea, are driven by the currents. A berg can plough through the pack just
like an icebreaker, compressing and breaking the floating ice ahead of it, and
if you are in a ship that seems likely to be caught up in such a turmoil you
will find it expedient to push and shove your way into whatever leads and
lines of weakness seem best calculated to get you out of the way.

Two days later, and without hazard, the wind changed and the pack
opened. Once free from the ice, we paid flying visits to Deception Island
and Hope Bay. The former is a great volcanic caldera – a broad, collapsed
crater – breached by the sea to form a wonderful natural harbour some
twelve kilometres wide at its broadest, and sixteen kilometres long. The UK,
Argentina and Chile – all of which claim this part of the Antarctic – all had
bases there. Ours was nearest to the narrow harbour entrance named
Neptune's Bellows, guarded by towering cliffs of black, red and orange
volcanic lava and ash. The west of the entrance is full of reefs, and marked
by a wrecked whale catcher on whose side some Fids, probably after a party,
had painted the inscription BAS PILOT NO 1. Soon we were anchored in
Whaler's Bay, where the BAS base lay next to a ruined whaling station with
its cemetery. An aircraft hangar stood nearby, alongside the runway from
which the twin-engined Otter aircraft operated. Steam rose copiously from
the black sand beach – clear reminder that volcanic activity was not over. It
was said to be the only place in the world where you could gather naturally-
parboiled krill. A few years later it got hotter than that, in a major eruption
which forced the evacuation of all three Bases, and (in a second stage) sent a
surge of ash, ice and debris through the British station, rendering the airstrip
useless.

Royce Longton, our new botanist, and I snatched some time amidst the
unloading of cargo to do some ecologising on the caldera rim. Then it was
on to Hope Bay, where Argentine and British stations stood close together
under the mountains at the tip of the Antarctic Peninsula, northernmost

point of the Antarctic mainland. Carl Skottsberg had made his fossil finds hereabouts in 1901, and the mountain that dominates the Bay is named 'Mount Flora' in recognition. It is flanked by two shapely cones that Fids at least know as 'Flora's Tits'.

Hope Bay had been one of the great bases for dog-sledging and about sixty huskies howled their greeting to us as we came ashore. Horror of horrors! John Green, Secretary of BAS and senior officer at Stanley, appeared with a Skidoo (a Canadian motor toboggan) and drove it up the slope. Heads shook in furious scepticism. Nobody wanted to recognize the shape of things to come. Lovers of real dogs hated the 'tin dogs' that were soon to supplant them.

A few days later, *Biscoe* and *Shackleton*, the latter with the Plastic Palace stacked in her hold, converged on Signy. We travelled in fine weather with wonderful views of icebergs – the biggest a huge tabular about 20 kilometres long. We passed Elephant Island, where Shackleton brought his men to safety after drifting for eighteen months in the ice of the Weddell Sea, after their ship *Endurance* had been crushed by heavy pack. It looked thoroughly unprepossessing, but Malcolm Burley (he of the 'splendid team') was to lead a highly successful Joint Services Expedition there in 1970-71, demonstrating how closely its flora and fauna resembled that of Signy and finding a moss bank overlying frozen peat 3 metres deep and 5000 years old.

You could spend an endless career leaping from island to island in this part of Antarctica, and collecting plants and insects. But our policy was to take Signy as our main study area and thoroughly analyze its ecosystem. So the first task was to get all the gear landed, and the Plastic Palace built and equipped.

I noted a well-recorded phenomenon as *Shackleton* appeared off Signy and slowed to anchor. A boat was lowered and a party made for shore. The new hands were togged up like a Polar version of Action Man – bright new anoraks or windproofs over heavy sweaters, gloves and Greenland boots. They looked splendidly photogenic in the bright sunshine. As the boat neared the jetty, Pete Tilbrook – 'Pete BL' – led the old hands out to start work. They were in shirt sleeves, battledress trousers and plimsolls.

This difference may partly reflect genuine acclimatization. But much of it, I think, was psychological and practical. In still, sunny weather the Antarctic can be comfortably warm (as Alpine ski slopes are if there is no wind). When a ship comes in and cargo has to be humped, the work soon peps up your internal warmth. The anoraks and sweaters don't stay on very long when you have a few hundred sacks of anthracite and scores of crates to shift.

We had a special team of builders to put the Plastic Palace up, and the work went quite well. But not without hiccups.

Dick Stocks, the chief builder, appeared one morning with a worried frown. 'I can't find any holding down bolts, to secure the steel frame to the foundations,' he said.

This was serious. On Signy the wind can gust to around 100 knots. The big plastic sections were light and bulbous, and needed to be secured firmly to the steel frame which in turn needed bolting into concrete blocks. No holding down bolts might mean a yellow plastic balloon taking off for the Stone Chute. The weather rammed the lesson home by producing a real snorter, gusting to 86 knots.

The problem was that three different firms had contributed to the job. One produced the plastic panels, floorboards and fittings. Another the steel frame. The third the quick-setting cement for the foundations. The bolts should have been supplied by Contractor Two, who assumed that Contractor Three was doing the job. Panic telegrams followed. In the end four things happened:

- Dick cast the foundation blocks with tapered recesses into which the bolts could be inserted and cemented later;
- a set of bolts was made rapidly in the workshops in Port Stanley;
- another set was flown out from England to Monte and conveyed thence to Stanley by the supply ship *Darwin*;
- *Shackleton* had to make an extra trip to the Falklands to bring the things to Signy.

All in all quite an expense. It reminded us how dependent Antarctic Stations were on efficient planning ten thousand miles away. And the point was rammed home when we tried to use the compressor to re-charge air bottles for the scuba divers. It had been sent to Britain the previous year for repair. It came out gleaming with new paint. It did not work. On dismantling, the dirt of last year's breakdown was still obvious; the flywheel wobbled, and the main shaft of the engine, in the words of mechanic Alf Amphlett, was 'gouged to buggery'. So there I was, with two expensive marine biologists and an assistant, all specially trained to dive, with no way of getting waterborne. Alf rose to the occasion, taking over and adapting a spare diesel generator engine. Again we saw why you had to have versatile craftsmen in the Antarctic.

The holding down bolts installed, the steel frame soon went up. It was only one storey high, with a broad flange around the edge on which the upper floor panels stood. These formed both walls and roof, arching to meet in mid-apex. Steel cables passed over the roof and were shackled to concrete blocks on either side of the hut, giving extra security against gales. All the panels were cramped and bolted together, with two strips of mastic to seal the joints. And this posed another problem. The supply firm clearly had

A new laboratory. The 'Plastic Palace' stands beside the old hut on Signy Island.

only two kinds of mastic – British and foreign. For them foreign apparently meant 'tropical'. It was as stiff as school pudding. We had to heat it with a blowlamp and hammer it into the grooves and then jam and screw the panels together while it retained some plasticity. As it was, the upstairs was a fraction longer than the downstairs.

But all was gleaming yellow and ready for a formal inauguration when *Shackleton* returned with Bunny Fuchs on 14 January (my 33rd birthday). We decided on a ceremony. A Foundation Stone was cast, the inscription made by cutting strips of plasticene with a V-pulley and laying them in mirror-writing on the smooth base of the wooden mould. To everyone's relief, all the letters were the right way round when the hardened block was finally removed.

BRITISH ANTARCTIC SURVEY
THIS STONE WAS LAID
BY
SIR VIVIAN FUCHS
JANUARY 15 1964

The Director, woolly cap perched atop, tapped it into place, made a few comments and drank a toast. No sooner had he gone than a little procession laid a smaller oblong slab beside the greater. A label read: 'LAID BY...' It was a burned, unleavened loaf. Somebody had had a bad day in the kitchen...

Not many weeks later, Bunny was back to witness the landing of some 350 drums of fuel for the new Rolls-Royce generators (the new fuel tank, into which diesel oil could be pumped directly from the ship, came next season). And with *Shackleton* and the fuel came our chief marine biologist, Pete ('Snork') Redfearn, who had been to Punta Arenas to have a bad tooth seen to. He had taken his opportunities. Under Bunny's increasingly frosty gaze, one 5-litre flagon of Chilean red wine after another was handed ashore. The Director gave the Base Leader firm instructions as to its use. Two days later I left Signy for the last time.

We put out into a strengthening gale. The sky was a mass of scudding grey, and the sea was short, steep and uncomfortable. But only a few kilometres away, shelter beckoned. A big tabular iceberg – about fifteen kilometres long and eight wide – had grounded on a shoal east of Signy. It made a good lee. We wallowed into it, leaving *Kista Dan*, just back from Halley Bay in the Weddell Sea, to ride the gale out in the open. Her skipper sounded a bit cautious...

We crept in beside the edge of the berg, standing off about two and a half kilometres from it. Suddenly, without warning, little avalanches of ice began to cascade down the cliff faces. A crack appeared, and a glass-green mass surged up from the depths. The Captain – David 'Frosty' Turnbull – issued two sets of orders simultaneously. The first could be summarized as 'Get the hell out of here!' – which was not as easy as it sounds as by then we had another small berg our port side, and could not turn until we had cleared it. The second order was 'Get Bunny!' Sir Vivian needed little getting. Pursued by all manner of Fids, with all manner of cameras, he appeared on the bridge. We stood and watched a fascinating spectacle. A slab of ice over a kilometre long and maybe 100 metres wide was peeling off the side of the berg. As it went it split into lesser masses of ice. On the radar screen, an apron of debris spread with amazing rapidity to halve the gap between us and the new ice cliff in about five minutes. Twenty minutes later a dozen fair-sized icebergs, their summits rising twenty to forty metres above the water, and with masses of smaller fragments between them, had spread to cover an area some ten square kilometres in extent.

The radio spluttered:

'*Shackleton*, *Shackleton*, are you all right, *Shackleton*, over?'

It was *Kista Dan* – whose view of us had suddenly been blocked by this screen of tumbled devastation.

We emerged and spent the night safely, but uncomfortably, in the open sea. Next day we headed for South Georgia.

This is, without doubt, the most spectacularly beautiful of all Sub-antarctic islands. It is big – over a hundred and fifty kilometres long and fifty wide – and high, rising to over 2,900 metres. The mountains soar up from the water's edge in buttresses and towers, rising to fluted ice crests from which great glaciers descend to calve small icebergs into the coastal seas. The coast is varied, with deep inlets, broad bays and many little tussock-covered islands and reefs. And the climate is just that bit warmer than at Signy, so that there is a border of red kelp in the shallow seas, and green tussock, short grasslands, wet sedgelands and *Acaena* heaths as a fringe between the sea and the icy hills. This injection of colour makes a beautiful scene even richer.

And the animal life helps. The island has the largest population of Elephant seals in the South Atlantic. It has a resurgent population of Fur seal that even in the 1960s was in the tens of thousands and is now well over a million. It has colonies of tall King penguins, with their orange-yellow flashes of feathering on the sides of the neck. Like the Emperors that are their closest relatives, they stand around a metre high and make no nest, incubating their eggs in a kind of brood pouch formed from their feet and a flap of feathered skin at the base of the belly. The young are, in contrast, a fluffy chocolate brown with dingy white tummies. And there are several other penguins (Gentoos, Chinstraps and Macaronis), large numbers of Wandering, Black-browed and Sooty albatrosses, many petrels, many skuas, and three kinds of land bird – a small pipit and two kinds of duck. The pipit and one of the ducks are endemic to the island.

In the 1960s BAS had a small station on Bird Island, at the extreme north-west of South Georgia, where biologists were studying Fur seals and albatrosses. The Fur seals provide one of the most striking stories of recovery from near-extinction in the animal world.

James Cook discovered South Georgia and named it for King George III in 1775 – his first Subantarctic landfall in his great circumnavigation of the southern limits of the world. It had one obvious natural wealth – Fur seals, whose pelts were then in great demand, not least for the China trade where the hairs were woven into fine felt. There were thousands of them in Possession Bay, where he raised his flag. The news travelled fast. By 1822, James Weddell calculated that no fewer than 1,200,000 had been killed, and recorded that the seals were almost extinct. The slaughter involved more than 2000 tons of shipping and 200 to 300 seamen every year. There was a small recovery – and more slaughter – in the 1860s and 1870s (as there was at Gough Island), and then it looked as if the Fur seals were gone for ever. Until 1923 when the RRS *Discovery II* found a small breeding colony on the Willis Islands, west of Bird Island. The population expanded from there, spilling over to the South Shetland, South Orkney and South Sandwich

Islands. And there is one reason why we can deduce that all these resurgent populations come from one group of survivors. About one in a thousand is white. Not an albino, but like Kipling's White Seal, dark-eyed and with a creamy yellow pelt. This is a much higher incidence of white-coatedness than would be expected if it just appeared as a random mutation, and it suggests that a rare genetic trait present in the remnant stock has been fixed in their offspring.

South Georgia in the 1960s was the scene of two active wildlife industries – whaling and Elephant sealing – but both were coming to an end. In 1962 there were four operating whaling stations – Grytviken, Husvik, Stromness and Leith – their names betokening their Norwegian and Scottish ownership. By 1964 they were on a care and maintenance basis. And the Elephant seal industry, which depended on the taking of the biggest males which were driven, roaring and rearing, into the shallow waters and shot and flensed there, also ceased. The demise of whaling also meant the demise of the British Resident Magistracy and administrative centre at King Edward Point, which looks across the bay to Grytviken. Curiously, just as the closure of the Administration looked more and more likely, approval was given for a massive new building – ordered by the Resident Magistrate as accomodation for all those he thought would flock to the island to study whales and other wildlife. It cost £200,000, and the package also included a new modern bungalow for the Magistrate. Both were ready just in time to be taken over by BAS, and then to be occupied by Argentine forces. Today, South Georgia is populated by unpersecuted birds and beasts, and Shackleton House at King Edward Point is occupied by a British military garrison.

Ernest Shackleton's presence looms over South Georgia. It was here that he, together with Worsley and Crean, crossed the unmapped icecap to seek rescue for his men, castaway on Elephant Island. It was here that he died in 1922 'after sixteen days of turmoil and anxiety' and after writing his last lines:

In the darkening twilight I saw a lone star hover, gem-like above the bay.

Shackleton is buried in the little whalers' cemetery at Grytviken, and a cairn and cross erected by his comrades still stands above King Edward Point, a landmark to all entering the harbour.

In 1964 Peter Tilbrook and I had over a week at the Point, waiting for *Protector* and for a three-week visit to the South Sandwich islands. The visit was my idea, and it stemmed from a strange happening in 1962.

This was a period when everyone was sensitive to explosions in remote places which *might* be due to the accidental or deliberate detonation of nuclear devices. Sometime in March the American burp-detectors recorded

HMS Protector *berthed at the old whaling station of Leith on South Georgia.*

an upheaval on the edge of the Antarctic, near an island named Zavodovski. Russian name? Russians in British Antarctic Territory? Russian explosion? *Protector*, as the nearest NATO warship, was sent to investigate. I was aboard because I was to travelling from the Falklands to Tristan to collect the Royal Society Expedition. Now we had a five-day deviation, and we were keen to make scientific use of it.

The South Sandwich Islands are a chain of eleven more or less active volcanoes strung out in an arc across a hundred and fifty kilometres of sea. They form a kind of bow-wave of crustal upheaval, where the rock plate that forms the floor of the Scotia Sea thrusts into the bed of the South Atlantic. They were Captain Cook's first Antarctic landfall after leaving South Georgia in January 1775. A seaman named Freezeland made the first sighting – of a tower of rock over 300 metres high that now bears his name. Behind it, receding into murk, was an ice-covered mass that Cook named 'Cape Bristol'. Southward was further ice-covered land he called 'Southern Thule', and northward a supposed headland that became 'Cape Montagu'. Cook thought (and doubtless hoped) that his discovery was part of the great southern continent he was seeking, and gave it the name 'Sandwich Land' after his patron the Earl of Sandwich ('Jemmy Twitcher', gamester, rake and inventor of convenience foods). Passing northwards, he found three islands – Saunders Island and two Candlemas Islands. It was not until 1819 that the

Russian navigator Thaddeus von Bellingshausen discovered the three northernmost members of the chain, naming them Visokoi, Leskov and Zavodovski Islands for various of his companions; he also proved that Cook's southernmost discoveries were all islands – and that Southern Thule is in fact three islands now named Thule, Cook and Bellingshausen.

It was pretty obvious that the 'burp' detected in 1962 was likely to be a volcanic eruption. But we decided to use the opportunity to have a look at as many islands as possible, since they were very little known. We started at Thule. I was landed by helicopter on a lava plain covered with dirt and penguin droppings, but supporting sparse lichens, green algal felt, and mites and springtails. Moulting Chinstrap penguins – looking incredibly scruffy – huddled around a boarded-up Argentine hut (for the sovereignty over these islands, like that of South Georgia and the Falklands, is disputed between Argentina and the UK). Meanwhile the helicopter staggered up in the heavy cold air to the crest of Thule – to find that in the midst of the ice cap, sheer rock and ice cliffs fell some 60 metres to a lake of gently steaming, emerald-green water.

We moved on, using the helicopter to buzz a shore party from island to island. On Bellingshausen Island (where I claim a first recorded landing) there was real excitement – for around vents belching out steam there were brilliant mats of liverwort, moss, toadstools and lichens. Heat and moisture had created oases in the cold Antarctic desert. Moving north we counted Fur seals on Saunders, and saw marks of a massive eruption through the ice cap of Bristol Island. But although it, too, was steaming like a simmering kettle it looked too old to be the origin of the burp.

We headed on towards Zavodovski. As we neared Candlemas Island, it was decided that we ought at least to go through the motions of looking for raised levels of radiation. That meant a cover story, and I provided it on 'Dr Boffin's Ten Minutes' – a regular briefing for the ship's company, who were politely interested in my various weird comings and goings.

'Tomorrow, we are going to land on Candlemas Island,' I said. 'And there's a special job to be done there. In 1911 a German expedition led by a man named Filchner called there' (all quite true) 'and reported radioactive rocks' (quite untrue). 'We think that was a mistake, but I am going to take a radiation counter ashore just to check up . . .'

I did. I passed the scanner over various rocks, while Marine Bufton, my helper, looked on in amusement. The needle stayed resolutely rock-bottom in the green. That gave me licence to explore this fascinating island – which clearly had a very old, quiescent southern half and a very active northern one, where steam rose from a sulphur-streaked cinder cone. Between the two lay a pair of lagoons, probably closed off from the sea as the northern cone was built up by successive eruptions. A Leopard seal basking on the shore eyed me malevolently as I walked by. On the slopes of the young volcano we found patches of warmed greenery like those on Bellingshausen, and geysers spouted above a hot pool where happy sailors, waiting for me to finish my collections, enjoyed a swim.

Next day we solved the mystery of the burp. For the seas around Visokoi Island and northwards to Zavodovski were streaked with floating pumice lava. Clearly there had been a massive undersea eruption. I organised gangs to fish with buckets from bow and stern and we soon had several boxes of rock samples. We also had a very unhappy Chief Engineer, who came all the way up to the Bridge to protest.

'Sir,' he said to Robin Graham, 'no doubt all this is good science and great fun for Dr Boffin. But this bloody muck is getting into our engine room water intakes and scouring the insides to buggery. I've had to shut the fresh water distillation plant down, and there'll have to be strict water economy until we get all the grit out. The generators don't like it either, and I won't swear for the engine cooling systems. Please get to hell out of here as fast as you can . . .'

We left, abandoning an attempt to land on Zavodovski Island and to trace the source of the pumice, which we associated with a shoal on the charts – clearly a submarine volcanic peak – to the north-west. The least recorded depth was 172 fathoms (about 280 metres).

Next year the ship came back, and got a shock. The depth was not 172 fathoms but around 15 – under 50 metres – in a crescentic shoal which was almost certainly the crater rim of a much enlarged volcano. One of these days it will break surface as the youngest member of the South Sandwich arc.

These brief days in 1962 had brought home to me the need to study these islands and their biology. So I arranged to 'borrow' *Protector* (by now commanded by Martin Ollivant) for three weeks in 1964, and put a scientific team aboard her. One party – including a geologist (John Tomblin), a botanist (Royce Longton) and a zoologist (Peter Tilbrook) – was to be landed on Candlemas Island, which was the most varied and interesting of the group, to stay for at least two weeks and make detailed observations. Pete had to have 24-hour power even there, so a small generator was included in the equipment! The second party, including a survey team led by Lt Cdr John Wynne-Edwards, a second geologist, Peter Baker (formerly of the Royal Society Expedition to Tristan), Bill Vaughan (formerly Seals Inspector at South Georgia) and I were to be mobile, hopping from the ship to the various islands in succession. We hoped that the surveyors would measure the distances from island to island exactly and that we could make other observations and take aerial photographs that would allow us to improve the highly sketchy maps. And Charles Lagus, BBC cameraman, came along for what promised to be a fairly spectacular venture.

It worked out pretty well. But there were hairy moments. The ship carried elderly Whirlwind Mark I helicopters and they were under-powered, albeit with very reliable engines. There was a lot of nasty down-draught turbulence. From time to time you would find yourself descending steadily to a grey sea heaving with ice, while the pilot put maximum lift on and hoped to claw free before contact (there were flotation devices on the choppers but they told us that they would probably make the aircraft turn over and float upside down). John Wynne-Edwards threatened to re-name the south-eastern point of Saunders Island 'Cape Adrenalin' because the helicopter conveying him nearly crashed against it twice. I well recall taking off from that same point (where we were based for a day's fieldwork), with the helicopter moving briskly upwards to hover, putting the nose down and clearing the land at fastest possible speed – only to find that the ship had vanished into a blizzard. Even a 4000-ton vessel seems very tiny when you are fifteen kilometres away and visibility is a mass of whirling snow.

But we made exciting discoveries. The very first volcano we came to – the tiny rocky mass of Leskov Island which everyone assumed would be thoroughly extinct – proved to have steaming vents and moss carpets on its summit ridge. We found more warm ground and moss on Visokoi Island. We went back for three days to Bellingshausen and made detailed observations of its steam vents and their rich plant life. Bill Vaughan counted the seals – finding several new Fur seal breeding colonies – and made detailed notes on the seabirds. The surveyors strung the islands together, moving some of their mapped positions several kilometres in the process. Sometimes it was frustrating – as when John Wynne-Edwards and I camped on Saunders Island on the only clear night during the whole visit, to try to fix the position with star sights – only to find that the wind had shifted and was blowing the plume of hot gas and steam from the main volcano right over us, so that the stars jumped and shimmered in the hottest of haze.

The Navy entered into the spirit of the thing:

> We fly off with Sparks and Chippy
> And Doctor Biology.
> Dozens of bearded weirdies
> Backed up by the BBC . . .

went the ships' paper (the Radio Operator and Carpenter had been enlisted as extra boffins for the duration).

We savoured the weird landscape of the group to the full. For ice and fire

Martin Holdgate measuring the temperature of gases emitted from a volcanic vent on Bellingshausen Island, South Sandwich Islands. Photograph: Charles Lagus, Camera Press.

make an odd combination. There are places where active craters pierce ice hundreds of metres thick. There are areas of wide ice-cap devoid of life, and close by them places where escaping steam warms the soil and, condensed into mist by the cold air, falls back as droplets to nourish the most vivid and luxuriant growths of liverwort and moss. There are hot pools alongside wide expanses of bare frozen ground. There are great cliffs of banded lava and ash, sombre in their tints of red, grey and orange. There are bluffs of rock and ice, intermingled with graceful ice-cones rearing up against a pale sky. There are areas of ashen hills and extinct craters, one of them bisected by the sea to show the layering of the ash about the harder lava plug of the central vent. It is difficult terrain, lapped by difficult seas, and there are not many places where you could land a boat. The helicopter established itself as an ideal facilitator of Antarctic fieldwork.

The weather was beastly. For nearly ninety per cent of the time there was more than seven-eighths cloud cover. For one third of it the visibility was less than 8 kilometres. It snowed often. But mostly it was just a cold, grey, dreary environment – and at the end of the three weeks the mists closed in for four whole days. We went up to the new volcanic shoal and dredged some pumice from its top. The ship met up with a Royal Fleet Auxiliary tanker and fuelled (for we were due to go home across the South Atlantic to South Africa). We put a larger party onto Candlemas (and promptly got weather-bound there). We went back to Zavodovski – where fog continued. We revenged ourselves by choosing names for this, the most active and smelliest of the eleven islands. We named the peak Mount Asphyxia, and the main headlands Fume Point, Noxious Bluff, Acrid Point, Stench Point and Reek Point. The staid referees of the Antarctic Place-Names Committee vetoed the first of them. We did not even try with Cape Adrenalin.

Life on the ship was an amazing contrast with the shore camps (not that these were uncomfortable, for the equipment and food were good). *Protector* adhered to the splendid imperial tradition that the officers changed into evening dress for dinner, and visiting scientists were treated as temporary members of the Wardroom. It was a strange experience to come on board in a shaky helicopter, your field gear damp and smelling of penguin mess, and an hour later to be showered, clad in dinner jacket and black tie, sipping rum and coke at the bar. At least, on most evenings – for once in the while they decided to hold a 'Fids night'. That meant that the officers appeared in every variety of grotty clothing (except that anything smelling of penguin dung or petrel vomit was barred). We, of course, made sure that our dinner jackets were immaculate and our bow-ties perfect. One has to maintain some standards after all . . .

The comfort in *Protector* was in real contrast to that in *Magpie*, outward to Tristan nine years earlier. No mess decks. No hammocks. You were roused by canned music, and the lyrics from *Oklahoma* are for me for ever associated with those first moments when my feet hit a gently rolling deck and I struggled to keep upright and wash in a basin whose contents seemed determined to cascade over the rim onto my knees. 'Oh what a beautiful morning. . .' was often a prelude to a grey sky, heaving swell and scant visibility.

Our time in the South Sandwich ran out and we left for Bouvet Øya (so named because it is a Norwegian possession, although discovered by a Frenchman, Captain J.F.C. Bouvet de Lozier, who sighted it in 1739: there are no records of subsequent visits until sealers arrived in 1808). Norway claimed it in 1927. We were to rendezvous there with the South African supply ship *RSA*, and jointly examine how suitable the place was for a weather station. By coincidence, Allan Crawford was to be in *RSA* – his third trip to Bouvet. It was also to be the third time that he and I met at various remote islands.

Bouvet is a volcano, like the South Sandwich, but it rises from the Mid-Atlantic Ridge, and is the next emergent peak as you go southwards from Gough Island. They say it is the most isolated island on earth – the one place

Some of these may be relict members of the ancient mountain fauna of a pre-glacial continent. In the Antarctic Peninsula, with its younger mountain ranges and retreating ice, recent immigrants from South America are commoner. But there is no doubt that the penguins evolved with the cooling continent, from birds that swam the temperate seas many millions of years ago, developing ever-better insulation and cold-adapted physiology as the temperature plummeted.

Although there are many tales of rivalry between the pioneer Antarctic explorers, and especially between Amundsen, Scott and Shackleton, each of whom wanted passionately to be first to the South Pole, the tradition of comradeship and co-operation lies equally deep. It is partly because those who go to the far south are not ordinary people. Apsley Cherry-Garrard summed it up in the much-quoted lines of *The Worst Journey in the World*, probably the finest of all personal accounts of Antarctic exploration.

> And I tell you, if you have the desire for knowledge and the power to give it physical expression, go out and explore . . . Some will tell you that you are mad, and nearly all will say, 'What is the use?' For we are a nation of shopkeepers, and no shopkeeper will look at research which does not promise him a financial return within a year. And so you will sledge nearly alone, but those with whom you sledge will not be shopkeepers; that is worth a good deal. If you march your Winter Journeys you will have your reward, so long as all you want is a penguin's egg.

Today the usefulness of polar research is still questioned, and countries remain governed by the mercenary mind. Short-term advantage counts for more than long-term equity. There are few votes in penguins' eggs. But polar explorers, like mountaineers, remain a fellowship. The sense of community among Antarctic scientists stems not only from their shared intellectual interests but from their experience of life in wild, harsh and beautiful places, sometimes basking in calm, sunlit serenity, and sometimes battered by shrieking storms and tumultuous seas.

The SCAR Working Group on Biology brought together scientists from Argentina, Australia, Belgium, Chile, France, Japan, New Zealand, Norway, the Soviet Union, the United States and the UK. Despite political divides, it was a close-knit group. We did four main things. We discussed research priorities, so that each national effort fitted within a wider programme. We co-ordinated certain field activities, such as the banding of birds. We held occasional symposia – the first in Paris in 1962 and the second, on Antarctic Ecology, in Cambridge in 1968. And we gave advice to the Treaty meetings, not least on conservation. Conservation was necessary because people with a sense of history – such as Brian Roberts – were well aware of a diversity of potential threats.

People think of the Antarctic as a clean, empty wilderness, but its early explorers had an eye to commerce and even a poet and romantic like Shackleton hoped to find new riches for his country. The great wealth of Fur seals discovered by Cook at South Georgia became the foundation of a valuable, albeit short-lived, industry. In the twentieth century many people got rich by exploiting the great whales, and the desire to understand them and manage their use was one reason for the outstanding research done by the *Discovery* investigations in the 1920s and 1930s – though these did not stop several species of whale being driven to the brink of extinction by 1970. Hopes of mineral wealth may well have helped sustain British Treasury support for FIDS during the period of extensive geological exploration led by Ray Adie. No deposits worth mining have ever been found, and the whole continent is now 'off limits' to commercial mineral exploration, but new economic bubbles have continued to swell. In my time in BAS, Russian biologists estimated that a sustained annual harvest of up to 70 million tonnes of krill might be taken, a quantity so vast that it would have equalled all other fishery landings in the entire world. There were worries about what this would have done to the whales, seals, fish and seabirds, many of which depend, directly or indirectly, on krill. Inigo Everson took up research on these matters and became an authority. The krill fishery was started, but never matched its theoretical promise and has now almost collapsed.

In 1964 it looked as if a new Antarctic sealing industry might also be about to start. A Norwegian ship, the *Polarhav*, went south to look at the possibility of exploiting the world's most numerous seal, the Crabeater, *Lobodon carcinophagus,* which abounds in the pack. Calculations (based on surveys from ships) suggested that there might be as many as 30 million of them (though we now think that 17 million is nearer the mark). *Polarhav's* cruise caught only 1127 seals, and the difficulties an industry would face were demonstrated when the ship got caught in heavy pack for ten days, but it set the conservationist alarm bells ringing. The Agreed Measures did not apply in the open sea, and guidelines we in the SCAR Working Group on Biology prepared in 1966 had no legal force. Brian Roberts believed that a new Treaty was needed, to control the prospective industry before it got started and became backed by vested interests and financial commitments. It took some time for him to win his case, but in 1972 the Convention on the Conservation of Antarctic Seals was signed in London. It was Brian's philosophy of regulating ahead of trouble that, years after his death in 1978, also drove the negotiation of CCAMLR, the Convention on the Conservation of Antarctic Marine Living Resources in 1980 and CRAMRA, the Convention on the Regulation of Antarctic Mineral Related Activities in 1988.

I suppose that it was my work with Brian on the Agreed Measures and then in the SCAR Working Group on Biology on the guidelines for regulating sealing that got me noticed in the conservation world. In particular, it drew me into the conservation section of the International Biological Programme.

The IBP was conceived as a kind of biologist's sequel to the International Geophysical Year. The first plan, by the President of the International Council of Scientific Unions, Sir Rudolph Peters, and the Italian medical scientist Guiseppe Montalenti, was to study the diversity of human populations and life-styles worldwide and document them (to use Peters' words) 'before civilisation stirred these up beyond genetic recognition'. That idea survived as the Human Adaptability Programme, led by the Oxford scientist, Joe Weiner, within a much wider IBP whose theme was 'the biological basis of productivity and human welfare'. Shorn of jargon, that meant looking at how different kinds of living systems around the world functioned, and how they might support (or limit) human societies. It was highly relevant to the issues environmentalists became concerned with in the 1970s, and even more relevant to today's buzz-concept, 'sustainable development'.

The broad theme of IBP was too wide for any single international organizing committee. It was, therefore, divided into sections. François Bourlière of France, who had hosted our first Antarctic Biology symposium in Paris in 1962, led the group on the productivity of terrestrial communities (PT for short). Max Nicholson, Director General of the British Nature Conservancy, convened CT, the section on the conservation of terrestrial communities. Other sections dealt with fundamental production processes (PP); fresh waters (PF); the seas (PM); the use and management of living systems (UM); and human adaptability (HA – Joe Weiner's group). The actual work, of course, was done by a host of scientists on the ground in various countries. The merit of IBP, like that of SCAR, was that it provided a framework for research within its over-arching central theme, adopted a consistent set of international methods (so that, with luck and good management, the results could be compared) and stimulated Governments to come up with a bit more money. It also helped biological research in the poorer countries (there was a good joint Anglo-Ugandan study, for example, on Lake George in the African Rift Valley). National coordination, as for SCAR, was through national Academies of Science, so that the Royal Society led in the UK.

Max Nicholson enrolled me in the Conservation Committee because he

A redoubtable conservationist. Max Nicholson, then aged 95, on an excursion to Loch Lomond National Nature Reserve in 1999.

saw the Antarctic Agreed Measures as something of a model. It was my first encounter with a remarkable man. Born in 1904, he became General Secretary of the 'think tank' Political and Economic Planning in the 1930s, and served during the second World War as a Director of Allied Shipping, attending both the Postdam and the Yalta Conferences. As a Deputy Secretary – the second most senior grade in the Civil Service – he was head of Herbert Morrison's office between 1945 and 1952. He combined this official career with a passion for ornithology, writing several books on birds. He was also a member of the Wild Life Conservation Special Committee chaired by Julian Huxley and Sir Arthur Tansley that led to the creation of the Nature Conservancy in 1949. In 1952 he stepped sideways into that 'parallel career' to become the second Director General of the Conservancy, and its real architect. With Peter Scott he was also the creator of the World Wildlife Fund in 1962.

Max was brilliant, idiosyncratic, tireless and years ahead of his time. He was also a crafty political operator, using his Whitehall skills to good effect in his new role. I have heard him say that his rivals in the Civil Service were so terrified that he would opt to return to become Permanent Secretary of a major Department that they saw to it that there was a steady flow of funds to the Nature Conservancy despite Treasury hostility. His capacity to build contacts and get his own way were both apparent in the IBP CT section.

It was through CT that I got to know a number of international conservationists. Among them was an American tax judge, Russell Train, who was about to change careers and have an immense influence on national and international environmental affairs. At his house in Washington DC – at a very well-lubricated party – I met a naturalist called Lee Talbot, who had spent six months in 1955 travelling halfway round Asia checking on the status of rare animals including the three kinds of Asian rhinoceros, the Asian lion, the Arabian oryx and the Syrian wild ass (which proved to be extinct in the wild). In 1966, Lee and I were members of a group that went with Max Nicholson to Brazil, viewing relict patches of the fast-vanishing coastal forests and flying to the great waterfall of Iguaçu in an ancient DC3 whose door security was strengthened with string. The weather was dirty. Dropping to land at a grass strip on the way we somehow scraped into a narrow clearance between cloud and tree-tops. 'Don't worry,' said Lee. 'These are marvellous aircraft. I've crashed in three, and walked away every time.'

Iguaçu is one of the three great waterfalls of the world. The river, a tributary of the Parana, falls 70 metres over a horseshoe of precipice in some twelve different cascades, amid dense sub-tropical rain forest. Flocks of swifts nest behind the curtain of falling water, darting through the spray to inaccessible ledges. Macaws shriek in the forest canopy. Both sides of the river, in Argentina and Brazil, are National Parks with a total area of over 200,000 hectares. The Parks are now a well-trodden tourist track, but they were less frequented in the mid-1960s, and we hoped to see real pristine wilderness. We were disappointed. It looked all right, until you walked into the forest. There you found a dearth of big, old trees and far too much bamboo. Lee and I walked one way, to meet the doyen American ecologist Ray Fosberg puzzling over the same problem. Some big stumps settled the argument. The whole forest on the Brazilian side of the falls had been logged, maybe thirty or forty years before. There was no ancient primary forest anywhere near (although we were assured of such growth 10 kilometres or so further away). The second growth was looking impressive enough, but some at least of the original diversity must have been lost. It was a first-hand encounter with a widespread problem of tropical conservation.

The governing body of IBP was SCIBP – Scientific Committee for the IBP – which, like SCAR, was a Special Committee of the International Council of Scientific Unions (an organization only slightly less complicated and less jargon-ridden than the United Nations!) It was a big Committee – there were nearly forty members – including the conveners of the various sectional programmes and about a dozen elected senior biologists from all around the world. To help co-ordination, other bits of ICSU doing apparently related work were asked to appoint representatives, and I was nominated by SCAR (when I stepped down in 1968, George Knox, who had by then become Head of the Zoology Department at Canterbury University, Christchurch and a leader in New Zealand Antarctic research, took my place and went on to become President of SCAR).

The bureaucracy of SCIBP was enlivened by occasional drama. Indeed, there was much more rivalry and argumentation than in SCAR. There was particular tension when the United States National Academy of Sciences decided that to get American biologists involved properly there would have to be two more international sectional programmes – on Comparative Physiology and on Systematics and Biogeography. Roger Revelle, a distinguished oceanographer who chaired the US National Committee, had the job of proposing the notion to SCIBP.

Joe Weiner, at his most withering, responded first. It went something like this:

'Mr Chairman, I am most grateful for this late recognition by our American colleagues of the importance of comparative physiology. But I am puzzled that they seem to think we need to have a new sectional programme for it. Let me just read a few sentences from the agreed mission of the Human Adaptability programme, which I have the honour to lead . . .'

There followed some pithy quotes on the theme of 'anything you can do, we are already doing better'. Roger Revelle got red and began to gobble like a turkeycock.

Max Nicholson followed. 'Mr Chairman, the programme of the CT section seems to me to cover the greater part of what our United States colleagues propose in their SB programme. Let me also quote . . .'

By the end of this dialogue, Roger Revelle's health looked seriously endangered. Fortunately, Jean Baer, our Swiss President, declared an adjournment, and a drinks party soon followed. I was buttonholed by Revelle, I suspect because I was a Brit. 'That man Weiner . . . and Nicholson as well . . . !' he protested. SB and CP never happened – but a number of outstanding American biologists stayed outside IBP in consequence. Anglo-American scientific friendship was not enhanced. I was not surprised when, in the queue at Le Bourget airport going home, I heard Professor Hal Waddington, a distinguished geneticist, talking to Ronald Keay, the Assistant Executive Secretary of the Royal Society. I caught one fragment:

'We must keep our eyes on Max . . .'

They may have been concerned with wider issues than IBP. For Max Nicholson was also deeply involved in the debate then going on over whether to establish a new British environmental research council. There was a feeling that while Government support for research on the basic sciences, medicine and agriculture was well managed by the Science Research Council, Medical Research Council and Agricultural Research Council respectively, environmental research was unduly fragmented. In 1959, Lord Hailsham, then Minister for Science, asked his Advisory Council on Science Policy for advice. They came back expressing worry about the lack of coherent support for research on natural resources like minerals, water, soil, land and fisheries. In 1961 a special Committee was told to consider the case for a new environmental research council, and in 1963 it said that this should be established.

But on what basis? One idea that floated around early on was that Max's Nature Conservancy, which already had the status of an independent Research Council, should be broadened to include research on freshwater biology and maybe marine fisheries as well. After all, it already included freshwater sites as nature reserves, and was embroiled with the fisheries Departments in arguments about the conservation of seals. Such an enlargement might have made it the channel for support to the Freshwater Biological Association, based at Windermere, and maybe a raft of marine fisheries laboratories as well. Max Nicholson had also been pressing for research on hydrology, and especially on the effects of different kinds of land use on water flow and evaporation, which it was proposed to study in two valleys on the Long Mynd in Shropshire, one forested and one grassy. Sir Solly Zuckerman, then Chief Scientific Adviser to the Ministry of Defence but himself a zoologist, chaired a group that considered three ways forward. One was the expansion of the Nature Conservancy into a biological research council. The second was to have a natural resources council dealing with biology and hydrology. The third was a wide-ranging research council embracing geology, meteorology, oceanography, hydrology and biology.

The argument swung this way and that, influenced (I am sure) by personalities and personal preferences almost as much as by dispassionate analysis of what might be best for science. Many of the candidate bodies were far from overjoyed at the prospect of being swept into a bigger entity.

Max Nicholson argued for minimal change that would turn the Nature Conservancy into a Biological Research Council. Lord Hailsham, as Minister for Science, came down in favour of a Natural Resources Research Council (state papers of the period show that he was not exactly the Nature Conservancy's greatest admirer). Some people wanted to deal even more harshly with the Conservancy, slicing it in two by putting its four research stations into the new Council and leaving the conservation branch as a slimmed-down operational body which selected and managed nature reserves and provided public information about nature conservation.

In 1963, following strong pressure from Sir Solly Zuckerman, the die was cast. There would be a new Natural Environment Research Council. The Nature Conservancy, the Geological Survey, the Hydrological Research Unit and the National Institute of Oceanography would be rolled into it and it would also grant aid (and exercise a near-control over) the Freshwater Biological Association, the Marine Biological Association and the Scottish Marine Biological Association. I remember Max Nicholson telling me, at about this time, that he thought that the British Antarctic Survey should also be a component. Such action would sever BAS even more completely from its colonial past. It happened in 1967.

I didn't know much about any of these manoevres in September 1965, when I went to see Jim Cragg to discuss Antarctic soils. Jim had moved from Durham to direct the Nature Conservancy's research station at Merlewood, on the southern edge of the Lake District, and one of his staff, Andy Bailey, had gone down to Signy to continue the soil studies I had started in 1962. We also got round to talking about family life. Lizzie's and my son, David, was just a few weeks old, having been born prematurely in Blackpool with a birth weight of just 2 lbs 14 ounces. Jim came straight to the point.

'Don't you think it's time you considered your future?' he said. 'You've a wife and two sons. Should you be going off to the Antarctic every other year for five months? I know it's enjoyable, but hopping out of helicopters onto icy islands is not the safest of jobs . . . ?'

He went on: 'Barton Worthington, our Deputy Director for Research, is leaving the Nature Conservancy to become the Director of the IBP. The Conservancy will need a new senior scientist who is good at co-ordinating research programmes. Why don't you apply?'

'Won't you be doing so? You're much more senior, and have all the right experience.'

'No. I don't want to work in London and I hate committees. And this new NERC organization is too bureaucratic for me. But you already work in London and you seem to be good at committees . . .'

I hesitated. For ten years I had made the life of the cold, remote and beautiful places at the far end of the world my special concern. I had built, and now led, a good scientific team and was becoming well known internationally. If I went on, I saw my way to writing the authoritative book on Antarctic ecology. Scientifically speaking, it made no sense to change careers. And the grip of those distant and lovely lands was still strong. On the other hand, Jim was quite right that it asked a lot of Lizzie and the children. Was it fair?

Anyway, I didn't really think that I had an iceberg's chance in the doldrums of getting the job. I was only 34, and a middle-ranking member of a body that had not yet been drawn into NERC. Barton Worthington's job was graded Deputy Chief Scientific Officer, and it carried the incredible salary of just over £4000 a year. But it seemed worth testing the water, and I applied.

Then Jim Cragg wrote, 'I've changed my mind and decided to apply myself.' He was already a DCSO, and my friend and mentor. I decided to withdraw. 'Don't,' he said. 'I have a feeling that they may be looking for someone in your age group, not mine, and we're at such different stages we're not really in competition.' The hat stayed in the ring. I was duly grilled by a learned Appointments Committee chaired by Professor Roy Clapham, who headed the NC's Scientific Committee. To my astonishment Jim Cragg's name was not on the interview list (I am good at reading such things upside down). Early in December I got a letter offering me the post. I phoned Lizzie. 'Guess what – we've got that job.' My mother immediately decided that we ought to be able to afford a nanny for the boys (she was wrong!). I wrote and accepted. But then came further astonishment. An embarrassed emissary from NERC appeared in Bancroft Road.

'We're terribly sorry,' he muttered, 'but after we had offered you the job we found that we had overlooked an application from another senior candidate.'

'Jim Cragg?' I asked. Naturally, the even more embarrassed emissary did not reply. But that was what had happened. Jim and I spoke. His comments on the competence of those concerned made me wonder whether I would be better off sticking to penguins. But he urged me to go ahead and do the job, and told NERC Headquarters firmly what to do with his papers. Very early in 1966 I found myself installed in a stately office in Belgrave Square, responsible to Max Nicholson and the Conservancy for a nation-wide team of scientists studying the British flora and fauna and trying to ensure that as much as possible of it survived into the next century.

I remember at least one moment of emotion about the change. Somewhere on the London Underground there was a poster urging people to visit the countryside. The art work was unusually good, and as I stared at it, it came home to me that I had been given a special responsibility to care for these lovely places: for what Hopkins has called 'landscape plotted and pieced, fold and fallow and plough' and for the diversity of 'dappled things' for which he gave glory to God.

The Nature Conservancy was an organization ahead of its time. It was the product of real vision. Julian Huxley and Arthur Tansley – one a zoologist, populariser of science and builder of organizations and the other a botanist, field ecologist and creator of British plant ecology – were very different people. But they were united in seeing that after the War new technology, new agricultural methods, new towns and all the other elements of social reconstruction would bear heavily on the surviving patches of wild countryside and the plants and animals that lived there. Yet these were not only beautiful and to be cherished in their own right, but natural laboratories for the young science of ecology. And ecology promised new insights into the relationship between life and habitat – into why things lived where they did, and how changing conditions guided evolution. As a tool, it could be a key to the planning of the human future – and a counter-weight if the economic and social imperative to make Britain agriculturally self-reliant led to unforeseen environmental destruction.

The Wild Life Conservation Special Committee that they chaired argued for a 'biological service' which would do ecological research, select and look after nature reserves, advise on ecologically sound management of land and living resources, and contribute to education. An 'Ecological Research Council' was to guide the service. As usual, the vision was eroded by established and sectoral interests, not least in the Ministry of Agriculture which did not want a lot of academic ecologists telling it how to develop British farming. As a result, The Nature Conservancy, created by Act of Parliament in 1949, had a narrower mandate that focussed almost entirely on nature conservation, although it was permitted to do research in support. Its first Director-General, Cyril Diver, was a distinguished amateur naturalist who had taken the job of Clerk to the House of Commons partly so as to have plenty of time for fieldwork during the long Parliamentary recesses! But the dominant influence was that of Max Nicholson, who took over in 1952. Under him, the Conservancy developed separate but interlinked Conservation and Research branches, plus sections providing advice and promoting environmental education. It was organized as a Great Britain body, but national differences (and political sensitivities) were recognized by the existence of Directors for Scotland and Wales.

One of the first things anyone has to do in a new job is to get to know both personalities and internal politics, and the Conservancy was more complicated than BAS in both respects. Max himself I knew fairly well, but his Deputy for Conservation and Management, Bob Boote – my 'opposite number' – was new to me. Bob also served as Director for England, while John Berry directed operations in Scotland and Elfyn Hughes led Wales from his base in Bangor. The Conservation Branch was regionalised, Deryck Fraser serving as Conservation Officer for England and steering its six regions, while Joe Eggeling, an experienced forester with years of service in East Africa, ran the Scottish Conservation Branch, with Regional Officers for the South, North West and North East. Elfyn Hughes directed the two Regions dealing with North and South Wales.

Unlike the Conservation Branch, the Research side of the Conservancy operated as a more or less unified Great Britain service, though Scotland did have a head of research, my Cambridge contemporary Dr David Jenkins, who acted as my deputy north of the Border. There were four main Research Stations and numerous outposts. The oldest laboratory was at Furzebrook, near Wareham in Dorset – on the edge of the Isle of Purbeck, where chalk grasslands and acid heaths, hard and soft coasts, the broad embayment of Poole Harbour and the nearby New Forest combine to give as much ecological diversity in a small area as you will find anywhere in Europe. Cyril Diver had himself done long-term studies at Studland Point, which was one of the first National Nature Reserves. Jim Cragg's domain of Merlewood, on the southern fringes of the Lake District, was the second Research Station – handy for limestone grasslands and fens, coastal marshes and acid bogs, oakwoods and mountains. Moor House, an old Appleby Castle shooting lodge and the highest inhabited house in England, served as an out-station. It stood in a great basin of peaty moorland where the river Tees rises under the cap of Crossfell – and this, too, was one of the earliest National Nature Reserves. I knew it well for it was here that the Zoology Department in Durham had done most of its field research.

Research staff also worked from the Scottish Headquarters in Edinburgh, on the isle of Rhum (which the NC owned in its entirety and which was both an important National Nature Reserve and a place for research on Red deer), and on Deeside (where David Jenkins and his colleague Adam Watson had been unravelling the complicated life of the Red grouse). Welsh research was centred on Snowdonia, where the mountain grasslands and the patches of ancient oakwood that clung to inaccessible crags were being scrutinized by a team led by Elfyn Hughes. But the newest research station was in England, at Monks Wood Experimental Station in Huntingdonshire, built as a lowland ecology centre and within easy reach of two large areas of ancient fenland, Woodwalton and Holme Fens, and right alongside Monks Wood itself, named for the nearby Abbey of Sawley. Its Director was Dr Kenneth

Mellanby, like me once an insect physiologist, who had been the founding Vice Chancellor of the University of Ibadan in Nigeria, and since his arrival at Monks Wood had become a keen observer of moles.

What were we trying to do? In a sense, the approach was not unlike that in the British Antarctic Survey. The research sought to understand why species of plant and animal were to be found in particular places, functioning in particular ways. Insights into the ecology of species and the conditions that led to particular patterns of vegetation could be used to guide management and ensure that as much as possible of Britain's wildlife remained for future generations to enjoy. The intellectual challenges were considerable, and the advent of techniques of systems analysis and mathematical modelling offered prospects of describing in new and rigorous ways how the various components of ecosystems fitted together and how the systems functioned as a whole.

My job was not to direct all the research projects – the station's Directors did that, and many of the specialist staff knew far more ecology than I did. Jim Cragg and Kenneth Mellanby were politely firm about our respective functions when we lunched together soon after my arrival. They saw my role as stitching the various programmes together to the satisfaction of our advisory Committees and NERC itself, making the case for research funds, and providing a buffer between the research teams and the central machine at NC and NERC Headquarters. 'Keep those bastards off our backs,' said Jim. It was pretty obvious that he was fed up with the whole system. Nobody was surprised when a few months after my arrival he left to become Professor at Calgary in Canada, and Director of a field station in the Banff National Park.

By this time, Max Nicholson had also retired and Duncan Poore – a fellow member of the IBP CT Committee – was appointed as Director. Duncan was a distinguished plant ecologist who had done pioneer work on the classification of British vegetation and then gone to work in Malaysia, at the University of Kuala Lumpur, where he became an authority on tropical rain forests. He, Bob Boote and I formed a triumvirate at Headquarters. Duncan led the process of recruiting Jim's successor, and they lit upon John Jeffers, then Chief Statistician at the Forestry Commission. 'We were very impressed with Jeffers,' Duncan reported. 'But we'll have to give him a computer.' It is hard to remember what a culture-breaking innovation that ancient and (by today's standards) weak and inefficient PDP 6 was, when it was first installed at Merlewood. John had almost everyone computer-literate within a few months. The ICT Revolution had arrived!

This was a time of what now seems astonishing growth in national scientific institutions. It was the era of Harold Wilson's 'white-hot technological revolution' and there were increasing sums of money for research, year after year. We were kept busy planning new developments. Should we have a new research station at Banchory on Deeside for work on Red grouse, other upland birds, deer and Scottish pine forest ecology? Should we build another research station near Norwich as the favoured centre for work on the 'soft' coasts of East Anglia? How should we judge between competing bids for research funding – and make sure that our science was not only good ecology but relevant to the active conservation that the Conservancy had to do? Amazingly, a lot of time went on deciding how to spend extra money, and employ more people.

'We've been allocated thirty new posts next year,' Duncan Poore once announced. 'What do you think we should do with them?'

'We need more Reserve Wardens,' said Bob. 'And better public information systems.'

'I would like to appoint a specialist on grasslands,' I countered. 'And we are weak on wetlands. Also, we have nobody looking at the ecological effects of herbicides, especially on fresh water systems . . .'

So it went on. I don't think it was altogether healthy. It was just too easy. Hunches became scientists so fast, and with so little hard argument, that we stored up problems for a future where resources were to get increasingly tight. But it was good to feel that the national need for science was recognized, and that we were part of a new movement that should lead to the wiser use of natural resources.

I found that the Conservancy was leading in a number of IBP projects. At Meathop Wood, Merlewood staff were analyzing how the many species in an oakwood contributed to its overall structure and productivity. At Moor House the earlier work of Jim Cragg's Durham Research Students was being tied together and supplemented so that we could model the moorland ecosystem ('model' in the new sense of describing in mathematical equations the rate and speed of the various processes that fixed, used and exchanged energy and built living matter or 'biomass'). In North Wales Elfyn Hughes led similar studies of grassland growth and production in the great basin around Llyn Llydaw, under the eastern crags of Snowdon.

Long ago I had vowed to follow biology because it would take me into wild and beautiful places. When I went to the Conservancy, I felt that it would give me a chance to do something for the British countryside I had known and loved since those childhood holidays at Asby. But I found that much of my time was actually spent in the London office in Belgrave Square, or in travelling to and from our research laboratories. Whereas in BAS I had led an active research team, and had the chance to do some original work myself, in the Conservancy I was little more than a scientific administrator. I think now that 35 was too early an age to make this transition. But at the time I was too busy to feel a sense of loss. And these visits did take me to the Lakes, Snowdonia, Deeside, Moor House, Welsh woodlands, Kentish coppices, southern downlands and many kinds of coast. I vividly remember one magical morning with David Jenkins on Deeside, when in the course of two hours before breakfast we watched otters on one of the lochs amid the heather and birchwoods of the Muir of Dinnet, dropped in on a blackcock lek, where half a dozen cock birds croaked and displayed in a circle to the delectation of any passing greyhens, and saw Red and Roe deer, an eagle and a fox as passing extras.

Another side of the job was involvement in bigger environmental issues. Max Nicholson had an eye for impending problems – especially those with a political dimension. In the early 1960s he had spotted two – oil and pesticides – which were to dominate national environmental concerns for more than a decade.

No doubt he understood about oil because he had been a shipping specialist and recognized the threat posed by ever-larger tankers carrying ever-greater cargoes in congested waters like the English Channel, bordered by rocky coasts and swept by storms. In April 1966 his predictions came true when the *Torrey Canyon* ran aground on the Seven Stones, east of Scilly, and presented the world with its first supertanker disaster. Cornwall saw miles of fouled and reeking beaches, contaminated harbours, and thousands of dead and dying seabirds.

Nobody had any experience of such a thing. The Government's Chief Scientific Adviser, Sir Solly Zuckerman, convened a scientific committee on which Duncan Poore represented the Nature Conservancy. The Services were mobilised. The Prime Minister ordered the RAF to bomb the wreck in the hope of burning the oil that remained in its tanks. It did not work very well, partly because success depended on the bombs penetrating the oil tanks and exploding within them rather than passing through the whole ship to the sea beneath. Booms to keep oil out of inlets were tested. They only worked in calm weather. Oiled sand was scooped up and dumped in inland quarries. Detergents were sprayed on a massive scale.

I saw what this did when I visited Mount's Bay one fine, breezy spring day in company with the Chairman of the Conservancy, Lord Howick (better remembered as Sir Evelyn Baring, the name he bore when Governor of Kenya). An enthusiastic young Naval Lieutenant was in command of four London fire engines, all pumping detergent onto the oiled beach. The white emulsion spread out into the blue-green sea.

'You're making your mark on the environment,' we said, not in our most approving tones.

Mount's Bay, Cornwall in 1967. Lord Howick, Chairman of the Nature Conservancy, strides towards a shore blackened with oil from the Torrey Canyon. *The sea beyond is white with detergent foam.*

Irony was lost on the Navy. 'You should have been here yesterday!' he countered. 'I had the whole bay white . . .'

We learned a lot. Perhaps the most galling lesson – which has not really sunk in even after thirty-five years – is that once oil gets into the sea there is very little worth doing about it. It is next to impossible to clean rocky shores without aggravating the damage. The detergents used in 1966 were much more toxic than those now available, and killed more marine life than the oil did, but even today cleaning techniques are far from perfect. Whereas, left to itself, the oil (which is, after all, a natural product) does decompose. After ten years shores should be more or less back to normal. Sandy beaches can be scooped up, and this may be justified on a limited scale if they are important for bathing – but they will clean themselves in time without the problem of disposal of lorry loads of smelly muck. Booms work well to keep oil out of sheltered inlets, and skimmers can remove it from calm water, but both are useless in a choppy sea. And cleansing oiled seabirds and seals – though much more efficient now than at the time of the *Torrey Canyon* when over 98 per cent of the victims died – is still an inefficient business. I doubt very much whether the millions of dollars spent cleaning up after the *Exxon Valdez* in Alaska helped the environment more than nature would have done for free, given time. The fact is that people hate feeling powerless and have an unquenchable confidence that they can improve on nature. Often they can't. Preventing tanker accidents, and designing ships to be as leak-proof as possible, pays much better than cleaning up after disasters.

This was, I think, the main lesson learnt from the *Torrey Canyon*. A Ministerial Committee on Hazardous Cargoes pressed the international body responsible for shipping, the Intergovernmental Maritime Consultative Organization, to draw up new international conventions. In 1969 one of these gave a coastal state the right to take action on the high seas if an accident threatened its shores. In the same year another agreement made shipowners responsible for the costs of damage, and required them to take out adequate insurance. The oil industry adopted the 'load on top' system under which ships did not wash out all their oily tank contents at the end of a voyage. The countries around the North Sea and English Channel agreed to co-operate to track oil slicks and work together if there was another tanker wreck. Yet despite all this, other disasters have occurred. It has taken a long time for improved ship designs, better navigation systems and tighter rules to bring oil pollution of the sea under something like control. And even today, irresponsible Captains still wash out empty oil tanks when they hope nobody is looking.

The Conservancy was well ahead of its time in its research on the impact of pesticides on wildlife. Its work began long before the American writer, Rachel Carson, published her fine – and alarming – book *Silent Spring* in 1967. Max Nicholson or Barton Worthington may have got the notion that the subject was important from an international conference convened by IUCN, the International Union for Conservation of Nature and Natural Resources, with which Max had close contacts, at Lake Success in the United States way back in 1949. But it was in the late 1950s that reports began to come in of dead foxes in the 'galloping grass counties' around Leicestershire, home of many of the most famous packs of foxhounds. The Conservancy was called in. It established that pigeons were being killed by eating seed corn dressed with certain kinds of pesticides – the so-called organochlorines, such as dieldrin and aldrin, themselves chemical relatives of DDT. The foxes were finding free suppers scattered about the fields – and paying the penalty in their turn. In 1957 concern over the amount of pesticides hitting the countryside led Government to agree with the manufacturers on a 'Notifications Scheme', under which the properties of new substances were reported to an Advisory Committee and the makers agreed to observe the safety precautions it proposed. The NC was on the Committee to advise on wildlife aspects.

The creation of Monks Wood as an experimental station was one consequence of these concerns. Kenneth Mellanby set up a Toxic Chemicals and Wild Life Section, headed by Dr Norman Moore and including outstanding ornithologists such as Derek Ratcliffe and Ian Prestt. Derek Ratcliffe established that when organochlorines were eaten by birds of prey, they laid thin-shelled and vulnerable eggs which were easily broken in the nest. Hence the population crash of birds like the Peregrine falcon and the Sparrowhawk. But this discovery opened up a whole can of political worms. The Conservancy was daring to question the safety of DDT and suchlike materials, hitherto looked on as wonder compounds and science's greatest blessing to agriculture. This in turn caused a mighty collision with the Ministry of Agriculture and the pesticides industry, who fought back on three levels – personal, professional, and political. It got quite dirty.

The political attack was predictable. How could the prosperity of British agriculture be weighed in the scale against the survival of a few birds – and moreover, raptors with hooked beaks and talons, and nasty habits when it came to game bird chicks? The professional critics argued that the research was incomplete, inconclusive and undertaken by a special interest group biased towards protecting wild life whatever it cost. Moreover (and here it got personal) the NC researchers were newcomers to the field whereas the Ministry scientists had been working on chemicals and their impact for years. They had better laboratories, and established reputations. The NC team were attacked as an emotional bunch of over-the-top bird-fanciers. It became fashionable to refer to Norman Moore (who is a baronet) sarcastically and with great emphasis as *Sir* Norman Moore, regardless of the fact that he has never used his title.

Some of the meetings were quite bitter, and although the worst was over by the time I was appointed, MAFF and the industry continued to fight hard against a strict, legally-based, Pesticides Safety Precautions Scheme in place of the loose voluntary Notification system. It is all well under the bridge now, but consider. Had there been no Nature Conservancy research team, would anyone have done the work on fox and bird deaths? Would MAFF, with its primary concern for agriculture, have devoted much effort to what must have seemed to many of its scientists a minor side-effect? Could they have been expected to take up unpopular cudgels against 'their own' industry?

Early 1966 I was more deeply embroiled in another politically sensitive conservation issue – the Battle of Cow Green. A place, to quote the leading Counsel on the other side, Peter Boydell QC 'which is not very green, and where there aren't many cows'.

The River Tees rises in springs and peaty gullies on the back of Crossfell and the other highest summits of the North Pennines. The beck that runs in a little limestone gorge near Moor House is one of its feeders, and the basin of Moor House National Nature Reserve is its uppermost catchment. As it gathered itself and became a river, the Tees used to flow sluggishly through a broad valley in the peaty moors before thundering over volcanic cliffs at Cauldron Snout and wandering along a rocky vale to cascade with even greater violence over another volcanic cliff at High Force. Upper Teesdale is renowned for rare plants, and many of them are 'arctic-alpine' relicts of the ice ages. They grow there partly because of the cool upland climate, but especially because of a crumbly limestone, cooked to sugar-like crystals when the volcanic layer was injected. This 'sugar limestone' forms alkaline, mineral-rich areas moistened by springs, and this is where the rarest plants live.

The upper Tees is one of northern England's finest rivers. But the lower Tees is industrial water, and in 1966 it was of great importance to ICI, whose vast chemical works at Billingham were one of the chief foundations of the economy of Tees-side. The company wanted more water. They made it clear that without it regional and indeed national prosperity was at risk. They pressed the Tees Valley and Cleveland Water Board to build a so-called river regulating reservoir in the upper Tees catchment (this is the kind of reservoir that stores water in times of heavy rainfall and releases it in times of drought, thereby guaranteeing a steady flow for abstraction by users downstream). But where should the reservoir be? Two big National Nature Reserves lay in its path – Moor House being one – and the whole valley between Middleton in Teesdale and Cauldron Snout was traversed by the Pennine Way and was cherished scenery. There was an outcry when the Board announced that they were considering flooding the valley at Dine Holm, in the heart of the area of highest scientific interest and finest scenery. The engineers turned hastily to the broad upper valley above Cauldron Snout, with its soggy bottom that was already almost a lake. It looked good. Quite a short dam would create a reservoir over three kilometres long and a kilometre wide. That should give lots of water for relatively little money.

Representatives of the Water Board, the engineers and ICI went to see Max Nicholson. He consulted the country's top mountain and moorland ecologist, Professor W.H. Pearsall, then Chairman of the Conservancy's Scientific Advisory Committee, who raised no objections. The water would barely encroach on Moor House NNR. It would only touch the margin of the proposed NNR lower down the valley. None of the areas of most cherished scenery would be submerged. Indeed, by injecting a large area of open water into a lakeless region the reservoir might even enrich the landscape. Max wrote an encouraging letter. If the lake was planned so that conservation and public enjoyment were catered for, he thought that the Nature Conservancy might even support it 'as easing public pressure on more important sites lower down the Dale'.

Oh dear! The rare plant botanists were incensed. Didn't the NC know that on Widdybank Fell there was a major outcrop of sugar limestone replete with rarities – and that nearly half of it would be submerged? There was a revolt. Two members of the Conservancy's Committee for England resigned. A number of expert and learned Societies joined together to petition against the plans. The Conservancy resolved that despite what Max had told the developers, it would resist the Parliamentary Bill that was to give permission for the construction of the reservoir. But how? Although a statutory Committee, the NC was part of NERC and NERC came under the Ministry of Education. The Conservancy's Memorandum of Objection had to go via NERC to the Department, for the Minister to consider. He in turn had to discuss the strength of the objection with his colleagues. The Ministry of Technology and the Treasury brushed the objections aside. How could a few acres of rare vegetation stand against the vital needs of Britain's greatest chemical company? Alternative reservoir sites were looked at. None was as attractive in economic and engineering terms as Cow Green. Ministers decided that the Government would not oppose the Bill. They did, however, agree that the Conservancy's objections should be explained to the Parliamentary Committees that would scrutinize it. I was told that I had to be the witness to do the explaining.

It was really like walking into a minefield. I knew nothing about parliamentary procedures – I hadn't even set foot in the Palace of Westminster since a school visit in 1947. Nobody in NERC seemed to understand the rules which applied to us as a public body. I had no brief beyond an instruction to make the best arguments I could for nature, in support of the Conservancy's Memorandum and in accordance with the arguments of a string of expert witnesses, many of whom (like Professor Harry Godwin from Cambridge) were members of Conservancy Committees.

I don't think we did too badly before the Commons Select Committee, where we swayed at least one Committee member to our side. When they reported back to the floor of the House there was a respectable vote against proceeding with the measure. But things were much more difficult in the House of Lords Committee (a Private Bill, like any other measure, has to go through both Houses). Here I found myself in a hotter seat, being examined as the first of the objectors rather than after Professor Godwin and other eminent independent scientists.

The proceedings in the Commons had shown that the Nature

Conservancy's original Memorandum missed quite a few points. But it was decided that we could not alter it for the Lords Committee, because it had been passed to the House by the Minister. Peter Boydell, who by curious coincidence had been a prefect at Arnold School when I was a very insignificant junior boy, cleverly manoeuvred me into admitting that in certain respects it was imperfect. He then encouraged me to expound key arguments that the memorandum did not cover. This provoked Lord Crook, a member of the Committee, to fury.

'I object very strongly to the way you have given evidence today,' he burst out, colouring with indignation. 'I have served many years in public life. I have given evidence and received evidence. I have never heard anything so improper as your testimony. You are not here as an independent expert witness. You are here as the representative of a public body which gave advice to the Minister. You are here, with the Minister's agreement, to answer questions about that advice – and not to arrogate to yourself the position of the Minister. Were you not briefed? . . .'

There was quite a lot more. It felt as if Big Ben had fallen on my head. Somehow I scrambled out without revealing that I had *not* been briefed on the constitutional points at all (I now know that Lord Crook, himself long associated with the Ministry of Labour and editor of the *Civil Service Argus*, was strictly correct even if cholerically intemperate). James Fisher, who was the next witness, for the National Parks Commission, quaked visibly for he saw himself in the same difficulty. Peter Boydell apologized afterwards, saying that he had not sought to provoke such an outburst, and Lord Grenfell, the Chairman, was similarly kindly (without, of course, criticizing his Committee member). The Bill passed. ICI put up a research fund and the doomed areas were thoroughly examined before the waters rose. Some rare species were transplanted. The worst fears of extinction proved unfounded. But no sooner had the reservoir been built than the case for it began to evaporate. New processes, new plant, recession, competition and other changes transformed ICI's operations. Although Cow Green has been used to regulate the flow in the Tees, and supply the industries at the river's mouth, I very much doubt whether today's needs would justify its building.

The Cow Green furore raised several serious questions. First, how authoritative can one be about the scientific importance of particular sites? Second, how on earth does one balance the value of a unique patch of vegetation against the need for water supplies? In 2002, following adoption of the European Union Directives on Habitats and on Environmental Impact Assessment, the burden of proof would have been different and the reservoir builders would have had to show that their need was imperative and that there really was no alternative. It is equally unthinkable that today we would allow the destruction of the remote and lovely hamlet of Mardale Green in the Lake District so as to enlarge Hawes Water for Manchester. But road schemes from Twyford Down to Newbury still slice through ancient woods and grasslands rich in plants and insects. How does one judge for the best – knowing that today's major construction projects are effectively irreversible, unless and until there is another Ice Age?

Cow Green also raised questions about how decisions are taken. I was attacked by Lord Crook for improper behaviour – for arrogating to myself the powers of the Minister. The rule is that Civil Servants can answer factual questions about what their Department has done, and can explain the basis of a memorandum or plan, but they should not discuss the reasons for a Minister's policy or decisions. The Minister is the only person to answer such questions. But it was stretching the point to apply this argument to the Nature Conservancy, which was a science-based expert body with specific functions assigned to it by Act of Parliament. The Conservancy was supposed to argue the case for conservation. It should not have been muzzled by the fact that it was part of a Research Council that answered to Parliament through a Minister. I do not think that the question could arise today.

Ray Beverton, the Secretary of NERC, was immensely supportive when Duncan Poore – who had sat through it all and taken me back to his flat for a large and steadying drink afterwards – telephoned and recounted Lord Crook's explosion. But Ray had a lot of problems of his own. It proved very difficult to merge the proudly independent fiefdoms that had been forced into NERC into a harmonious whole. Bunny Fuchs defended the autonomy of BAS by ensuring that the Foreign and Commonwealth Office and the Governor of the Falklands, as High Commissioner for British Antarctic Territory, had a strong control over its funding and a major influence on its programme. Max Nicholson had ensured that the Act of Parliament creating NERC required the Council to maintain 'a Committee called the Nature Conservancy' with some functions delegated by statute. The other Directors defended their corners with equal vigour. Ray Beverton, himself an outstanding biologist and warmly liked as a man, worked steadily to build confidence – but he felt obliged to stand on his dignity as the chief executive of the whole Council, and with the part-time Chairman, Sir Graham Sutton, the Accounting Officer (or official can-carrier) for what it did with all its money. NERC had growing pains that lasted for several decades.

The Council was clearly uneasy about having a body like the Nature Conservancy within it. For NERC was a *research* Council. A group of some twenty eminent scientists whose role was to make the case for spending the taxpayer's money on environmental studies, and to see that it was well spent on good science, within themes of real priority. The Council was good at – say – assessing the needs and opportunities for research on freshwater biology, and balancing these against the demand for more finance for geology. But it was less happy about its responsibilities for field conservation, including spending money on nature reserves, and it was profoundly uneasy when it came to our work to promote conservation through a strong voluntary network of County Naturalists' Trusts or our opposition to developments like the Cow Green Reservoir. 'For heaven's sake, Dr Holdgate,' said Donald Maclean, Ray Beverton's scientific deputy, 'what has all that got to do with *research*?'

Maclean was a hydrologist and he had a probing scientific mind. He loved asking sharp questions about proposals from the various bits of the NERC empire.

'Why on earth do you need all these Nature Reserves?' he demanded one day. 'What's the basic rationale? Can you convince me that they're more than a lot of pet sites chosen by enthusiastic old buffers who like to watch birds there?'

In one way that question prompted the Nature Conservation Review that Duncan Poore, Bob Boote and I started in 1967. Cow Green also demonstrated the need to identify the most valuable sites ahead of a threat, and be ready with a credible dossier of hard facts about their scientific importance. We persuaded Dr Derek Ratcliffe of Monks Wood to lead the project. Derek was probably the finest all-round naturalist in Britain, with deep knowledge of plants, vegetation, birds and mammals. We began by asking all the Regional Officers of the Conservancy to review the entire land surface in their regions (using maps, records and the personal knowledge of staff and local naturalists). They listed the places they thought stood out, on the basis of a set of criteria Derek defined.

What criteria? That was the first difficulty. How objective – how 'scientific' in Maclean's sense – could we be? Size was clearly important because large areas of habitat support more individuals, and are likely to have a greater variety of aspects, elevations, soils and local climates. Diversity was also important – how many habitats and species did a site actually contain? Rarity of habitat, vegetation and species could also be measured fairly objectively. But there were more difficult criteria, including 'typicalness', 'position in an ecological or geographical unit', 'naturalness' and 'fragility'. Should the reserve series include the typical and commonplace as well as the rare and unusual? Should it cover the range of ecological and geographical variation over the country? Should we weight the selection in favour of those areas that appeared to have suffered least from human impact? Should a special effort be devoted to fragile sites – but might fragility itself disqualify if it meant that conservation was too difficult or even impossible? The criteria went on to embrace recorded history, potential value (that is, the extent to which conservation management could make a site better) and 'intrinsic appeal' – this last recognizing that some features do stir both naturalists and the public more deeply than others. Flowery meads, purple heaths echoing with the hum of bees, woods full of bird-song, or cliffs white with seabirds are deeply attractive, and people want them safeguarded, although one job of the Conservancy was to see that less conspicuous and less appealing species, such as beetles and snakes, were not overlooked.

Specialists in the various habitats – woodlands, heathlands, coastlands, chalk and limestone grasslands, moorlands, wetlands, mountains and so on – were invited to look nationally at the sites chosen by the Regional staff. Derek Ratcliffe then did a final, overall, assessment. It took ten years before the results appeared in two massive and fascinating volumes. The Review drew attention to a lot of wonderful places that had gone unrecognized (including my own childhood playground, the limestone scars above Great Asby, and the limy springs, fens and species-rich heaths around Sunbiggin Tarn). And it confirmed that Julian Huxley's and Arthur Tansley's committee – Donald Maclean's 'enthusiastic old buffers' – had been pretty sound in their judgement. But it also revealed a deep scientific argument about survey methods. For John Jeffers and others argued that the review was too subjective: it was based on the personal knowledge and value judgements of naturalists. John would have been happier with a study that began by looking at the measurable features of the landscape and climate, sorted these into groups by computer, characterised vegetation and fauna at randomly chosen sampling sites within each habitat group, and then looked at how a reserve series might best safeguard the range of variation thus defined. The two approaches might be expected to converge of course, and the more 'mathematical' one would need to be extended by the more subjective one, which would be better at finding rare sites of outstanding 'quality', but there was concern that the methods Derek Ratcliffe used did not admit of the more objective assessment. The argument still rumbles on.

One of the most important National Nature Reserves was (and still is) the isle of Rhum, in the inner Hebrides, just across the sea from Skye. Once it had been the home of crofting communities, whose ruined dwellings lay near the shore at Harris and Kilmory. But it had been depopulated in the nineteenth century, and now the Conservancy owned the whole island, and the only people living there were Conservancy employees. This made it an ideal site for research and for experimental conservation – for example by the re-establishment of woodlands of native oak, birch and other species.

David Jenkins and I debated long about how the research on Red deer, for which Rhum was a focus, should be developed. He thought we should divide the island into two with a deer-proof fence, to test ideas about how the habitat would respond to different levels of grazing. We took a specialist team to the island to discuss these ideas on the ground. We tramped up the hills and spied deer in remote glens. We stayed in Kinloch Castle, a time-warp, an Edwardian mansion with all the original fittings. The bedroom doors even had the cards bearing the names of the last house party. The baths were immense cast-iron contraptions with multiple brass controls, letting water at you from all manner of improbable angles. There was a huge automatic organ, driven by rolls of punched paper.

The Castle had been built by the Bullough family, and Lady Bullough had given it to the Conservancy. She remained keenly interested in our work, right up to her death in her hundredth year. John Arbuthnott, Master of Arbuthnott, who was our Chief Factor (Scottish land agent) wrote her newsy bulletins and made ready for her burial on the island. 'When I go, you're not to keep me waiting about!' she directed. When Lady Bullough died, I represented the Conservancy at her funeral at Moulton near Newmarket, among the matchless green paddocks of racehorse-land. It was a Top Class funeral, tail-coats, top-hats and all. But I missed the really unique event, which was on Rhum.

The family mausoleum is at Harris, on the west coast of the island, in a lovely bay that sweeps under the knees of Hallival and Askival, the high hills. A little pillared Doric temple, all alone in an empty basin. The Newmarket undertaker rolled Lady Bullough smoothly to Mallaig, at the end of the Road to the Isles.

'Where's the ferry?' he demanded, as the Rolls came to a halt on the jetty.

'Down there,' said someone, pointing to a small fishing boat.

'But what do I do with Her Ladyship – and the Rolls?'

'You lash the coffin on the fore-hatch – do it tightly as it's going to blow – put a tarpaulin over it, and put the hearse in yon herring curing shed . . .'

They put out into rough weather, to find a cortege of Land Rovers awaiting them on Rhum. Over a rough track, with deer lolloping out of the way. Out to the Mausoleum, where John Arbuthnott had the tomb all ready. Out with a broom to sweep away the deer droppings and make all seemly. A quick consultation. 'Which way is east?' 'Turn her around, Jack.' So Lady Bullough was laid to rest, correctly orientated. The Head Undertaker was seen taking a photograph. 'One for the records,' he said. 'My most unusual funeral.' It was, indeed, a far cry from Newmarket.

It did not follow that the Nature Conservancy sought to *buy* every site considered worthy of becoming a National Nature Reserve. The Treasury loved Nature Reserve Agreements because they were much cheaper. Under one, the owner managed the site under the scientific guidance of the NC, receiving a modest payment for extra costs incurred or revenues foregone. NRAs had many merits beyond cheapness, not least because they involved the owner and his staff positively as allies for conservation. But sometimes we did want to buy land – maybe because we needed freedom for research, or maybe because conservation did not fit easily with normal management practices. One such site was Glenfeshie.

This is a magnificent area on the west side of the Cairngorm mountains, the biggest block of really high ground in Scotland and the haunt of many arctic and alpine species. We wanted it as a site for research on Red deer, where we could test what we had learned on Rhum in a mainland setting. The vendor was willing. The Department of Education was content both with deal and price. Even the Treasury raised no objection. Then the Scottish Office stepped in. The deal was blocked.

'The Secretary of State considers that too much land has already been sterilised for conservation in the Cairngorms,' we were told. I am sure the Secretary of State was indeed advised that public ownership of this land would be a mistake. But why? Deer forests were a major land use in the Highlands. It was common knowledge that too few deer were being shot, and that the resulting overstocking was causing erosion, land degradation and a halt to the regeneration of the native pinewoods. But many landowners were reluctant to change their traditional management and kill more animals. Our plans were designed to help the Red Deer Commission, the Scottish Landowners Federation and the Minister himself by demonstrating new approaches that would have produced better deer in a better environment. Did the Minister understand this?

I suspect that the real reason was that our acquisition would have tilted the balance in the Cairngorms towards conservation and away from development for tourism. There was already controversy over plans to expand the skiing facilities on Cairn Gorm, in the north of the hill massif. Some of the Minister's advisers were strongly in favour of these developments. The senior Civil Servant who worked most closely with the Conservancy was later jailed for his involvement in what became known as 'the Poulson affair'. I still wonder whether this was a factor influencing the decision. Be that as it may, we had to fall back on an agreement with the new private owner, Lord Dulverton. He supported conservation, and it worked fairly well, but we did not gain the freedom to manage the deer as tightly as we had hoped. Had we done so, we might have made Glenfeshie a 'model' estate blending scientifically sound deer management with forest regeneration and what is now called 'ecotourism'.

The NC was unique in blending research with field conservation. But it was not easy to link the two. The conservation staff wondered how useful a lot of the detailed studies on ants, or spiders, or moorland beetles would be when it came to practical management. The research side argued that you couldn't save species or manage reserves without scientific knowledge. Sometimes this was self-evident, as when we got worried about the impending extinction in Britain of the Large Blue butterfly. This strange and beautiful creature lays its eggs on wild thyme. The caterpillars, which graze the thyme, exude a sticky, sweet, secretion much cherished by a particular kind of red ant, whose young they resemble. So enticing is the secretion that ants carry the caterpillars into their nests – where they repay the protection and hospitality by eating their hosts' young. Eventually they pupate underground, still safe among the ants, emerging in due course as the next generation of butterflies. Complicated, even bizarre? Indeed. And you need plenty of thyme, in herbage of the right length, which in turn supports plenty of colonies of the right species of ant. Jeremy Thomas showed that this in turn depended on the right kind of management of the heath, and that grazing regimes were critical. The Large Blue has now been reintroduced, and is thriving in sites in the south-west of England managed according to his prescription. It would not have been possible without the research.

We tried to promote contact between researchers and managers by creating what we called 'habitat teams'. They reflected the fact that we had people at several research stations studying woodlands, or grasslands, or heaths, and we had woodland, grassland or heathland management questions in several regions. The solution? Link all the researchers dealing with a particular habitat and the person in each region especially keen on it in a team – or, as we would say today, a network. The hope was that there would be two-way communication so that those planning research would know what their conservation branch colleagues needed, and the latter would know what their research colleagues were up to. In a sense it was an internal piece of machinery to bring what Lord Rothschild later called 'customers' and 'contractors' together. It worked – to some extent. The problems? Everyone was very busy and meetings took time and were expensive. It was difficult to get the teams together, especially as field conservationists and committed researchers alike grudge the time they spend in committee rooms. It would have been easier today, when 'virtual' teams can be linked electronically.

My move to the Conservancy in 1966 did not altogether cut me off from the far south. Until 1968, I still chaired the SCAR working group and represented SCAR on SCIBP. Duncan Poore encouraged me to organize the 1968 SCAR Symposium on Antarctic Ecology in Cambridge, and gave me time to edit the proceedings. He also let me take six weeks to go back to Gough and Tristan with Nigel Wace, to see what had changed after ten years of human occupation of the weather station on Gough and how the new lava on Tristan was being colonized by plants and insects. Happily, we were stuck on Tristan in bright weather, with a strong wind that closed the harbour to boat work. As a traveller himself, I'm sure Duncan read my delight in the deadpan telegram I sent him, which read something like this: STORMBOUND TRISTAN LIKELY DELAYED TEN DAYS FORTU- NATELY ABLE TO DO FIELDWORK REGARDS = HOLDGATE. Out of this visit came a monograph on man and environment in the Tristan islands and a new wildlife conservation ordinance, approved by the island Council and enacted by the Governor of St Helena in 1976.

Tristan and several other islands also erupted into global politics in the late 1960s, when a Defence Review threw up the so-called islands strategy – the notion of building airfields on a series of remote relics of empire around the world, so that the proposed F-111 strike aircraft could hop from one to the other on its way to any trouble spot, anywhere. A V-bomber equipped with cameras and long-range tanks flew from the Cape to photograph Tristan, Gough and various places in the Indian Ocean. The photos provided gratifying reassurance that Allan Crawford's map of Tristan and John Heaney's map of Gough were pretty good efforts. They also led to discussions of whether an airstrip could be built on the Settlement plain of Tristan or the upland plateaux of Gough. Both were rejected, but the elevated coral atoll of Aldabra in the Indian Ocean looked a better bet. It was bigger, sunnier, uninhabited and unincumbered by mountains. The RAF, with American support, wanted to go ahead.

Conservationists were outraged. Aldabra is the home of the only population of giant tortoises in the Indian Ocean, along with a flightless land rail and other endemics. An expedition reported to a Royal Society meeting early in 1967, and there was almost unanimous scientific agreement that the airfield would be an indefensible disaster. The Nature Conservancy objected strongly, but Ministers still seemed unswayed. I remember attending – no doubt as Duncan's deputy – a meeting convened by the Minister for the RAF, Lord Shackleton.

Eddie Shackleton was better known to me from his polar connections. The youngest child of the great Antarctic explorer, he had himself been on expeditions to the Arctic and become something of an authority on Nansen. I had encountered him when he came to lecture at the Scott Polar. But his main career was in politics, as Labour MP for Preston for many years and then as a Life Peer. As Minister he had to look after the RAF. As an individual, he was a keen conservationist.

The meeting in his office followed predictable lines. A series of high-ranking RAF officers said that global security depended on the new Anglo-American strategy. Giant tortoises could be moved somewhere else, but only Aldabra could keep the world safe. We said that Aldabra sparkled in the world's natural crown, one of a handful of elevated coral islands, with unique wildlife that would not survive an airfield. We urged a thorough scientific study before any decision was taken.

Shackleton listened. He sat on the fence with the skill learned in thirty years in politics. As I recall, he did not rule the scheme in or out, but did accept that much more study was needed before it went ahead. We all got up to go. 'Hold on a minute,' he said, as I prepared to follow the pale blue uniforms. The door closed. 'Tell your Director,' he said, 'that while I am here this plan will not go ahead. What I need is the best scientific argument you can give me. I'll see to the rest.' It was arranged that my colleague Morton Boyd, then Regional Officer in the North West Highlands, should join a joint expedition that involved government engineers and Royal Society scientists. Morton reported the impossibility of blending airfield and nature reserve. There was a lot of political manoevring, but the outcome was that Aldabra stayed an island for science, and it is now a World Heritage site, administered by the Seychelles Government. At the latest count, there were over 150,000 giant tortoises there – more than anywhere else in the world.

I never got to Aldabra but exploring by proxy drew me into the British Schools Exploring Society. Founded by Surgeon Commander George Murray Levick, one of the doctors on Scott's last expedition, the BSES took British schoolboys into 'wild and trackless country', to learn self-reliance by trekking, camping and fieldwork. Clive Jermy of the British Museum (Natural History), who had been with a BSES Iceland Expedition, felt that they needed more scientists on the Council and persuaded me to join. I agreed, because I thought that the aims of the Society were important, but I found the Council even more bureaucratic and argumentative than NERC. Half the meetings seemed to be taken up with squabbles over the Rules. Audrey Murray Levick, the Founder's widow, who had herself served for many years as Secretary of the Society, was a powerful personality who felt proprietorial about its traditions – and she dominated the Council. There was little chance of getting serious discussion of how to modernize the kind of exploration the Society did. There was immense preoccupation with fund-raising, through a Dinner and Ball, orientated towards High Society. This was not my scene. I resolved to resign.

I left it too late. The Vice President, Colonel Ralph Greg, appeared at Belgrave Square. 'The Chairman's resigning,' he said. 'Mrs Murray Levick is going to step down from Council. We want you to take over as Chairman.

The President, Lord Tweedsmuir, is keen to talk to you about how the Society should develop.'

I was persuaded. It led to ten years in the Chair, to major changes in the Society, and through a partnership with Brian Ware of Brathay Hall in the Lake District, to the creation of a Young Explorer's Trust as a kind of forum in which all our national bodies concerned with young people's expeditions could share experiences and promote exploration and outdoor adventure.

I still think that this is very important. There is in every one of us a delight in wild beauty, and a zest for adventure. Exploration brings challenge, builds skills of living in difficult terrain and weather, and above all gives what Geoffrey Winthrop Young called 'the joy of comrades and the thrill of strife'. BSES gave young people this experience and built those skills. It started in rather elitist mode, being restricted to boys from recognized Public Schools – but it soon broadened to take young people from all kinds of secondary school, and also both police cadets and erstwhile young offenders. Later on still – long after my time – it included girls, recognizing that they are just as tough and resourceful on the hills as boys. Long after that start with BSES I worked with Brian Ware and John Hunt (of Everest) to create the Foundation for Outdoor Adventure, which argued that worthwhile challenges could be found in almost any environment. City schools taught abseiling down disused railway viaducts and canoeing on disused canals. Short trips to the hills enthused young children who had never ventured off the streets.

Everyone (or almost everyone) applauds the adventurer. Yet today's society seems designed to make his or her life difficult. Our culture seems to work on Mrs Ramsbottom's principle – as set out in Stanley Holloway's Blackpool epic, *Albert and the Lion*. When Albert was swallowed by the lion he had provoked:

> Mother said no, somebody's got to be summonsed
> So that was decided upon . . .

Nature is dangerous. Even the gentle English hills can become savage places, fiercely icy and swept by 'whirlwind-swivelled snow'. A climber's skill is to move safely through potential danger, recalling like Geoffrey Winthrop Young's cragsman that:

> In this short span
>   between my finger tips on the smooth edge
>   and these tense feet cramped to the crystal ledge
> I hold the life of man . . .

It is right to train and prepare so that skills are at their highest and dangers are foreseen and avoided. But those who seek adventure on the mountains or at sea know that there are hazards, and sometimes things go wrong. Captain Scott was content to write that 'we took risks, we knew we took them: things have come out against us, and therefore we have no cause for complaint.' Today some lawyer or other would probably be exhorting the relatives of those who died with him to sue the expedition organizers for damages. I believe strongly in the doctrine of reasonable risk, and that hazards have to be accepted as part of the price we pay for the exhilaration of adventure. It would be a tragedy if the modern preoccupation with safety and the compensation culture that is linked to it were to frighten off leaders who give freely of their time and experience to bring to new generations of young people a taste of the thrills of adventure.

I spent four years in the Nature Conservancy. Much of it was London-based and Committee bound (we had moved to a larger house at Hoddesdon, in Hertfordshire, in 1967 to make the commuting easier). Most of the Committees were far from memorable, but there was one around 1969 which does stick in the memory. The Irish Minister of Lands called on the Bird Conservation Committee chaired by Sir Peter Scott. There was a small, special, entertainment fund (from royalties on one of Max Nicholson's books, I think), and it was used on a very jolly lunch at a nearby hotel. The talk came round to grouse. The Minister was briefed on the Conservancy's research.

'I'll tell you a tale,' said he. 'When I was a boy in the bogs of Western Mayo there were lots of grouse. My granddad told me the best way to catch them. First, you have to make some poteen. Take a bottle in your coat pocket, and the fermented potato mash or grains you have distilled from in a pail. Cut a trench in the bog, narrower at the top than the bottom, and build the turves into a little shelter. Strew the grain or potato mash in the trench and get yourself into the shelter to taste the poteen. The grouse hop along and smell the mash, and in a while they're having their party in the trench while you're having yours in the shelter. While they're sleeping it off, out you come and wring their necks ...'

Adam Watson and David Jenkins doubted the truth of this tale. The credibility of Ministers was diminished.

Birds hit the headlines in the autumn of 1969. There were storms in the Irish Sea. Quite normal, as any Blackpool resident knows. But they drove ashore thousands of dying seabirds – mostly Guillemots, but with a few Razorbills. They had little body fat left, were clearly exhausted, but were not fouled by oil. Something else was killing them.

Ray Beverton, as Secretary of NERC, announced an Inquiry, and appointed me to chair it. We drew together experts from NERC Institutes and several Ministries. We sent birds for analysis. The labs found that many had high concentrations of polychlorinated biphenyls (PCBs) in their livers. PCBs were at that time important industrial chemicals, used in transformers and other equipment. They had never been identified as an environmental problem – but they did have some chemical similarities to DDT and they did accumulate in bird fat and internal organs. There was quite a lot in the fat of some healthy birds we collected from outside the area of mortality. The conclusion was that the birds had been stressed by the storms, which coincided with the moult after the breeding season. The PCBs would have been mobilised as the birds used their fat reserves. Passing to the liver and kidneys, they would have weakened the birds further, tipping the balance between survival and death. It wasn't conclusive but Monsanto, the chief manufacturer of PCBs in Britain, announced soon afterwards that they were giving up making them. They are now very much 'black list' substances. Once again, nature had proved a watchdog, alerting us to a problem that had got through all the safety nets and screening processes.

It was pesticides and pollution that caused my departure from the Conservancy. It happened early in January 1970. The telephone rang at Belgrave Square. Ray Beverton.

'The Prime Minister wants to visit Monks Wood, with the Secretary of State and Sir Solly Zuckerman. It's part of a tour of laboratories working on pollution. They're calling at the Warren Spring Laboratory at Stevenage first. Please would you and Duncan put a programme together and let me have it . . . ?'

In the late 1960s, pollution became a political issue. The wreck of the *Torrey Canyon* had already prompted the creation of a special committee in Whitehall to look at the whole question of threats to the environment from ships that carried dangerous cargoes. In 1967 Rachel Carson's *Silent Spring* appeared, to be followed in 1968 by Paul Ehrlich's *The Population Bomb* and by a solid report from the American Chemical Society on *Cleaning our Environment*. These set off echoes in the UK. Anthony Greenwood, then Minister for Housing and Local Government, sent a note to the Prime Minister, Harold Wilson, in November 1968 which suggested there might be a Committee or Commission to review all the arrangements, scientific, governmental and procedural, for controlling pollution. It is clear that he had been prompted to do this by one of his Parliamentary Under Secretaries, Wayland (Lord) Kennet, who was watching the environmental scene closely (and was, incidentally, Peter Scott's half-brother). Sir Solly Zuckerman, by then Chief Scientific Adviser to the Government, was a frequent visitor to the United States and was also convinced that the new environmental movement demanded a political response in Britain.

In the autumn of 1969 the Prime Minister took action. He told the Labour Party Conference that 'we must deal with the problems of pollution of the air, the sea, the rivers and the beaches.' He appointed one of the most brilliant members of his Cabinet, Anthony Crosland, as Secretary of State for Local Government and Regional Planning – and as a kind of 'overlord' co-ordinating all the environmental actions of the Government. In December 1969 Harold Wilson announced that Mr Crosland was to be supported by an expert Central Scientific Unit on Environmental Pollution in his own office, and that the Queen had agreed to the appointment of a Royal Commission on Environmental Pollution to provide independent high-level advice on what should be done. Unusually, it was to be a *standing* Royal Commission, which would prepare a series of reports, rather than one that just examined a single issue and proposed a Government response. The Committee on Hazardous Cargoes was broadened into a Committee on Environmental Pollution. It was a remarkable package, for hardly any country had a senior Minister or a high-level Council or a special scientific unit at that time. Much of that package has survived the ensuing thirty years.

We bustled about to lay on a display at Monks Wood. The visitors were to be briefed on what the station, the Conservancy and NERC did. They were to see the work on pesticides and wild life – especially birds. They were to be told about the 1969 seabird wreck in the Irish Sea – something Anthony Crosland's office already knew about, for they had been represented at my final meetings. They were to be given ideas about the need for more work on the subtle, long-term effects of chemicals in the environment, and the value of wild life as an indicator.

The motorcade arrived – to find about a hundred local farmers, cross about a recent agricultural price settlement, waiting for them. The PM and Secretary of State went off with the farmers' leaders into the Conference Room to argue it out. I found myself giving Sir Solly a preview of the display and talking about our research. It was my first meeting with a great, controversial, figure of modern British science.

Solly Zuckerman was an extraordinary man. A young Jewish medical student from Cape Town, he had come to London as a post-graduate Scholar, risen through a series of scientific posts, married the grand-daughter of Rufus Isaacs, first Marquess of Reading, and become Professor of Anatomy at Birmingham, Fellow of the Royal Society, long-time Secretary of the Zoological Society of London, and an increasingly powerful scientific influence in Government. This last link began in wartime, when he studied the impact of bombing. His persuasive demand that bombers be switched from nightly pounding of German cities to a precision attack on rail communications in France made a huge difference to the success of the

Normandy landings. Cynics noted that as a zoologist he had published a book on the Social Life of Monkeys and Apes – 'ideal qualification for working in Whitehall.' As Chief Scientific Adviser to the Ministry of Defence he had been involved in many key decisions about nuclear hardware and became an early and steadfast opponent of the nuclear arms race, arguing that the only value in nuclear weapons lay in their deterrence as things too terrible to be used.

Although his advocacy of the Test Ban Treaty and then of balanced nuclear disarmament ruffled some American feathers, he built and kept extraordinarily close contacts with his opposite numbers there, and had unique access to the highest levels of American science and defence.

'I'm the only man in Britain,' I remember him saying, 'who can arrive in Washington, pick up the phone to Admiral Rickover's office, and be talking to him face to face that same day.' He made much of that contact – sometimes infuriating the British Embassy by arriving unannounced, and departing without telling them what he had been doing.

As Chief Scientific Adviser to the Government, he made certain that the voice of science and the voice of Solly were heard everywhere (and at times it seemed as if he had trouble separating them). He was charming, brilliant, vain, persuasive, tyrannical and a past master of Whitehall intrigue. I found him rather overpowering, but he set out to charm – not only me, but the scientists waiting for the Prime Minister.

In due course Harold Wilson had worked his charm on the farmers, and they departed, mollified to the point of giving him three cheers. He insisted that his tour should not be truncated. So we all went round again – with an increasingly bored-looking Anthony Crosland standing back from the exchanges. He was quite prepared, I think, to let his scientific advisers deal with laboratories and crystallize the policy issues for him. He certainly saw no need to pore over microscopes or smelly bird corpses. The visit ended with an upbeat little speech from the PM to the staff, a very brief word from the Secretary of State, and departure. Next week, the telephone rang. 'Somebody called Day, from the Cabinet Office,' said Joanna, my secretary.

'My name is Bernard Day. I'm the Establishment Officer at the Cabinet Office. Sir Solly Zuckerman wants you to come as Director of the Central Scientific Unit on Environmental Pollution. Please would you come over for a talk with me and with Mr Cox, who heads Mr Crosland's Office?'

CHAPTER SIX

Cleaning our Environment

SOMETIMES THINGS happen suddenly and change the whole course of life. This was such a happening. I had not applied for the job. I wasn't sure that I wanted to leave the Conservancy. Why did I let myself be, as it were, annexed by Zuckerman and his official machine? A feeling of pride at being asked, at the age of 39, to take on a key scientific job in the so-called corridors of power? A feeling that action against pollution of the environment was important, and that I could and should contribute? A tendency to go with the tide of opportunity? Ambition (for it was a promotion)? Maybe a mixture of all of these.

Central Government was a new and strange world. I had never worked closely with any Minister before, and Anthony Crosland was not only very senior but very intelligent, very easily bored, and very good at showing it. Bob Cox, head of his office, was a senior Under Secretary who had served for many years in the Ministry of Housing and Local Government. He tried hard to teach me a modicum of Decent Behaviour in Civil Servants – but it was pretty obvious that I had missed the training normally given to anyone well before they get to Under-Secretary level. I'd never been in a Minister's Private Office, never in Treasury, never in a team working on any Parliamentary Bill, never in a job where the skills of routine administration and the delicacies of handling Parliamentary Questions are absorbed by guidance and experience. It was very much like being the new boy at school.

There were also built-in stresses. A Central Scientific Unit was expected to be *scientific* – that is, to amass and evaluate evidence, provide scientifically-robust analyses of the various threats pollutants might pose, question assumptions and challenge policies that appeared ill-founded. Working within the office of a senior Minister, the Unit might be expected to feed him arguments with which to question his colleagues and propose more effective actions. But the Whitehall view appeared to be much more limited. The Unit was to be small. It would not do original research, depending instead on experts in Government laboratories and institutes like those in NERC. It was to confine itself to coordination. It was to work mainly to and through the interdepartmental Official Committee chaired by Solly Zuckerman and made up of more senior Civil Servants than myself. It was to have a 'dotted line' reporting responsibility to Sir Solly, as the Chief Scientific Adviser. As became clear later, he saw this as giving him a considerable measure of control over what we did.

But the first need was to get the Unit started. By April 1970 we had the core in place. Les Reed came from the Warren Spring Laboratory to be our expert on air pollution. Ian Prestt came from Monks Wood to cover chemicals and ecology in general. Nigel Harvey from MAFF supported us on agricultural matters. We selected a specialist on water pollution and its treatment. Within a month of taking over, I was arguing with the Cabinet Office to be allowed a team of eight rather than the five scientists the Civil Service Department was minded to sanction. My case was simply that 'the field we have to cover is wide, we must have sufficient expertise to win the respect of departments and other organisations with which we must deal, and we must have sufficient officers to be able to undertake reviews of specialist fields for the Royal Commission without detriment to our other work.' Under Bob Cox, an Assistant Secretary, Daphne Wilde, was already in post as Secretary to the Royal Commission. Later, Bob persuaded officialdom to give us another Assistant Secretary, Michael Macfarlane Davis, to share the increasing burden of minute-writing and inter-departmental and international representation.

The Royal Commission was also just beginning. It was led by Sir Eric Ashby, botanist, former Professor at Manchester, former Vice Chancellor of Queens' University, Belfast, and in 1970 Master of Clare College, Cambridge. Official papers now in the Public Record Office reveal that he was Solly Zuckerman's choice. Anthony Crosland had originally favoured the Duke of Edinburgh and had been 'warned off' at Harold Wilson's express behest. His next choice, Dr Beeching, axeman of the railways, was also vetoed by the Prime Minister as 'too ICI, too industrialist'. We were fortunate in the final selection. Eric Ashby was not only a good scientist but a man of immense common sense, balance, sound judgement and consideration for others.

The Royal Commission members were chosen, as they still are, to cover a wide field. But it was more heavily weighted towards science than today. In addition to the Chairman it included one of our great ecologists, Frank Fraser Darling; the Chairman of NERC, Professor Vero Wynne Edwards; a geologist, Launcelot Fleming, who added a second dimension since he was also the Bishop of Norwich; and Sir Solly Zuckerman himself. Being member of a Royal Commission and Chief Scientific Adviser to the Government at the same time was unprecedented – but Solly was unique! Then there was an economist, Wilfred Beckerman of Oxford University; a media tycoon, Aubrey Buxton, Head of Anglia TV (who was also a good naturalist and conservationist); an industrialist, Neil Iliff of Shell; and a mandarin turned leader of the voluntary bodies, Sir John Winnifrith of the National Trust, former Permanent Secretary of the Ministry of Agriculture. Their first self-chosen task was to review the whole national approach to pollution and advise on new action. Anthony Crosland himself took a keen interest in their work, and attended their first meeting. Bob Cox and I attended all Commission meetings and were encouraged to join in the discussion.

Both the Royal Commission and the Central Unit had many sources of information. According to Dr Harry Atkinson, then a member of Solly Zuckerman's office, there were already about ninety departments, industrial groups, research teams and committees addressing various aspects of pollution. But 'the environment' as a unifying theme was new in Whitehall, which did not take all that kindly to cross-cutting concepts or coordinating units that interfered with departmental fiefdoms. Perhaps this helped explain why the Foreign and Commonwealth Office was one of our strongest supporters from the start, for they, too, had to take an across-the-board view, relating what was done at home to a surge of actions around the world. The Unit became deeply involved in international work, and I formed a close partnership with Ronald Arculus, who headed the FCO Science and Technology Department.

Our offices were at Great George Street, between Whitehall and St James' Park. Anthony Crosland occupied a magnificent panelled chamber upstairs, with Bob Cox in an only slightly less splendid room nearby. Not far away, at the heart of the building, was a circular corridor girdling offices that overlooked the round central courtyard. This was a true corridor of power, for it was the home of Treasury grandees. In early spring, the rooms on the south side were cordoned off and labelled 'no access except on budget business'. Legendary mandarins – the highest ranking Permanent Secretaries – stalked those corridors and lunched (as we did) in the Cabinet Office mess. They were courteous, gifted men (yes, all men), with 'urbanity of manner'. They did not exactly follow Chesterton's exemplar in also possessing 'unconsciousness of sin', but many behaved as if they were appointed as the arbiters of secular sinfulness.

Solly Zuckerman sent me on a tour to meet the custodians of pollution policy in the various Ministries. I found that Departmental empires were stoutly defended. The Ministry of Housing and Local Government had particular responsibility for pollution, because it looked after clean air, water and waste disposal. Clean air had become a major concern after the Great London Smog of 1952/53 had killed nearly four thousand people – mostly elderly sufferers from lung or heart weakness, or both, but also some frail infants. The Clean Air Act of 1956 had followed, and MHLG was busy pushing local authorities to create 'smoke control areas' in which only smokeless fuels could be burned. Richard Adams was the Assistant Secretary in charge, although the book about rabbits which he wrote in his spare time (*Watership Down*) soon catapulted him to fame and full-time authorship. Water policy – clean drinking water, sewage treatment and clean rivers – fell to the MHLG Under Secretary, Jack Beddoes, and the Chief Water Engineer, Jimmy Glenn. Then again, there was the Alkali Inspectorate, led by Frank Ireland – the oldest industrial air pollution control body in the world – which regulated emissions to air from the biggest and most polluting factories and power stations. It had an established culture that I soon heard all about.

If mandarins were arbiters of secular sin, it soon became clear that they judged foreigners as the principal environmental sinners. There was a deep satisfaction with British achievements. The Clean Air Act was hailed as a world leader. The Alkali Inspectorate was held up to me as 'first and best'. The MHLG was satisfied that the environment was in a healthy state and did not need much new effort to stay that way. The Central Unit soon got the message that we were expected to proclaim our national way of doing things abroad. For there was deep hostility to the foreign cult of emission standards – of fixing in law how much of a specified pollutant would be permitted in a particular kind of discharge to the environment. The MHLG attitude to industry was one of partnership. Voluntary codes of conduct were preferred to mandatory ones. The same culture prevailed in the Ministry of Agriculture, where pesticide use was regulated under a voluntary Pesticides Safety Precautions Scheme.

'We don't believe in fixed standards like those the Americans are proposing,' Frank Ireland explained. 'Our system is much more flexible and efficient. The law requires any scheduled industrial process – and that means all the dirty ones used in large factories – to use Best Practicable Means. That's the technology we judge combines efficiency and economy. We tell industry the standard of cleanliness we expect them to achieve using b.p.m. We can revise it upwards whenever new technology comes along. And we discuss it with the industry so that most of the time they clean themselves up voluntarily. Prosecutions are rare . . .'

'Isn't that just too cosy? Where's the incentive to do better? Supposing we find that pollutants are doing serious damage to health, livestock, crops or wildlife and there's no technology good enough to ensure safety?'

Such questions tended to provoke irritation, or a rather squashing comment like one I remember from the MHLG Deputy Secretary, Richard Chilver:

'Frank Ireland's the best chemical engineer in the business. His professional body has just given him a medal. Don't you think that someone like that can be trusted to do his job efficiently?'

I was told by Bob Cox that part of my job was to probe and ask awkward questions, and he clearly expected that we would upset people. But the relationship with Solly Zuckerman was not an easy one: it never is easy to report two ways at once.

As 'environmental overlord' Anthony Crosland was particularly concerned with three departments – MHLG, the Ministry of Transport and the Ministry of Public Building and Works – which between them handled the bulk of urban pollution issues. The Secretary of State was interested in reports that the United States was about to crack down on motor vehicle exhausts, demanding 'forcing' standards that no technology could yet deliver. There was consternation in the Ministry of Transport. 'Neither practicable nor economic – quite foolish,' said our experts. Solly Zuckerman took a team to Washington DC for talks on a range of scientific topics. Before we left, Bob Cox told me to find out what was behind the US action on vehicles, and report to my Secretary of State, who wanted to meet with Transport and Technology Ministers and officials and discuss what (if anything) the UK should do.

We went. We met Lee DuBridge, then Chief Scientific Adviser to the US Government. We heard a detailed (and to me convincing) explanation. Air in California, and especially in the Los Angeles basin, had become fouled with oxidant smog, much of it originating in a witches' brew of car exhaust that produced irritant fumes in still air in sunlight. People's breathing was suffering, and citrus fruit was blighted within forty miles of town. Even in the Eastern United States, summer ozone levels rose above the threshold which sensitive plants like tobacco could tolerate. And the tobacco crop was important in Virginia. They judged that, left to itself, industry would not take the necessary action and that there would be serious costs to human health and agricultural production. So they were imposing tight standards that new cars would have to meet by a set date. It was the antithesis of the British approach, and certainly far from cosy. There was an orchestrated scream from the motor industry in Detroit – but Washington was unmoved, and confident that the industry would deliver, when forced to it. It was all many miles removed from our friendly partnership with those that we were supposed to be regulating.

I wrote a full report when I got home, and sent it to Anthony Crosland, with a copy to Solly Zuckerman. And Solly exploded.

'What did you mean by sending that report to the Secretary of State?' he demanded. 'The meeting in America was my meeting. You came as one of my delegation. If anyone is to brief the Cabinet it is me. What you did was wrong . . .'

I was taken aback. Didn't I work for Crosland? And hadn't he specifically asked for a report? Bob Cox was no help. 'Typical,' he said. 'The old lion and the young lion. You'll just have to make your peace with him . . .'

Peace was, in due course, restored – though the incident made me very wary. But Solly was a redoubtable champion of science. He was highly valued by the Prime Minister, Harold Wilson, to whom he had direct access. He was respected by many senior Ministers. He was enormously influential in nuclear matters, where his close personal links with senior Americans buttressed his power. He gained practical leverage by chairing the Committee that brought key officials from all Departments together to discuss what should be done on environmental issues. Another element of strength was his jealously-guarded dignity and seniority. I recall being in his office one morning and hearing two Private Secretaries debating a request from a junior Minister for an interview.

'Of course, Sir Solly will see him,' said the more senior. 'But he comes here. Sir Solly goes to see Members of the Cabinet and Ministers of State. Junior Ministers come to him.'

In that spring of 1970, we in the Central Unit, guided (and frequently pressed) by Solly and his Committee, were especially concerned with the preparation of a White Paper promised by the Prime Minister and Secretary of State. It was to review all sectors of the environment and tell the public what Government was doing about all perceived pollution problems. It was also to point out gaps in present arrangements and indicate how they would be filled. Our Central Unit had to compile it, although each Department would approve its respective bit and the final text would be agreed by a Ministerial Committee and ultimately by Cabinet. And we were in a hurry, because Ministers wanted to publish by the middle of July.

The task was like turning over stones.

'Do we have a policy on the pollution of the sea?' Bob Cox asked me one day.

'I don't think so – if you mean a coherent, overall one. MAFF have a policy on the kinds of waste they allow to be dumped in particular places. They also do a lot of pretty good research. MHLG have a policy about effluent discharges to rivers and coastal sewers. Scotland, Wales, and I suppose Northern Ireland, must have their matching policies. But I don't think anyone's ever tried to pull it all together.'

'That's our job, then. Please would you write a paper by Monday, so that we can discuss it and put it to Solly's Committee?'

The White Paper was to be a landmark document. Indeed, by some time in May the draft was getting so immense you could have seen it across many a desk. Then Bob Cox summoned the team.

'General Election in June.' he announced. 'Parliament's last sitting is on 29 May. Last date for publishing Government documents is 28 May. Wayland Kennet is to write a shortened text of the White Paper over the weekend. We're all to be available on the telephone so that he can check things . . .'

That Saturday in Hoddesdon, the phone rang. Lord Kennet.

'Lead,' he said. 'Why are we bothered about lead in petrol?'

'We aren't,' I replied (for we weren't at that time). 'The Americans are, because it will poison the catalysts they'll have to put on the back ends of their cars if they are to meet their new exhaust standards. Some people argue we should cut it out because it's a poison, but our medical advisers say that there's no evidence that we get significant amounts from petrol. They say our main sources are diet and lead plumbing in old houses – there's a real problem with acid water in Glasgow, which dissolves water pipes and cisterns. Children who pick at flakes of old-fashioned lead-based paint and eat it also have high blood lead levels.'

'Thanks,' said the Minister. The White Paper fell back on that time-honoured escape clause: 'The Government will nevertheless continue to keep this matter under review.'

Whatever the defects evident with hindsight, the White Paper – Command 4373, *The Protection of the Environment. The Fight Against Pollution* – was an important document. It was the first ever across-the-board statement of Government policy in its field. It is clear, concise, and being written by a single hand (and that of a professional writer at that) it has better than average literary quality. For years it was the only Government overview of pollution, by either of the ruling Parties.

The Royal Commission also got into its stride. Its first Report, which appeared in February 1971, resembled the White Paper in ranging across the whole field. Eric Ashby himself wrote a good deal of the introductory chapters. It is interesting to compare the two documents with where we are thirty years later.

The White Paper starts off by saying that 'the degree of control we can exert over pollution is a major factor in the quality of our civilization.' It goes on to specify three essential foundations for action: knowledge, both of ecological science and of control technology; the right economic analysis and priorities; and the right legal and administrative frameworks. Turning to the environment itself, the Paper is enormously taken up with smoke – from domestic fires (which still, in those days, burned a lot of coal in inefficient old grates), from industrial furnaces, and from badly-adjusted diesel engines.

But it also worried a little over two future problems – how to stop the rapidly increasing population of motor cars from creating the kind of smog the Americans were already acting against, and how to react to the possibility that carbon dioxide emissions might warm the climate – or that dust and vapour from more and more aircraft in the stratosphere might cool it.

Noise was highlighted as everyone's pet hate, but the Government stopped short of using the White Paper to announce their intention to ban Concorde and other civil aircraft from flying at supersonic speed over land in the UK, so causing a 'sonic boom' on the ground. They decided that they had to calm French nerves first. The Government also thought that proposals by the United Nations Economic Commission for Europe for tighter standards for emissions from motor vehicles were 'without merit', but decided that this confrontation, too, had no place in the White Paper. None the less, there were plenty of positive noises. There was concern that too much nitrate from fertilizers might get into drinking water, that too much land was becoming derelict and that sewage treatment was inadequate. The Government announced that the voluntary controls on pesticides would be replaced by a legally-binding system (Monks Wood wins at last!), that it wanted to launch a Clean Rivers programme and that it would do something about oil pollution from ships. Finally, it supported an active international programme, including a major British involvement in the United Nations Conference on the Human Environment, to be held in Stockholm in 1972.

The Royal Commission looked farther ahead. The economic system needed to ensure that the costs of pollution were borne by the polluters. The training of those actually trying to control pollution needed to be improved. The Clean Air programme was welcomed but more needed to be done about motor vehicles. We needed better sewage treatment, tighter controls over the disposal of toxic wastes, controls over the dumping of wastes at sea, and better control of noise. The Commission announced it was going to study the pollution of estuaries and tidal seas. It called for international monitoring, especially of pollution that might affect the climate. And it expressed concern over the disposal of radioactive wastes.

Smoke. Noise. Nitrate. Pesticides. Oil from ships. Dumping at sea. Radioactive wastes. Toxic wastes and dereliction. Making polluters bear the costs of pollution. All these were topics of their time, and many remain so today. But it is interesting to see the beginnings of concern over the problems of the 1990s – climate change, and the mounting impact of road transport.

In June 1970, against all the pollsters' expectations, Labour lost the General Election and Mr Heath moved into Downing Street. As Labour would have done had they been returned, he restructured government, creating a Department of the Environment. He appointed Peter Walker as its first Secretary of State. Mr Walker presided over an immense Department that amalgamated the former Ministry of Housing and Local Government, the Ministry of Public Building and Works, and the Ministry of Transport. He also inherited Anthony Crosland's responsibility for coordinating everything that all Departments did about pollution. Crosland's former special office was closed down and Bob Cox left for the Home Office, to serve as the Deputy Secretary responsible for prisons, leaving me heading both the Scientific Unit and the Royal Commission Secretariat. And official papers, now released under the 30-year rule, reveal that we were at the centre of a power struggle.

The Foreign and Commonwealth Office wanted to keep the Central Unit in the Cabinet Office, because they saw its separation from executive departments as a strength. They pointed out that President Nixon had just announced his intention to establish an Environment Protection Agency in the USA, and thought the Unit might turn into a distinctively British nucleus of something similar. Eric Ashby approached Sir Burke Trend, Secretary to the Cabinet, with a similar plea. But the Civil Service Department, pressed by Sir David Serpell who was to head the new DOE, fought back. Serpell was blunt. 'If a "Ministry for Environment" is set up, its Minister ought to have responsibility for the Central Co-ordinating Unit – indeed it would surely seem very odd if he didn't.' He got his way, and the Central Unit was twitched away from the Cabinet Office and from Solly Zuckerman (some of whose power had departed with Harold Wilson). At the time, I was quite pleased. I had found Solly a confining presence; indeed, when David Serpell told me he had 'fought hard to get you away from Zuckerman,' I responded, 'I will remember you in my prayers!' It did make sense for the Unit to remain close to the Minister it was meant to support. But we did lose some of our independence when we were removed from the Cabinet Office.

I hoped to have the same kind of link with the new Secretary of State that we had enjoyed with the old, and the omens seemed good when Peter Walker summoned me about a week after he had taken up office.

'I intend to make action against pollution a cornerstone of my Ministry,' he said. 'Your Unit will be part of my central office. And the first thing I want to do is take lead out of petrol . . .'

David Serpell took a different view. I think that the last thing he wanted was a bevy of scientists running in and out of the Secretary of State's office. He may well have feared that we would start acting rather as Ministers' special advisers do now, and become an independent influence within the

Department. Indeed, from what I got to know of Peter Walker I think that this might easily have happened. Instead, Serpell told me that I should report through Richard Chilver as the Deputy Secretary who looked after clean air, water, noise and wastes. This put us alongside the policy directorates in the hierarchy and meant that any challenge to their approach would be argued out at one of Richard's weekly meetings rather than in front of the Secretary of State. But David Serpell was happy with the notion that we should harass other departments.

'Your role is that of the mosquito,' he said one day. I ventured to differ. 'Gadfly. Mosquitoes suck blood delicately – and incidentally, only the females do it. Gadflies deliver a powerful nip.'

'OK,' said Sir David. 'Gadfly. But remember that nipped cows kick . . .'

The Civil Service in those days was rather different from today's model. For one thing, Ministers were much less involved in the management of their departments (it all changed when Michael Heseltine arrived in DOE in 1979 and established his management information system for Ministers, known as MINIS). Civil Servants handled the implementation of established law and policy, and staff management was left to the Permanent Secretary. Civil servants also represented the United Kingdom in a wide range of international negotiations. Matters went to a Minister when problems arose, or when a new initiative seemed desirable. And, of course, Ministers asked questions and themselves proposed new actions or new laws, seeking official advice on how to achieve these goals. Sometimes that advice had to be 'drop it, Minister, it won't work' – just as sometimes Ministers would say to officials 'your advice may be technically sound, but politically we can't do it that way.' Often ideas were thrown around in dialogue, so as to see whether they were worth following up. The Civil Service prided itself on being able to give impartial advice to Ministers of any political party (when a General Election was in the offing, manifestos were crawled over and parallel briefs prepared for new arrivals of different political complexions, suggesting how their particular party pledges might be implemented). There were no personal political advisers within Departments, and a straw poll at the time would, I am sure, have dismissed any proposal to appoint them as unnecessary, money-wasting and likely to lead to confusion and conflict.

The culture of service was strong, and in my view admirable. Most of the 'fast stream' civil servants had good academic degrees and outstanding minds to go with them. They could have made much more money outside government. They were there because they wanted to serve the community. They did not seek limelight, and were content to work in an atmosphere of confidentiality. I agreed then, and still do, that such confidentiality was necessary. The news that a new law on this or that was being examined would obviously ruffle affected interests, and might allow a speculator to make a lot of money. Public consultation was essential – but only when Ministers were clear that the idea was one they wanted to pursue. And since Ministers were (and are) publicly accountable for everything, the Civil Servants advising them were sworn not to divulge the nature of the advice they gave – for this could weaken the Minister's position especially if the advice was not taken. Many of us were bound to develop a close working relationship with individual Ministers, and this had to be based on trust. Ministers had a right to expect that the zany notions they may have floated in confidence – or the many false starts that are inevitable on the road to final policy – would not be revealed by their advisers. In that period we all accepted the discipline. Leaks were almost unheard of.

The scientific culture did not fit altogether easily into this world. We were trained to question established theory, and to make independent evaluations of evidence. The fact that something was official policy, or even enshrined in statute, did not make it immune from challenge. That was one basis for our 'gadfly' role in the Central Unit. It also made us uncomfortable colleagues. And there was a further complication. We had our professional links outside Whitehall. We continued to attend scientific meetings. From time to time we were invited to speak from professional platforms – something administrative Civil Servants hardly ever did. It was far easier for us to return to that professional world than it was for administrators who had locked themselves into a lifetime career when they entered the Civil Service. All this led to a certain jealousy and a feeling that however useful we professionals might be, we did not quite 'belong'.

The contrast between Richard Chilver and myself could not have been greater. Richard was a Civil Servant of the old school. His interest was in overall policy, not second-guessing what his Under Secretaries were about. He was highly intelligent, courteous, and selective in what he did. He wrote clear, thoughtful memoranda in his own hand. He saw his role as screening and guiding what went to Ministers, so that they were given well-digested arguments that focussed on key issues and were not cluttered with technical detail. And his careful, leisurely style carried over into his daily life. When we had a power cut that stopped the lifts in the Three Terrible Towers of Marsham Street into which the Department moved in 1971, Richard could be seen climbing the stairs to the eighteenth floor very slowly, pipe in mouth, doing *The Times* crossword puzzle as he went . . .

For his part, Richard was clearly convinced that 'steady as she goes' was the right policy for HMS Britannia. Writing to Solly Zuckerman in May 1970, when there was mounting concern over the quality of public water supplies, he emphasized that 'we shall find it increasingly necessary to concentrate expert personnel and money on essentials at the expense of side-shows.' I am pretty sure that he saw the new environmentalism of the 1970s as a side-show and a recipe for wasting time and money. The result was to tip the efforts of the Central Unit more and more towards the international scene. Here, we had a pretty free hand – I think because it was a relatively fluid area on which Ministers had yet to take a view, and because it kept us from nipping colleagues in DOE who were carrying out policies that had already received Ministerial blessing.

Britain thought of itself as a world leader in environmental action and Peter Walker, who took great pride in being the first Secretary of State for the Environment anywhere, wanted this leadership to be recognized abroad. When France and the Federal Republic of Germany appointed Robert Poujade and Hans-Dieter Genscher as their Environment Ministers, he invited first one and then the other over for talks. The Heath Government was committed to taking Britain into the EEC, and these discussions were part of the process of getting closer to Europe. We were delighted when M. Poujade, noting that better sewage treatment had restored oxygen and fish to the Thames, announced that he would return '*pour Thamesefier la Seine*'. History does not record how the Académie Française reacted to that unlovely new French verb.

In June 1970, Ronald Arculus of the Foreign and Commonwealth Office pulled together a memorandum on British priorities among the many international bodies that were jumping on the environmental band-waggon. We in the Central Unit were very much involved both in developing this policy and in attending the top-priority international meetings. It was agreed that global environmental issues that needed regulation – like oil pollution from ships, or noise from aircraft – should be addressed within specialized United Nations Agencies like the Intergovernmental Maritime Consultative Organization or the International Civil Aviation Organization. We also gave high priority to the World Meteorological Organization and World Health Organization. Despite our rude words about vehicle emission standards, we accepted the United Nations Economic Commission for Europe as the right place to negotiate regulations at European level (though all that would change if Mr Heath succeeded in getting the UK into the European Economic Community). We didn't think much of the Council of Europe, but it had done quite well as a place for discussion of nature conservation and pesticides, and was supported in those two limited fields (which Government at the time did not regard as of first importance). OECD, the Organization for Economic Cooperation and Development, the 'rich countries economic club', was, in contrast, seen as a real heavyweight and we agreed it was the place to sort out policies important to the developed world. Finally, we loathed the idea that NATO might get into the environmental action through its Committee on the Challenges of Modern Society (CCMS for short), brainchild of American Senator Daniel Patrick Moynihan who wanted to give the alliance 'a human face'.

My first experience of these things was at the newly-formed OECD Environment Committee in 1970. As is not unusual, the main session was preceded by a 'fix-it' discussion the evening before. This took the form of a dinner, hosted by the United States to win support for the election of their delegate, Christian Herter Jr, to the Chair. He got it. Next morning I found myself sitting for the first time behind a label UNITED KINGDOM and speaking as if I was all 56 million Brits. It felt a bit odd, even though my brief had been agreed with all the responsible Departments and I had a Foreign Office colleague and representatives from the Scottish Office and the Department of Trade and Industry to see that I kept on the rails.

Over the following two years, that Committee ranged over many topics but two stand out in my memory. The first was our discussion and adoption of the 'Polluter Pays Principle' which is now Holy Environmental Writ but was then quite revolutionary. The central idea is that environmental costs must be 'internalized'. If I run a dirty factory, pouring effluent into the river or unfiltered fumes into the air, I may make cheaper products, but everyone else around pays for it in the shape of ruined fishery, expensive treatment to make the river water fit to drink, dirtied laundry, corroded buildings, unhealthy air and so forth. If the Government pays for the clean-up, taxpayers' money is being used to subsidize me, and those who buy my cheap products. The 'P.P.P.' says that I and others like me must bear the costs of meeting whatever standards for emissions to air and water society demands. In turn, of course, I will pass those costs on to those who buy my products, as is only fair since they are the beneficiaries. Simple. But the recognition that when the environment is polluted costs fall on society as a whole was an important advance in the 1970s, when people had tended to look on the waste-dispersing capacity of nature as a 'free good'.

The other debate was less harmonious. It was on air pollution, and especially on the long distance movement of sulphur dioxide. Coal contains up to 4 per cent sulphur, and in early days when a lot of coal was burned in towns, mostly in inefficient old grates, sulphurous smoke reached lethal concentrations – as it did in the smog that killed so many people in London in December 1952. By the 1970s urban air was well on the way to being clean, but big power stations dotted about in the countryside beside the rivers that supplied their cooling water were still squirting millions of tons of sulphur dioxide through tall chimneys into the upper air. Much of the British emission was wafted away on the westerly winds to rain down over Scandinavia as dilute sulphuric acid. It was reported to have killed aquatic life in thousands of kilometres of Norwegian and Swedish rivers, and to have destroyed a number of valuable salmon fisheries. Erik Lykke, Norwegian delegate to the OECD Environment Committee, argued that this was a clear breach of the polluter pays principle, and that the UK and other 'source countries' should clean up their emissions.

As United Kingdom delegate, my brief was to be sceptically defensive, but to agree that an international research programme on the long-range transport of sulphur pollutants over western Europe should be set up under OECD auspices, and this was done in 1972. Leslie Reed bore the brunt of what were often difficult discussions, which went on for four years. At home we encountered a barrage of defensive argument from the Central Electricity Generating Board. One of their staff claimed that the deposited sulphur was probably a good thing because light sandy soils like those in the British East Midlands were deficient in it – CEGB was actually helping the farmer! Others argued that acid rain either did not happen in Britain (regardless of the fact that a Manchester Public Health Officer actually discovered and named it in the nineteenth century), or was no problem because our soils contained so much lime that it was quickly neutralized. However the CEGB did do some good research into the causes of acidification in Galloway lakes, and in 1974 we set up a joint review group led by the Central Unit and NERC to draw together all the scientific evidence we had about the situation in Britain. Meanwhile, the basic ploy was to argue scientific uncertainty and to point to the weaknesses of some of the Scandinavian research as justification for inaction.

The problem brought up the question of burden of proof. Should there be scientific certainty before large sums of public money were invested in systems to scrub the sulphur oxides out of power station flue gases? The British attitude was that action should be shown to be necessary by 'sound science', and that even then the costs of damage should be balanced against the costs of control. In other countries, and among environmental non-governmental bodies, more and more voices were heard demanding that action should be taken if there was a reasonable likelihood of risk, even if the scientific proof was incomplete.

There were also questions of international responsibility. How much should the British taxpayer pay to protect the Norwegian environment? The Treasury and the CEGB argued that Norwegian acid rain must result from the emissions of many nations, including Norway itself. In 1972, at the Stockholm Conference, we accepted that all States had a responsibility to ensure that their emissions did not damage the environment of other states. But the industry still argued that it was wrong to make it incur costs when the scientific case was unproven. The debate rumbled on for a decade (and I will come back to it), and it was not until 1987 that Britain adopted the 'Precautionary Principle' which in essence says that if there is a reasonably strong probability that something will cause environmental damage, action should be taken without waiting for scientific certainty.

The Nordic countries were among the first to wake up to the environment. Sweden created a National Environmental Protection Board in 1969. In the same year their Ambassador to the UN, Sverker Åström, proposed a UN Conference on the Human Environment and invited everyone to Stockholm in June 1972. The Central Unit was deeply involved in the preparations. Bob Cox, Richard Chilver, Jim Jones (Deputy Secretary in the Ministry of Transport) and I visited Stockholm in June 1970 and had long talks with Professor Arne Engström, Chief Scientific Adviser to the Swedish Government. It was my first time in that lovely city, but as is so often the case, most of the hours were spent in committee rooms. Arne Engström explained that environmental issues had created a new political movement in Sweden, especially among young people. The UN Conference was seen as the start of a new world environmental order. New Conventions would regulate dumping of radioactive waste in the oceans, ensure the safe transport of oil, control the transport and storage of persistent poisons and prevent acid rain. The Swedes were also very keen to expand monitoring of the environment.

I am afraid we were not as supportive as we should have been. Richard Chilver said that international standards were appropriate only where pollution crossed frontiers or where international trade was involved. For the rest, it should be left to countries to protect their own environments. We found ourselves in greater agreement with the Americans, who were also making a big environmental pitch at home and abroad. President Nixon gave great prominence to the fight against pollution in his Message to Congress in February 1970, He created a three-man Council on Environmental Quality, chaired by Russell Train (President of the US Conservation Foundation and host of that memorable party for the IBP CT Committee back in 1966), with a geologist, Gordon Macdonald, and a journalist, Robert Cahn, as members. Lee Talbot became a senior staff officer. The CEQ was a bit like our Royal Commission, and it produced annual reports on the condition of the United States environment. Later in the same year the President created a powerful Environment Protection Agency under an industrialist, Bill Ruckelshaus. For many years the Americans were truly leaders in global environmental matters, and they were very active in the preparations for the Stockholm Conference, which dominated the first two years of my time in the Central Unit.

Maurice Strong, the dynamic Canadian Secretary General of the Conference, was determined that it should achieve something beyond talk. At 'level one' he wanted it to raise world-wide awareness of environmental issues. The vehicles were to be press publicity, meetings, and a popular book *Only One Earth: the Care and Maintenance of a Small Planet*, written by two outstanding thinkers, Barbara Ward and René Dubos. The second level was to be the Conference itself, whose Declaration would, he hoped, be a world Charter for the Environment. The third level was to consist of practical outputs, among which Maurice included an integrated system for monitoring what was happening to the world (code-named 'Earthwatch'), an international Convention (or Conventions) to protect the sea, especially against the dumping of wastes, an information system so that anyone with a problem about a nasty substance could find out what was known about its properties, and a continuing UN Secretariat to coordinate international action within the family of nations. Surprisingly, all these things happened.

The PrepCom (Preparatory Committee) was the planning forum. But the Level Three actions were remitted to IGWOGs (Inter-Governmental Working Groups) on Marine Pollution, on Monitoring, and on a Register of Sources of Environmental Information. The UK, led by Peter Walker, took them seriously. We made a bid for leadership in IGWOG I on Marine Pollution, convening a meeting in London which Richard Chilver chaired, in which the frameworks of both a global and a European Convention to stop the dumping of dangerous wastes in the sea were discussed.

At that time, such dumping was a hot issue. Events like the seabird wreck in the Irish Sea had sparked an outburst of near-hysteria. The headlines yelled at us: HAVE WE DONE IT AT LAST? HAVE WE POISONED THE SEA? A Dutch ship, the *Stella Maris*, became notorious when she cruised in the full glare of the press from Rotterdam into the North Sea to dump a cargo of 650 tonnes of chlorinated hydrocarbons. There was a scream from Norway, which was close to the proposed dumping grounds. It was decided to go further into the North Atlantic, but when the vessel put into the Faeroe Islands for fuel, it was refused her. Finally, she was recalled by her owners, who had been leaned on by the Dutch Government (there was no Greenpeace to harass such vessels in those days). Scientific assessments suggested that all the dumping to date was on so limited a scale that it was little more than a few nasty drops in the vast oceanic bucket, but there was real cause for concern because there was no agreed international law. And it was evident that the more nasty drops ships like *Stella Maris* were allowed to deposit, the more unhealthy the bucket would become.

The IGWOG on Marine Polution in action! Martin Holdgate, as UK delegate, discusses a point with the United States in Reykjavik, Iceland, in the spring of 1972. Photograph: Icelandic Photos.

Governments agreed that we needed new international rules to control dumping at sea, even if this was only a minor source of marine pollution (most of which came from rivers and coastal outfalls). A Convention controlling dumping in the north-east Atlantic was rapidly agreed in Oslo early in 1972. The IGWOG on Marine Pollution met in London and agreed on a very similar framework for a global agreement. Both texts owed a great deal to a British draft, and by being so centrally involved we had a big influence on what was finally agreed. However the second IGWOG meeting in Ottawa, in the old station opposite the imposing railway gothic towers of the Chateau Laurier hotel, went badly wrong. The problem arose because our Canadian hosts, and especially our Chairman, Ambassador Alan Beesley, wanted to change the agenda and talk of much wider Law of the Sea issues. This, and Alan's rather haughty style, infuriated Arne Engström (who, of course, saw a tangible achievement for Stockholm slipping away). He stormed out of the room. I followed.

'Martin, I go to phone my Prime Minister and withdraw my delegation...'

He calmed down, but the week achieved almost nothing. So, with the time before Stockholm running out, much turned on session three in

Reykjavik's Loftleidr Hotel, overlooking the city airport. Two weeks. Almost success. The UK convened a fourth session in London, just before Stockholm, in the hope of tying up the loose ends. They all came unstitched. We were left with no more than an agreement that the UK would convene a final meeting after the Stockholm Conference at which every effort would be made to complete the negotiations.

We took the other IGWOGS seriously, too. I attended the one on Monitoring, in Geneva in September 1971. Lizzie, Robert, David and I drove there from the Chiemsee near Munich, where we had been on holiday. It was appallingly hot, and while I yawned away in the meeting rooms, Lizzie found the ice cream bills mounting astronomically (and in Swiss francs too) and that the lake steamers were the cheapest way of keeping a 15 year old and a 6 year old – not the most compatible of ages – more or less happy. Fortunately, the burden of the IGWOG on information about nasty substances fell on John Peachey (coincidentally one of Jim Cragg's former Durham research students) whom we had snatched into CUEP as an expert on information technology. John held off a German bid for an all-singing-and-dancing Information Centre and won support for a 'Referral System' – a kind of network, serviced by a modest central switchboard which put people who needed data in touch with those who had it. He defended the concept successfully at Stockholm – where we found another of Jim's research students, Bill Banage, now a Professor and Minister for Animal Resources in Uganda, leading his country's delegation. We had an excellent reunion lunch, officially approved as Hospitality to a Friendly Minister.

Peter Walker took immense trouble over the Stockholm Conference. He decided that the team he was to lead must represent the country as a whole (there was a laudable attempt at that time to make environmental policies multi-partisan, recognizing their long-term nature). That meant finding out what a wide range of people thought. So he set up four independent Working Groups to canvass public opinion. Sir Eric Ashby chaired one on pollution (its Report was called 'Nuisance or Nemesis?'). Sir Ralph Verney's group covered natural resources – 'Sinews for Survival'. Dennis Stevenson led a group that looked at the role of the citizen – 'Forty Million Volunteers'. And Raine, Countess of Dartmouth (later Countess Spencer) chaired a group that looked at culture and the arts. The Central Unit provided the Secretariats, and Lady Dartmouth was, at times, rather demanding. Her report had on its cover a Snowdon photograph of a nymph swathed in soft draperies and standing in a fountain. Ken Evans, who headed the Secretariat for the four groups, alleged that the first photograph was nude. 'Tony!' came the rebuke. 'That won't do. Tell that girl to put some clothes on and get back into the water.'

Peter Walker, of course, led the Delegation to Stockholm, with Eldon Griffiths, Parliamentary Under Secretary, as Ministerial alternate, and there was a Ministerial presence for Scotland as well. But he also invited Anthony Crosland as 'shadow' Secretary of State, Sir Eric Ashby as Chairman of the Royal Commission, the three other Chairs of independent Working Groups, representatives of the CBI and TUC, and a host more. We must have taken a delegation of thirty in all, not counting the half dozen Secretariat that operated our office. I shudder at the cost, but it all worked very well. There were, of course, some odd moments. One came when we learned that the American scientists Sherwood Rowland and Mario Molina had calculated that aircraft flying high in the stratosphere might destroy the ozone layer which shields us from damaging solar ultra-violet radiation. Ministers feared that this might be the basis for an attack on Concorde! The UK and France leapt to its defence. Sir Alan Cottrell (who had taken over from Solly Zuckerman as Chief Scientific Adviser in 1971) and Sir John Mason, Director General of the Meteorological Office, were summoned to Stockholm. They sat at the UK desk during the discussion of air pollution, looking thoroughly bored. Ozone depletion was never mentioned (which is curious, for Rowland and Molina were right, although chlorofluorocarbons, not Concordes, were to prove the villains of that piece). There was far more muttering about acid rain caused by sulphur oxides from power stations, on which Sweden had produced the first good study, but even that was not pressed home as an issue.

Stockholm was not really a world conference. Far too few developing countries attended (many saw it as of little relevance to their most crucial problems of poverty and under-investment). Russia and all the eastern bloc except Romania stayed away in protest at the admission of West, but not East, Germany (though they were active in the PrepCom, and were in daily touch with Maurice Strong throughout the proceedings). But it was the first big Conference of its kind attended by the People's Republic of China, and when they disagreed with a draft resolution they tended to castigate it in bizarre language full of reference to 'running dogs of fascist imperialism' (having had quite a lot to do with China in later years I suspect that translation as well as dogma was at fault). One session went on until 3 a.m. before a formula was found that removed a Chinese objection nobody else really understood. Jim Jones, who had just taken over from David Serpell as Permanent Secretary of DOE, was sitting with me at the side of the hall listening to all this. At about 1.30 a.m. Jim could stand it no longer.

'This is what the Foreign Office is paid for,' he asserted. 'Look at Meg Rothwell at the UK desk. She's loving it. I need a Scotch. Let's tell them we're going.' We did.

Stockholm was a qualified success. It established the principle that the environment was important enough to warrant attention at world level. Its Declaration established some significant points – including the responsibility of all states to see that their actions did not harm the environment of other states or the 'global commons' outside the limits of national jurisdiction. But it is perhaps best remembered for creating UNEP, the United Nations Environment Programme. Maurice Strong went on to be its first Executive Director, while Mostafa Tolba, the Egyptian Minister of Education and Science, who led his national delegation to Stockholm, became his Deputy and eventual successor. But there was quite a bickering over what kind of animal UNEP should be. The rich countries – who were dominant at Stockholm, and who were already criticising the cost of the UN – were clear that there should be NO NEW UN AGENCY. The existing Agencies wholeheartedly agreed. Their refrain was 'anything that needs doing, we are already doing or can do better than anyone else' (shades of Joe Weiner and Max Nicholson). The UK and USA pressed for 'a small co-ordinating Secretariat of no more than 50 people' who would service a Governing Council of 32 States, drawn from all continents, that would decide the priorities for UN work on the environment. The actual work would be done by the existing Agencies, especially the World Health Organization, the Food and Agriculture Organization, the World Meteorological Organization, and the various Regional Economic Commissions among which ECE, the Economic Commission for Europe, had already created an intergovernmental group of Senior Advisers on Environmental Problems (this was to be the spur to the regional Convention on Long-Range Trans-Boundary Air Pollution which finally got to grips with acid rain). And a voluntary Environment Fund was to be created, with a target value of US$100 million a year, to pay for the additional work the Agencies could not otherwise do.

There was an even more passionate debate over where UNEP should be based. There were, at one time, at least eight places on offer – Mexico City, Paris, Geneva, London, Vienna, Rome, Nairobi and Stockholm itself. The developing countries were adamant – it had to be in a Third World capital. The choice was narrowed to Mexico City and Nairobi. Nairobi won. The Secretariat would stay in Geneva until 1973, and then move to the new Jomo Kenyatta Conference Centre in the middle of the city, pending construction of a permanent Headquarters, on land to be presented by the Government of Kenya. As a permanent member of the UN Security Council the UK was allocated a seat on the UNEP Governing Council.

Stockholm also left business unfinished. The Convention on the Dumping of Wastes at Sea was one of them. But the British offer to host a

Peter Walker opens the conference that agreed the London Convention to protect the sea against the dumping of wastes. Photograph: Keystone Press Agency.

final negotiating session was accepted, and in October 1972 we all met in the gilded, be-mirrored, Long Gallery of Lancaster House (the modern Queen Elizabeth Conference Centre had not then been built). As head of the host country delegation, I was destined for the Chair. Peter Walker came to open the proceedings. As I escorted him out, the instruction was simple:

'You bring me an agreed Convention in two weeks' time – or don't bother to come back to the Department...'

He was joking – but the joke was on him. For by the time we adopted the Final Act of the Conference, with the agreed Convention, he had been moved to head the Department of Trade and Industry. Geoffrey Rippon, who replaced him, had none of Walker's dynamism or understanding of the environment.

The London Convention was my first experience of chairing a tricky piece of international negotiation. It wasn't helped by the room. The Long Gallery is beautiful, but it fits its name. If you sit in the middle, as the Chair must, the table stretches to a remote distance either side. Far away at the edge of sight there was a delegation sign FEDERAL REPUBLIC OF GERMANY. The letters were so small as to be unreadable. You just had to memorise faces and places. Another and more agreeable problem at Lancaster House arose because each morning, at 11 a.m., a military band marched past to serenade the Queen Mother at Clarence House. We decreed a Royal Coffee Break as the stirring strains swelled to make negotiation inaudible.

The negotiations were conducted in the seemingly-polite formal language diplomats use. Everyone addressed everyone else as 'distinguished delegates'. A Head of Delegation would be referred to as 'The Distinguished Ambassador representing Ruritania'. Dissent would be gift-wrapped: 'My Delegation considers that the form of words proposed by the Distinguished Delegate of Utopia, while admirable in its idealistic sentiments, is not altogether realistic . . .' And so on.

It's rather like the Civil Service, where when someone opens a remark with the words 'with respect, I would like to suggest . . .' they mean, 'you've got it wrong, and I will now put you right . . .' I once heard an old-style Civil Service Under Secretary address a junior Minister: '. . . with the very greatest of respect, Parliamentary Under-Secretary of State . . .' That meant 'you incompetent ass, you're talking nonsense, but since you're one of our Ministers I'll have to explain things to you.' Diplomatic negotiation sugars pills with courtesy, but the pills can none the less be poison.

We saw that at Lancaster House. The Russians were out to squash the Japanese (probably they were having another rumpus over the Kuril Islands at the time). The Japanese wanted the Convention to allow them to dump some concrete blocks in which they had encased cadmium waste (cadmium had been identified as the cause of itai-itai, or 'ouch, ouch' disease, a painful condition of the joints). The Russians were having none of it. The Japanese had no flexibility and there were language difficulties. In the end, they were forced to accept cadmium-containing wastes as 'black list' material not to be dumped at sea. Their Head of Delegation lost immense face and almost shambled into the final celebratory party, murmuring, 'Very sorry, very sorry,' in a broken voice.

Another awkward part of the negotiations was what to do about radioactive wastes. Here Britain and France were the ones with the problem. In the late 1960s both countries dropped consignments of intermediate-level material ('hot, but not too hot' as somebody put it), encased in drumfuls of concrete, at points in the sea chosen by the Fisheries Ministries as posing no hazard to marine life or the human food chain. The point began to be made that there could be no certainty of safety, and that special care was needed because once dumped the material was irretrievable. Spain was especially uneasy about dumps in the Atlantic, west of its coast. When negotiating the Oslo and London Conventions we therefore met strong pressure to put radioactive waste on the 'black list' of undumpables. Under industry pressure, both Britain and France resisted. We were luckier than the Japanese, for on this issue the other countries were willing to accept a 'formula' (which many people would call a fudge). Radioactive substances were listed as banned 'except for those certified by the International Atomic Energy Agency as appropriate for dumping at sea'.

This made the IAEA (a UN body based in Vienna) the certifying authority and if they said that a particular kind of radioactive waste, packaged a certain way, was safe to dump, dumped it could be. But the pressure on the Government from other countries (like Spain) and from public opinion (urged on by the new, active NGOs like Greenpeace) to abandon sea dumping continued. There was a last-ditch demand by the industry that the option be kept open, and a good deal of money was spent modifying the dumping vessel so that the drums could go straight down through a well in the middle of the ship, rather than over the side where Greenpeace inflatable boats could easily get in the way. But no further dumping was ever carried out. We would have lost nothing – indeed saved money – by accepting a total ban at the time when we agreed the Conventions. By holding out for the option we blackened our image to no practical advantage.

The Oslo and London Conventions were valuable advances in their time, but we were all aware that they only dealt with a small part of a big issue. Most of the mess in the sea comes down the rivers, or through a miscellany of coastal drains. The French Government decided to make this its focus of concern, and invited all the north-west European countries to meet in Paris in 1974 to negotiate a new Convention that would control the pollution of our regional seas from 'land-based sources'. Things moved fast – perhaps too fast – and we concluded the Convention in only two sessions, each of two weeks, in the French Government Centre in the Avenue Klébèr. The meeting was under pressure because M. Cabouat, who was in the chair, was also leading for France in Channel Tunnel negotiations which were boring steadily forward. I was particularly pleased to get agreement to a clear definition of pollution, right at the start of the text:

> The introduction by man into the environment of substances or energy liable to cause hazards to human health, harm to living resources and ecological systems, damage to structures or amenity, or interference with legitimate uses of the sea.

This was important to us Brits because it made it clear that pollution came through human agency (natural background was excluded), and was of significance for the damage it did, not only to resources but also to ecology, amenity and potential use. The argument underpinned our commitment to environmental quality standards, which we were pressing in a European context.

But there were lighter moments, and some niggles. The Spanish delegate, Jaime de Iturriaga, and the German delegate, Henning Wegener, fell out over something and became sarcastic, referring to one another as 'my dear colleague'. Time was wasting away. The Chairman got fed up, adjourned, and (I suspect) took them both out to dinner. We, the Brits, went and had a meal and some good red wine. We resumed around 9.30 p.m., pleasantly relaxed. Suddenly, through a warm Burgundian haze, I heard the Chairman.

'Perhaps the United Kingdom delegate will give us a form of words for that?'

(I should explain that, rather unusually for negotiations in France, we were drafting in English.) I woke up and asked Kevin Chamberlain, our Foreign Office lawyer, what it was all about. Scribble, scribble, scribble. 'The United Kingdom, please.' I read my text which, quite frankly, said nothing very much, as it was intended to submerge two irreconcilable positions in generalization. I heard Kevin's voice: 'Gobbledegook!' I regret to say that I extended my hand behind my back and waved two fingers at him rudely. The Danes, our neighbours, broke into unseemly mirth. The incident convinced me that international law is not best written under pressure, late in the evening, after a good Parisian dinner.

One of the controversies at Stockholm had been over the fundamental issue of 'limits to growth'. At the simplest biological level it is obvious that any area of land can only produce just so much of a crop, or just so much beef or mutton. One of the great achievements of human history has been in agriculture, lifting such production to heights our ancestors never dreamed of. But there must be an ultimate theoretical limit. In 1971 the Club of Rome published a book by Denis Meadows and others that used a simple mathematical model to explore what those limits might be if you made various assumptions about the interactions between human population size, agriculture, environmental resources, industry and pollution. It was not meant to be a prediction of doom, but of course that was just how it was viewed. It seemed to imply that the continuing growth in human numbers – the 'population bomb' of another American writer, Paul Ehrlich – and the pollution we all generate would overwhelm the Earth.

The report exploded like a bomb among the developing countries – many of whom had fast-growing populations, acute and mounting poverty, and serious environmental degradation. Far from seeing it as a cautionary tale, they condemned the report as a wicked attempt by the rich countries to heap blame for all the world's ills upon the poor. The barrage of emotional vituperation did nobody any good. The issue was whether there was any value in modelling world systems in this way, in the hope of understanding them better and adjusting policies so as to avert disaster.

Alan Cottrell, as Chief Scientific Adviser, invited Denis Meadows and other members of his team over to give a presentation of their work in Whitehall. This led to a decision to create a Systems Analysis Research Unit in DOE, to explore some of the trends and interactions in greater depth. They built their own world model, code-named SARUM, and had a lot to do with a big study in OECD called Interfutures – or, more explicitly 'the future development of advanced industrial societies in harmony with that of developing countries.' If I have to summarize its several hundred pages in a short conclusion it would be: 'There can be a good future for both developed and developing countries if we give proper heed to the environment, cooperate to help the third world develop, set the right governance structure in place, and have the political will.' Which might be called a blinding glimpse of the obvious. The key word is one of the shortest – 'if'.

A year after Stockholm, the new UNEP Governing Council convened in Geneva. By then it was clear that the organisation would be bigger, and its programme wider than the United States and United Kingdom had wanted. Some of the new Environment Fund was to be earmarked for the Earthwatch function – and for a Global Environmental Monitoring System (GEMS) in particular. Some was to go on IRPTC – the International Registry of Potentially Toxic Chemicals. Some was sought for more action on marine pollution, especially regionally (and the Regional Seas Programme became one of UNEP's outstanding achievements, catalysing a whole series of new regional Conventions). But the draft programme presented to the first session of the Governing Council was heavily weighted towards what were seen as developed country interests – especially action against pollution. The Third World, present in far greater numbers than it had been in Stockholm, revolted.

The dichotomy had been obvious even before we got to Stockholm. Many developing nations had told Maurice Strong that 'the rich countries produced almost all the chemical pollution and had the money to put it right.' They went on to stress that *their* problem was 'the pollution of poverty', due to under-development, insufficient aid and trade barriers set up by the developed world. It is a tragic fact that this is still a persistent refrain thirty years later. North-south tensions had been heightened by the publication of *Limits to Growth*. Maurice had cooled things down before Stockholm at a special meeting in a motel at Founex, on the autoroute east of Geneva, and he convened a follow-up at Cocoyoc in Mexico. But the cracks were thinly papered and they tore open at the first Governing Council.

Deadlock. First week ended. No programme. Second week. Deadlock continued. Maurice began to talk of resigning. The Bureau, made up of the President, three Vice Presidents, and a Rapporteur, one from each of the five UN Regional Groups – Africa, Asia, Latin America, East Europe and Western Europe and Others (the Others including the USA, Canada, Australia, New Zealand and Japan) – met. They decided that the programme should be redrafted by two people, one from the developing countries and one from the developed world. The former chose Taghi Farvar, a lively and highly articulate Iranian. The developed countries chose me. There followed the unusual spectacle of a serving British Civil Servant being given a confidential briefing by Konstantin Ananichev, head of the Soviet delegation, on what the Eastern Europeans could and could not accept.

Taghi and I sat all day in a little office, occasionally sallying forth for food and consultation. By about 7 p.m. we had a programme. At 9.30 p.m. we were with the President of the Governing Council, the Jamaican Ambassador Don Mills, and about twenty other key figures mandated by the Groups. At about 5 a.m. we had an agreed text and slipped out through a violent thunderstorm for a few hours sleep. At 10 a.m. we met again in full Council. The President decided on an all-or-nothing approach.

'Distinguished delegates, we have before us a delicately balanced package. It was produced by two of our colleagues, who worked on it all day yesterday. A larger group of us spent the whole of last night scrutinizing it on your behalf. I believe that it represents a balanced agenda. In the spirit of compromise and consensus I urge you now to adopt it *en bloc* and without further debate. Can we please agree that, and so adopt our programme for the coming year?'

A brief pause, and the gavel came down. 'Thank you.' Sighs of relief, not least from Maurice Strong. But of course the paper still bridged some pretty deep fissures. Several opened out yet again in later years.

The early 1970s were a time of rapid growth in environmental awareness: new initiatives sprouted like mushrooms in a dark cellar. Most developed countries, and many developing ones, created new ministries and agencies. National and international laws multiplied. Books – many of them prophetic of environmental doom – cascaded onto the news-stands. And non-Governmental Organizations proliferated. There had been several hundred in the wings at Stockholm, where Maurice Strong had raised a few conventional eyebrows by going out of his way to meet and encourage them. Some, like Friends of the Earth and Greenpeace, were beginning to flex activist muscles. They were looked at suspiciously by groups with a tradition of working with Government, and industry clearly viewed them as Public Enemies. But Ministers soon recognized them as voices to be listened to with at least half an ear, and expected their officials to do likewise. The omens of change were evident, and touched even the established fiefdoms of the DOE.

But the biggest change began almost imperceptibly, and indeed had little impact on my life at the Central Unit. In 1973, after Gaullist rebuffs and domestic false starts, the United Kingdom finally entered the European Economic Community. The various directorates in DOE did not think it would make much difference to our environmental policy. For we still saw ourselves as among the world leaders. Had we not been the first country in Europe to have a major environment department, headed by a member of the Cabinet? Had we not played a leading role in a wide range of international actions? Was not the Royal Commission on Environmental Pollution unique in Europe? Did we not have the oldest laws and agencies for environment protection in the whole EEC? Were we not even then preparing a new Control of Pollution Bill (enacted in 1974) which would greatly expand control over noise, waste disposal on land, and the pollution of air and water? Had we not been among the leaders of action to deal with marine pollution in the Oslo, London and Paris Conventions? The expectation was that we would be able to carry on much as before, using our established laws to implement the handful of Community environmental measures that had so far been agreed.

In 1973, however, the European Commission produced the first draft Community Environmental Policy. It alarmed many in Whitehall by its breadth and style. The UK set to work to ensure that it was restricted to topics that really did affect the Common Market. We could see sense in harmonising standards for goods that were traded across frontiers, and we also supported the adoption of the Polluter Pays Principle by the Community because it would help even out the playing field of manufacturing costs. But we were determined to avoid incursions into town and country planning or nature conservation, which were seen as domestic matters for member states.

Experience in the OECD Environment Committee had shown that there were differences between the UK and most other European countries over how we set standards. The German delegate to the OECD Committee, Peter Mencke-Glückert, had argued that legally enforceable limits for pollutants in discharges to air, rivers or the sea were a rational consequence of the Polluter Pays Principle and a way of evening up the competitive playing field. But the British thought that the important thing was to keep concentrations of nasty substances below the threshold at which they could do damage. Emissions which did not breach this 'environmental quality standard' were acceptable and a legitimate use of the 'absorptive capacity of the environment'. As one of our policy papers put it: 'The capacity of the environment to receive wastes and render them harmless is a resource which we can use but must not mis-use.' The divergence, along with the question of how firm the scientific evidence must be before new actions were taken, was to be a major cause of debate as European environmental policy expanded in the late 1970s and early 1980s.

But all this was far ahead as 1973 gave way to 1974. UNEP remained my international priority, and in 1974 we held the first meeting of the Governing Council in its new home city, Nairobi. I found myself elected a Vice President – perhaps in recognition of that long negotiation over the programme a year before. It was a bit awkward, as my boss, John Jukes (Richard Chilver's successor as Deputy Secretary), was titular head of the UK Delegation, and somebody had to break the news of my elevation when he flew in a day or two later (I think that Jock Taylor, who had succeeded Ronald Arculus at the FCO, did the deed). We gathered in the new Kenyatta Conference Centre, in an auditorium that looked like a flying saucer about to take off. The Kenyan Foreign Minister, Dr Mungai, took the chair, Mzee Jomo Kenyatta gave a welcoming speech, and everything went smoothly. So smoothly that I have no recollection of the discussions!

It was my first visit to Kenya, and those were days when security was not a serious problem. We wandered around the town freely. Jock Taylor and Meg Rothwell took one of our two hired cars and went for a walk on the Ngong Hills before breakfast, encountering nothing more dangerous than a young buffalo. Fifteen years later, you had to leave a guard on your car and take another with you on your walk. We went to Nakuru National Park to see the immense flocks of pink flamingos that frequent this Rift Valley lake, feeding on the brine shrimps that abound in its shallow, salt-rich, water. We visited the larger sister lake at Naivasha with its numerous snorting hippos. We drove into the little Nairobi National Park, where you can see lions, cheetah, rhino, hippo, giraffe, buffalo, ostriches, zebra, wildebeeste and much else within sight of the towers of the city. We had a day at Tsavo, where vast numbers of elephants were clearly destroying the vegetation and heading for a disastrous population crash. And I got a snapshot of history when the British High Commissioner, Sir Antony Duff, took me to the State Opening of Parliament. President Kenyatta made a brief, eloquent, speech in English and a longer and obviously even more stirring one in Kiswahili. Afterwards, Antony Duff introduced me to the Vice-President, Daniel arap Moi, an ex-schoolmaster. He struck me as an honest, pedestrian, rather dull but dependable man, in vast contrast to the charismatic Kenyatta. There was no sign of the transformation that power would bring.

But I had been getting restless in the Central Unit. I think there were two main reasons for this. First, I was doing a great deal of international travelling, coming home tired out and scarcely seeing the family. Second, I felt that some of the fire had gone out of the action. We had pushed forward a number of useful international measures, and helped with reviews of policy at home (some of them leading to publications in our own *Pollution Papers* series). But we seemed to have lost the thrust of novelty and Prime Ministerial backing that ruled in 1970. We missed Peter Walker's drive and enthusiasm. The policy Directorates in DOE remained strongly sectoral and set in their ways. Environment protection was a rather small appendage to a massive Department dominated by highly visible political issues like housing, local government finance, planning and transport. These involved vast amounts of public expenditure, and exposed Ministers to intense public and Parliamentary scrutiny, so it was understandable that they gave them priority. We had also lost Solly Zuckerman and his demanding pressures. The gadfly's nippers were getting blunt. The cows were developing immunity.

All these were niggles rather than strong convictions, for in other ways I enjoyed life in CUEP, ensconced high in the northernmost of the Three Terrible Towers and looking from my desk over Westminster Abbey, the Houses of Parliament, the bend of the river, St. James's Park and Buckingham Palace. But there were domestic concerns as well. Robert was clearly unhappy at Haileybury, the famous public school near our home in Hoddesdon, where we had sent him partly because my boyhood hero, Bill Stewart, assistant to Father in Brighton, was now Master. We were not happy about the school prospects for David either. And over the horizon came a new opportunity. NERC – yes, NERC – now chaired by my old supervisor Professor Jimmie Beament, was looking for a Director for the Institute of Terrestrial Ecology, and that Director could be based either in Cambridge or at Monks Wood. I phoned Jimmie and declared an interest. Lizzie had a long talk with Father (by now retired) who was taking a keen interest in David's education. He leaped at the bait.

'I can think of nothing that would make me happier,' he wrote, 'than you being back in Cambridge, and David going to the Perse.'

But that telescopes a lot of history. What was the Institute of Terrestrial Ecology? It hadn't been there when I left the Nature Conservancy for the Central Unit in 1970.

In 1971, in the midst of preparations for the Stockholm Conference, Duncan Poore and I met for lunch. He looked grave, but also excited.

'The Conservancy has passed a resolution asking Ministers to take us out of NERC,' he said. 'We are clear that conservation is a matter of national environmental policy. It has to be based on research, but most of the things we do don't fit in a Research Council. We ought to come under the Secretary of State for the Environment.'

I remember agreeing in principle that he had to be right. Conservation of habitats and species involved land use policies. There was a clear relationship between the work of the NC and that of the National Parks Commission which did come under the DOE, and there were also links with town and country planning which absorbed a good deal of Departmental manpower. But I expected problems. There were.

One central problem was that the Chairman of the Nature Conservancy, Lord Howick, opposed the resolution passed by an overwhelming majority of his colleagues. Far from feeling bound by their collective decision, he urged the NERC Council to ask Margaret Thatcher, as Secretary of State for Education and Science, to reject it. I remain surprised by this, for I remember Evelyn Howick as an honourable man: in his place I hope that I would have resigned. For his part Ray Beverton saw ways of turning the revolt to advantage. He told the Council that the problem arose from a fundamental defect in NERC's own Charter, which required them to establish a Committee called the Nature Conservancy and could be read as giving the latter a measure of autonomy. Vero Wynne Edwards, as Chairman of NERC, wrote to the Prime Minister in October 1971 dissenting from the Conservancy's judgement but announcing an internal committee of enquiry under Dr Cyril Lucas, Director of the Marine Research Laboratory at Aberdeen. Lucas talked to NC staff and found that most of the research branch, headed by Kenneth Mellanby, wanted to stay in a Research Council. Many were angry that Duncan Poore had not consulted them, although it is hard to see how he could have done so without breaching confidentiality with Conservancy members. Cyril Lucas concluded that the Conservancy should stay in NERC, abandon its role as a pressure group for conservation, and focus on research on scientific issues relating to land use change.

In November 1971 Lord Rothschild played his hand. Victor Rothschild – who had lectured to me in Cambridge twenty years earlier on fertilization, with especial reference to sea urchins – had long since moved from academia, first to head Shell's corporate research and then to lead the Government's 'Think Tank' – the Central Policy Review Staff in the Cabinet Office. One of the first reviews he had done concerned research. How could value be secured for the vast sums of public money then spent in Government laboratories, Research Councils and the like? His answer was a 'read across' from the private sector. Give the money to the people that needed the knowledge research should provide – 'the customers'. Let them commission the research from the laboratories – 'the contractors' – whether they be Government labs, Research Councils, Universities or even industrial centres. This would establish a market and let the customer choose the contractor that seemed best able to deliver quality and relevance, at the right time and at least cost. Enshrine the relationship in a written agreement – a contract. So came the 'customer-contractor principle' that was all the rage in Government research after the Rothschild report was published.

There was an obvious lesson here for the Conservancy, and Rothschild made it explicit in his Report. He said that 'the whole of the countryside programme should be financed by the DOE and the Scottish Development Department.' He considered that these Departments should become the Nature Conservancy's paymasters. The Government seized on these proposals, Alan Cottrell became a channel for people's comments, and in March 1972 the House of Commons Select Committee on Science and Technology took evidence. Duncan Poore argued for complete independence under the most appropriate Minister (obviously the Secretary of State for the Environment). The new Chairman of NERC, Sir Fred Stewart, said that his Council, including Lord Howick, believed that the NC should stay in NERC.

In the summer of 1972 Ministers decided that the conservation functions of the Conservancy should indeed come under DOE. It would be reconstituted as a new Quango (Quasi-Autonomous Non-Governmental Organization) with a part-time salaried Chairman and members appointed by the Secretary of State for the Environment. The issue was whether the research side should move with their conservation colleagues or stay in NERC. Neville Heaton, a recently retired DOE Deputy Secretary who had held the Countryside Policy portfolio, was appointed to advise Ministers on a solution. I remember arguing with him (as Duncan Poore also did) that some at least of the research should go into the new Quango, thus preserving the combination of science and operations that was such a unique feature of the Conservancy and reached back to Huxley and Tansley. But, prompted by Rothschild, Ministers decided otherwise. The research branch was to be left in NERC as an Institute of Terrestrial Ecology. Money was to be transferred from NERC to the NCC for the latter to use to commission the research it wanted. The Nature Conservancy Council Act of 1974 followed, splitting the Conservancy asunder. Sir David Serpell, not long retired from DOE, became the first Chairman of NCC, with a hidden mission 'to teach them sound administration and proper Civil Service behaviour'. Duncan Poore, whose boats had been irretrievably burned by the confrontation with NERC, departed to work for the International Union for Conservation of Nature and Natural Resources in Switzerland.

Bob Boote became Director of NCC, and Ian Prestt left CUEP to become his Deputy. I left to direct ITE.

Jim Jones urged me not to do it. 'It's not only that we want you to stay here,' he said. 'It's that it's never any good warming up cold porridge. You've really done that job already. You'll find NERC very frustrating after having been the supremo of UK international environmental policy. Don't do it. I can re-jig your work here if you need a change after four years.'

I didn't listen, but in many ways he was right. Although there were good family reasons, and although David did go to the Perse School, and then to Cambridge's wonderful Hills Road Sixth Form College, it was one of my career mistakes although it might have worked out had I stuck to it. But in April 1974 I found myself back in NERC (though on secondment from DOE). There I was, back in charge of Furzebrook and Merlewood, Monks Wood and Banchory, and a new station at Penicuik near Edinburgh that had been built to house the NERC Tree Biology Unit under Professor Fred Last. There I was with John Jeffers as my Deputy, Jack Dempster (Kenneth Mellanby's successor) as senior zoologist, and Fred Last as senior botanist. The four of us were to be a Management Group, overseeing programme strategy and scientific quality.

ITE presented one of the challenges you often find in a scientific institution. How to weld a scatter of 300 scientists from different disciplines, located at ten different places, with widely varying temperaments and work styles, into a coherent whole? And there was a new challenge faced by all manner of research establishments at that time – how to impose a customer-contractor system on scientists whose work had hitherto been largely self-chosen and self-driven?

With Ray Beverton's advice and help we established a discipline-based hierarchy. The primary dichotomy was into a Division of Plant Ecology and one of Animal Ecology. They had various sub-divisions. These met occasionally for what were really specialist symposia. The institute was directed professionally by the Heads of Division and Subdivision, although in a day to day sense 'the boss' was the Officer in Charge of the station where someone worked (rather as in BAS, where the geologists had all been responsible professionally to Ray Adie, the atmospheric scientists to Joe Farman and the biologists to me, but everyone on a Base was under the authority of the Base Leader).

I think the system worked – more or less – and did build cohesion and some sense of identity. But there was an inevitable tension. Research scientists are there because they have original ideas. Their chief wish is to get on with their experiments and observations. Most of them hate spending time in talk-sessions, unless the subject is close to their research and will help it forward. And gathering fifty people from all over even a small country like Britain for a divisional meeting costs a lot of money as well as disrupting a lot of timetables.

But the customer-contractor business demanded tight management. The chief difficulty was that scientific research is not like the manufacture of a commodity. Whatever the inspiration:perspiration ratio, you cannot do without the former. Unless the problem the customer has also inspires the researcher, good commissioned work is unlikely. If researchers have curiosity, drive and skill, it may be wholly destructive to take them off work that excites them simply because a customer won't pay for it. We tried to shield the best creative scientists by supporting them from the substantial funds that NERC retained for basic research, but we also had to earn back the money transferred from NERC to the new NCC. We decided that we had to know what every researcher was up to, so that we could charge for time spent. Everyone therefore had to produce a project plan for each significant bit of work. It had to have a title. An objective. Methods. Locations. Timetable – set out as a 'critical path network' showing how the stages inter-related, and depended on one another, and where the whole thing should have got to at particular times. And it had to include 'criteria for success' – the achievements by which the project should be judged.

The Management Group examined every Project Plan and often suggested changes. John Jeffers then put the reference number, lead researcher, title, and points on the critical path into the computer. People started getting little postcards from Merlewood:

'1 March 1975. Project 101 should be at stage 2. What stage has actually been reached? If there is delay, what are the reasons? If changes are proposed, what are they?'

People didn't like it. 'Fussy bureaucracy!' 'This is no way to do research!' 'Bloody interference!' 'Get lost!' Or words to those effects. But the customer-contractor system made something like this inevitable. Even so, a fly appeared in Rothschild's ointment. The transfer to the NCC of money to commission research had been seen by NERC as a paper transaction, and it had been assumed (unwisely) that the conservation agency would still get its research from its old research branch, now ITE. But markets don't work that way. Derek Ratcliffe, as NCC Chief Scientist, found that ITE did not cover all the topics on which he now needed knowledge, while NERC's overhead charges were much higher than those of a University. He began to shop around, just as Rothschild had intended. That in turn meant that to keep staff in employment, ITE had to find other customers – and to close down areas of research that nobody would pay for, or stations that were uneconomic to operate. Again, people didn't like it.

There were, of course, good moments. It was fun to be once more concerned with the British countryside and with ecology. To visit lovely places. To have more time in our sunny Cambridge house that looked across open fields to the gentle chalk upland of the Gog Magog Hills. But there were negatives. One of the most extraordinary was NERC's failure to use my four years' experience both in central Government and as an international negotiator. Ray Beverton was always a friend, and we got on well together, but institutionally he was quite stand-offish. Certain things were done by Headquarters, and certain things by Directors of Institutes, and that was that. Jim Jones was right: I had flopped back into a small pond, and the banks were too confining. But I *did* get a book about pollution written.

And there were occasional strange happenings. One of the strangest was at a scientific conference in Birmingham in 1975. Sir Peter Scott was there, in his capacity as Chancellor of the University. I knew him fairly well because the Nature Conservancy had supported the Wildfowl Trust at Slimbridge, which he had created, and one of my more enjoyable tasks had been to go and discuss their research with him and his Director, Geoffrey Matthews. From the Scotts' sitting room, with its vast picture window, there was a wonderful prospect of pools where duck and geese thronged. In winter it was full of Bewick's swans, which breed in the Arctic but spend the cold season on ice-free estuaries and meadows farther south. Peter and Philippa Scott had worked out a way of recognizing individual birds from the pattern on their black and yellow bills. I have one letter from Peter which says it all: '300 Bewicks swans in front of the window under the floodlights as I write – all known by name. It's a magical sight.'

Peter Scott is remembered as a fine naturalist, wildlife artist, pioneer of nature programmes on television, champion glider pilot, Olympic yachtsman and dashing commander of small naval vessels in the second World War. He was all those things and more. Energetic, exuberant and dedicated, it was he that really created the Species Survival Commission of IUCN (the World Conservation Union) and with Max Nicholson he was the force behind the World Wildlife Fund (now World Wide Fund for Nature). But once in a while his open mind, linked to his enthusiasm, led him into trouble. Never more so than in 1975 when he went public, initially at the Birmingham meeting, over the Loch Ness Monster.

There are legends of monsters (in Gaelic *each uisge* or water-horse) in several Scottish lochs, including Morar which, at over 300 metres, is the deepest in Britain. Similar tales attach to some Scandinavian fiords. Is anything there? To an ecologist the notion of a lot of big animals in a relatively small and unproductive lake like Loch Ness is inherently improbable. If they were air-breathing they would have to surface to 'blow' and surely they would be seen quite often? If they were prehistoric survivors they must have lived outside their present habitats for most of their history, for Ness and Morar were filled with solid glacier ice until around fifteen thousand years ago. To sustain a viable population there would have to be dozens of them at any time, and surely some bodies would have been washed up?

But the notion of an animal mystery like Nessie appeals to the romantic in most of us – it is something we would *like* to be true. And in the 1950s and 1960s there were some remarkable discoveries of 'living fossils' like the big coelacanth fishes in the deeps of the South Indian Ocean. In 1972 Dr Robert Rines of the Massachusetts Institute of Technology lowered flash-equipped cameras into Loch Ness and took some strange pictures at a time when sonar screens in the boat above suggested that two large moving objects were scattering small ones, presumably fish, before them. Two pictures showed what looked like a diamond-shaped flipper or paddle attached to a rough-skinned body. In 1975 more cameras caught images that at least looked like parts of a large animal. Peter sketched them for me as we talked in Birmingham, and said that the Curator of Reptiles and Amphibians at the Smithsonian Institution in Washington DC and the Professor of Comparative Zoology at Harvard agreed. Some critics did begin to suggest, however, that they were waterlogged tree trunks.

Peter Scott was convinced that the pictures provided evidence of a large animal in Loch Ness. He thought that it might look like a plesiosaur (a long-necked, air-breathing aquatic dinosaur). He felt that there was enough evidence to lay before a scientific meeting and the Royal Society of Edinburgh, Heriot-Watt University and the University of Edinburgh agreed to convene one. But before it happened the media erupted in frenzy. The sponsors withdrew. The meeting was transferred to the House of Commons, hardly the best venue for science. Scott and Rines published a paper in *Nature* explaining the evidence and giving Nessie a scientific name, *Nessiteras rhombopteryx* (the Ness monster with the diamond-shaped fin). The media promptly delighted in the fact that the Latin name is an anagram of 'monster hoax by Sir Peter S' although Rines countered by pointing out that the letters also spell 'yes both pix are monsters. R.'

Peter and I exchanged letters about this in December 1975. He wrote a full account of the story. With hindsight he felt that one problem had been over-enthusiasm on the part of Bob Rines, coupled with obscurity in the photographs themselves. Peter's judgement was that 'the 1975 pictures could conceivably be gnarled tree trunks floating in mid-water, which the 1972 flippers could not. On the other hand some and perhaps all the 1975 pix <u>could</u> be part of an animal . . . In my view the 1972 flippers can only be animal.' He was in no doubt of Rines' integrity.

A balanced conclusion by an honourable man. It has all been quiet since then. Myself, I would love to see a plesiosaur in Scotland, and it would create the biggest ecotourist boom on the planet. But I don't think I ever will.

Early in 1976, not long after I had received Peter Scott's letter and account, Margaret Moxham, my PA, came in. 'DOE on the line. Sir Ian Bancroft would be grateful if you would pop in to see him. His office suggests next Wednesday at 11.00. OK?'

Ian Bancroft had taken over as Permanent Secretary from Jim Jones. He came to the point.

'Joe Lyons is retiring in July. We need a new Director General of Research. We'd like you to do it. It means promotion to Deputy Secretary. You would be Head of Profession for our scientists and line manager for about 2500 people at the three laboratories – Building Research (which includes Fire Research and the Forest Products Laboratory at Prince's Risborough), Hydraulics Research at Wallingford, and Transport and Road Research near Bracknell. And you'll have to manage a research budget of around £50 million a year . . .'

CHAPTER SEVEN

Science and Policy

I TOOK THE JOB. I think it was a mistake. First, almost all the research at the various stations was on aspects of the physical sciences and engineering, about which I had only a layman's knowledge (I think this was lost on Ian Bancroft and the other top Civil Servants, for whom a scientist was a scientist). Second, it had very little to do with converting science into policy, as we had done in the Central Unit.

I found that DOE had taken Rothschild seriously. There were three Departmental Research Programme Review Committees – one combining the Environment and Transport sides of the Department (or the two Departments after Transport was separated in the summer of 1976), and one for each separately. There were also two independent 'external' Research Advisory Councils, CHRAC and PATRAC, dealing respectively with Construction and Housing, and Planning and Transport. There were 15 Research Requirements Committees where 'customers' (mostly Under and Assistant Secretaries from the policy Directorates) and 'contractors' (mostly from our own laboratories) met to discuss what should be done and how much should be paid for it. The research was divided into 84 subject areas. The machinery was run by a Director of Research Requirements, Bill Reiners, himself a specialist in building operations and economics. His Directorate had five staff Divisions, each covering a fairly homogeneous group of RRCs, while a Research Administration Division supported the Director General of Research (me) in various ways.

My predecessor, Dennis ('Joe') Lyons, was a physical scientist, had been Director of TRRL and was most interested in how the research establishments were run and the quality of the work they did. He was happy to leave the policy side to Bill Reiners. But this didn't work for me, as a biologist who couldn't really judge the physical sciences and was anyway more interested in how the results of the research were converted into action. I paid my routine visits to the labs, and enjoyed the education they gave me, but I never felt that I was really one of the team. The Directors – Jimmy Dick at BRE, Alec Silverleaf at TRRL, and Robert Russell at HRS – were all friendly and welcoming, but I sensed that they felt the same way. And perhaps there was a touch of foreboding, for as Ian Bancroft had put it when I was appointed: 'The main trouble is, you're much too young. You

could be in the job for fifteen years, if you stay through to retirement at 60.'
Bill Reiners supported me loyally, but it was difficult for him too, as I was
clearly much more interested in what had been his unchallenged 'patch'.
And we began to have cuts – in manpower and resources. The white hot
tide of technological revolution was turning and the Government – by now
once again Labour – trimmed our manpower and expenditure as part of an
economy programme. It was the start of a squeeze that continued for the
whole of my remaining time in the Civil Service. In the process much of the
structure Joe Lyons and Bill Reiners had built up was demolished again. In
my first year, we cut the RRCs down to six, dealing respectively with
Planning and Countryside; Housing; Building; Environmental Protection;
Highways and Road Safety; and Transport Planning and Transport
Industries. The subject areas were compressed to 62. Bill was not happy, and
took early retirement.

The job took me outside DOE, for it meant automatic membership of
the Research Council system – of NERC, of the Science Research Council
and of the Advisory Board for the Research Councils which presided over
collective policy and allocated funds. So, in a month or so I was translated
from a Director under NERC to a member of its Council – and
immediately I made a serious mistake.

The Council welcomed me warmly. But one of the earliest pieces of
business was who should replace me at ITE. To start with, I took the correct
low profile. Then came the crunch. A sub-Committee had recommended
that John Jeffers be appointed. Some members of the Council wanted a top
research ecologist rather than a statistician with a reputation as a rather
demanding manager. It got heated. I was asked for a view. I commended
John. Debate continued. I allowed myself to become irritated, and made a
badly-judged intervention to the effect that as a customer for work at ITE,
our Department would be disturbed if a competent leader, recommended by
a properly constituted appointments Committee, was set aside for reasons of
personal prejudice. That did it. The matter was settled in John's favour, but
the atmosphere was soured. I was held to have used threatening language,
and Professor Richard West, head of the Department of Botany at
Cambridge, resigned from NERC in protest. I had been on friendly terms
with Richard for over twenty years, and was very cross with myself!

The Research Council world proved to be far from harmonious. Indeed
some of the bodies I attended seemed to have been designed for confrontation. The Science and Engineering Research Council (as SRC became) had
four Boards, two of which dealt with 'big science' (the Astronomy, Space
and Radio Board and the Nuclear Physics Board) and two with 'smaller'
science (Science Board and Engineering Board). The first two demanded

massive installations, while the others worked largely through University support. When it came to bidding for funds it sounded rather like a street market, as the Chairs pressed their superior claims or denigrated their critics.

'The future of this country, as a serious contributor to fundamental science, depends on our making a full contribution to the Large Electron-Positron collider at CERN in Geneva/the Joint European Torus for nuclear fusion research at Culham/the European Space Agency/the UK Infra Red Telescope at Hawaii . . .' the refrain would go.

'These massive projects are siphoning off resources that would support far more productive science in the Universities, and much more of it because the money would go so much further,' came the counterblast. 'We should cease this juvenile preoccupation with glamorous big gadgets . . .'

It was entertaining (at times) but I am not sure that it was a mechanism for sound judgement.

Rather similarly, the Advisory Board for the Research Councils was structured for 'creative tension'. There were three kinds of member – the HORCs (Heads of Reseach Councils), the Departmental Chief Scientists, and the so-called Independents. The first two blocks had obvious vested interests – the former to win as much as they could for their own outfits, and the latter to get funds allocated to match Departmental priorities. But the 'Independents' – mostly from Universities, but with one or two industrialists – were just as prone to canter off on their pet hobby-horses, and especially the stallion of University advancement. There were times when people talked right past one another, leaving the Chairman and the Secretariat from the Department of Education and Science, headed by Deputy Secretaries Walter Ulrich and Richard Bird, to pick what consensus they could from the cacophony.

A great deal of the research for which I was responsible bore on major policy questions – that, of course, was why we did it. Some remains relevant to the issues of today. For example, probably as a direct result of the OPEC cartel's elevation of oil prices in 1974, both TRRL and BRE were working on energy efficiency. TRRL research showed that the shock of a steep rise in the price of petrol led drivers to drop their top cruising speed to a more economical 50-55 m.p.h. But this reaction wore off, and speeds (and fuel use) rose again. However, increased motoring costs did lead people to defer buying a new car, and this was counter-productive in environmental terms since older cars were more polluting and less energy-efficient. Such experience made me sceptical of a later proposal by the Royal Commission on Environmental Pollution for a 'fuel duty escalator' which deliberately increased the tax on petrol at a faster rate than inflation. I feared that rather than persuade people to switch from their cars to their feet, their bicycles or public transport, it would prolong the life of dirty old bangers.

TRRL also did pioneer research on road pricing. The idea is simple, and very logical. The road network ('infrastructure') is provided by the community as a whole. If people were charged so much a mile for using it, and the charge was highest on congested city roads, lower on motorways, and least on country roads, there would be an incentive to use the network efficiently, and maybe to switch to buses on town routes where cars were excessively expensive.

The problem was that to make it work throughout the country every car and every lorry would have to have some kind of meter, tripped by roadside or road-bed devices that indicated which price zone the vehicle was in. (You would feed the meter with credit cards bought at petrol stations or post offices, just as pay-as-you-go mobile phones are now fed.) The cost of equipping every vehicle and price-zone boundary was seen as excessive – and what happened if meters went wrong, or tourists came into the country with un-metered vehicles?

BRE was also working on how to use energy more efficiently in buildings. Indeed it had built a terrace of three houses specially for the purpose. These explored the possible merits of solar panels, exchangers that drew heat from air leaving the house to warm air coming in, and heat pumps that worked like back-to-front refrigerators, drawing low-grade heat from outdoors and concentrating it to warm the interior. This and other research showed that there were cheap and easy ways of making houses more energy-efficient, some (like loft insulation and reflective sheets on the walls behind radiators) with a pay-back period measured in months. The work led to campaigns and grants to improve insulation, and to new building regulations that enforced higher standards. Even after twenty years, however, we have a long way to go. Yet increasing the efficiency of energy use in buildings would be the cheapest and most effective single means of helping to counteract global warming and its attendant climate change.

There was a vast array of other research. At TRRL, I saw work on the strength of box-girder bridges (there had been some tragic collapses) and puffed into one of the first breathalysers. At Hydraulics Research I marvelled at a massive model of the Thames Estuary, built to simulate the changes in tidal flow and height that would occur if the third London Airport was built on Maplin Sands. At Fire Research there were fascinating (and harrowing) studies demonstrating the dramatic speed at which suffocating and toxic smoke spreads through shopping malls. They used one of the vast airship hangars at Cardington, built to house the R100 and R101, for test burns of materials in specially-built small houses. At British Rail's

A visit to a Research Station. Martin Holdgate, as Director General of Research,
examines an electric moped at the Transport and Road Research Laboratory.
Photograph: TRRL.

laboratory at Derby, which we helped to finance, I discussed work on a new
battery which used sodium and sulphur in place of the traditional (and
heavy) lead-acid systems, but had the drawback that it worked at 300 degrees
Celsius – not the kind of system to expose if a vehicle crashed in a
rainstorm. And so on, through an immense and diverse portfolio of projects.

With the example of Solly Zuckerman in mind, and more immediate
experience in the Central Unit on Environmental Pollution, I naively
assumed that one job of the Departmental Chief Scientist would be to work
with specialists in the research laboratories to make sure that the results of
all these studies were presented to Ministers, with proposals for changes in
policy if the research clearly showed this to be sensible. In fact, I found that
as research supremo you hardly ever came into contact with Ministers.
Indeed, I scarcely met Peter Shore, who became my Secretary of State on
the Environment side, or Bill Rodgers who took the Transport job after the
DOE was split by Harold Wilson in the summer of 1976. I sent them
annual, formal, reports and saw them in larger meetings or when one or

other came on a visit to a Research Establishment. But research was seen as a service at one remove from policy, and my job was to manage a programme that cost around £40 million a year, not to interpret its results.

This separation was a direct consequence of Rothschild. His report had made the 'customers' – the policy Under Secretaries – the commissioners of research. It followed that it was for them to incorporate the information that research provided in the advice they gave to Ministers. This worked well enough in technical areas where the customers knew the scientists in the laboratories and were used to talking to them. For example, the people in DOE concerned with formulating Building Regulations worked closely with the specialists in the Building Research Establishment, and the links between the Highways side of the Department of Transport and the TRRL were also close. It worked less well when Under Secretaries felt that they had enough information to do their job, and did not want the delay or trauma of change that research could indicate. Some actively discouraged studies that might undermine policies only recently approved by Ministers. But either way, the Director General of Research had little opportunity to act as a departmental Chief Scientific Adviser in the Zuckerman mode. My job was completely different from that of the DOE Chief Economic Adviser, Humphrey Cole, who gave weekly briefings on current economic trends to meetings of Permanent and Deputy Secretaries, and was accepted as a commentator on a wide range of policy issues.

That was my difficulty. If I tried to 'do a Solly' and press a distinct scientific view, I cut across the machinery, and found myself intervening in the relationship between my own staff and the policy directorates that drew on their work. If I tried to inject some independent questioning into the policy-making process, I commonly ran up against barely-concealed irritation from fellow Deputy Secretaries, on whose patches I was trespassing. The job of Director General of Research was wrong for me, and I was wrong for it. Years afterwards I remember complaining to Alec Silverleaf that it was a non-job. 'I agree,' he said. 'That's why I turned it down . . .' The implication that I was given the job as something of a last resort did little for my self-esteem!

Looking back, I think the best contribution I could have made would have been to use the departmental Research Requirements Committees to debate what research was all about. We should have given them challenging policy papers that probed deep into the uncertainties of current knowledge and demonstrated the value of research in preparing for inevitable change. Our work in CUEP had demonstrated that it was difficult to control pollution unless you understood the properties of pollutants, the environmental media in which they dispersed and the sensitivity of the targets they attacked. The same kind of argument applied in many other fields of what were, essentially, science and technology-linked Departments. We could and should have used the external Advisory Committees, CHRAC and PATRAC, to bring sharp independent minds to bear on the Department's long-term problems. We should have added PERAC – Pollution and Environment Research Advisory Committee – instead of asking the Royal Commission to take time out from its studies to give occasional scrutiny to our pollution-related research. As it was, I look on the period between 1976 and 1980 as the least rewarding and least useful period in my professional life.

Besides the Research Council machinery, I found myself involved in a host of other committees. Only two stand out in memory: the National Electronics Council and the Civil Service Science Management Committee. The Electronics Council was the creation of Lord Mountbatten, who had been ahead of his time in understanding the importance of electronic communications in the Royal Navy, and had taken on almost a missionary role to promote other aspects of the electronics industry. The Council drew together industry, Whitehall, and the Services. By the time I joined it, however, I think it was some way behind the cutting edge: its components had all in various ways 'got the message'. But it was memorable because of Mountbatten himself. Even in his late 70s he was an imposing figure. He did not so much chair the meeting as loom over it. When he decided to retire, in around 1977, he secured Royal succession in the shape of HRH the Duke of Kent. Mountbatten came for his last meeting, doubtless en route to some glittering function, in gong-bedecked uniform as Admiral of the Fleet. The Duke was an excellent chairman, with a deeper knowledge of industry, but he never quite achieved the same presence!

The Civil Service Department's Science Management Committee was a total contrast. Its job was to advise on the management of the Science Group – that is, all scientists in Government. I was an ex-officio member, and eventually became Chairman. Much of its work was anodyne, but in 1978 there was anxiety about how some of Lord Rothschild's reforms were working out. He had tried to secure more movement of scientific professionals into management roles, as happened in industry and seemed obviously sensible in a Civil Service that had to deal with a host of technical issues. But the schemes he had called into being seemed to have failed. Why?

John Ashworth, who had become Chief Scientist in the Central Policy Review Staff (now headed by the economist Sir Kenneth Berrill following Rothschild's retirement), convinced Berrill, Sir John Hunt (then Secretary of the Cabinet) and Ian Bancroft (promoted from DOE to head the CSD) that we needed a review of the Scientific Civil Service. Five of us were given the task, with an excellent support team. We dug up a lot of information (the final report we published in 1980 runs to 140 pages, of which half are statistical and historical appendices). We found that although in that period, Government employed five per cent of the nation's scientists, it didn't seem very sure what to do with them. Like Rothschild, we emphasized that in today's world, scientific knowledge was indispensable in framing many aspects of Government policy. We agreed with him that in a modern technological society, more people trained in science should find their way to the top of the Civil Service. We argued that the careers of specialists should be managed to spot those whose longer-term futures lay in more general policy. We called for a lot of detailed changes in how scientists were recruited into Government and managed once they had got there. But by the time we reported the Government had changed again. Mrs Thatcher clearly had more fundamental worries about the Civil Service. Our report earned a coolly polite commendation from Paul Channon, then Minister at the Civil Service Department. Not long afterwards, Ian Bancroft was summarily retired to the House of Lords, and the Civil Service Department was abolished. I suspect our Report remains deeply buried under Whitehall dust.

The Chief Scientist job had one or two international appendages. The most curious was responsibility for funding, via the Royal Society, the UK contribution to IIASA, the International Institute for Applied Systems Analysis, housed in a beautiful former Imperial palace at Schloss Laxenburg near Vienna. IIASA was a product of the desire to warm the Cold War through east-west contacts in science. Systems analysis was hailed as an approach of common value. Teams based at IIASA built complex models of environmental and economic systems, designed to have greater realism than those used in the Club of Rome's book *Limits to Growth*. A massive energy systems model was compiled by a team led by Wolf Hafele of Germany. 'Buzz' Holling, Professor of Biology in British Colombia, led another team that looked at the assessment and management of environmental systems.

The Royal Society was responsible for certifying the scientific value to the UK of what was going on in Laxenburg. The Chair of the National Committee for IIASA when I took over as Chief Scientist and British paymaster was Sir Kingsley Dunham, Foreign Secretary of the Royal and Professsor of Geology at Durham. We used to attend Councils in Laxenburg once or twice a year, hearing presentations of the research, discussing plans and budgets, and winding up with a social evening at a local hostelry where the wine flowed freely. It was all quite congenial.

But things changed sharply in around 1981. First, Kingsley Dunham retired, and responsibility for IIASA affairs at the Royal Society passed to the Treasurer, Sir John Mason, Director General of the Meteorological Office and a hard-headed physical scientist with a much more challenging and sceptical attitude to the kind of work IIASA was doing. Second, IIASA got into hot political water.

The trouble was almost inevitable, given its structure as an east-west bridge. Not all the Soviet appointments to the staff were there purely for science. One of their senior administrators was picked up transferring secret envelopes on an Oslo street corner. More seriously, the on-line computer links between Moscow and Laxenburg and onward to Western institutions allowed Russian hackers to find out more than was tolerable of the workings of an American Super Cray computer. The United States pulled out of IIASA in a dudgeon. I was asked whether the UK should follow, and turned to the Royal Society Committee for advice. John Mason orchestrated a thumbs-down, and although the new Chairman of NERC, Sir Hermann Bondi, attempted a rescue mission the funds were cut and we withdrew. I am not sure that we lost anything much.

The General Election of 1979 which took Margaret Thatcher to Downing Street brought Michael Heseltine as Secretary of State for the Environment and Norman Fowler to the post at Transport, where he was supported by an energetic young Parliamentary Under Secretary called Kenneth Clarke. Their style was very different from that of other Ministers I had worked for. They began to probe deeply into the management of the Department, and into things that had previously been left to officials. Michael Heseltine clearly believed that the Civil Service had much to learn from the private sector. Whitehall hummed with an anecdote about how, as a young and new junior Minister at the Department of Trade and Industry under the Heath Government, he had opened up the theme at a meeting with the Department's most senior officials.

'I'm a great believer in the private sector!' he enthused. 'It gives great opportunities for young people to take responsibility and succeed. Look at me! By the time I was thirty I had made my first million!'

He turned to a small and rather insignificant-looking official standing nearby. 'What had you done by the time you were thirty?' he demanded.

'Well, Minister, I had let off three Atom Bombs,' replied the little man – Dr Ieuan Maddock, Chief Scientist and a distinguished nuclear physicist, who had been closely involved in testing Britain's nuclear deterrent.

It is not recorded whether Heseltine felt at all chastened. Certainly he did not weaken in his quest for more transparent and accountable management in the Civil Service. Soon after arrival in DOE he established MINIS – Management Information System for Ministers – which required a clear statement of the objectives, manpower and budget of each part of the Department and led to presentations at which Ministers could quiz officials about why they had set out priorities and taken action as they had. I had to explain the research programmes and their management.

My very first meeting with our new Secretary of State unloosed a cold wind of change. He went through our lists of research establishments, and associated ventures.

'Why do we spend nearly half a million a year in supporting this Centre for Environmental Studies?' he demanded. 'I am told that it is dominated by Marxists. The social research it does may be fine in the academic world, but it isn't Government's business. I want the place closed. You tell them I'm stopping their grant from the end of next year!'

DOE was represented on the Centre's Council by Wilfred Burns, the Chief Planner, and me. We broke the news to Professor Peter Willmott, who had just become the Director. I remember pointing out that it was beyond the power of Government to close the Centre, and suggesting to Peter Willmott that he had the option of finding new funds, at least for a scaled-down outfit. But he didn't, and the Centre closed.

'And why have I got all these Research Stations?' Heseltine went on. 'Building? Fire? Forest Products? Hydraulics? What do they all do? How do we decide their programme? Why can't they be privatised?'

I explained about the customer-contractor principle, and the role of Building and Fire Research in underpinning building and fire standards and providing an impartial, expert foundation for a fair range of Government policy. 'OK,' came the response. 'Set them on one side for the present. But this Hydraulics Research Station. What does it do?'

'Well, Secretary of State, it's a world leader in exploring whether engineering works on rivers or coasts, or in ports, will cause erosion and silting up. They build models – and do mathematical analyses. They've built a huge model of the Thames estuary to explore how an airport on Maplin Sands would affect sandbanks and coastlines elsewhere. They serve several Government Departments, and a lot of local authorities – and are contracted to work for many big engineering firms.'

'It sounds as if they could do all that – and be more flexible and competitive – in the private sector. Please go and privatise the Station!' Norman Calvert, the Chief Establishments Officer, and I did just that. It was tricky – especially maintaining staff and Trade Union confidence that the new employment and pension would be as good as the old – but it worked. HRS became Hydraulics Research Limited and succeeded. It set a precedent. Indeed, it was the beginning of a process of privatising, converting to semi-independent agencies, and cutting back the central

Government research estate which continued over the following twenty years.

Ken Clarke was also an exacting scrutineer of the Transport research programme. 'Why on earth are we doing all this?' he demanded. 'It may be very interesting, but how does it improve government *policy*? How does it deliver value for money?'

I tried a reasoned explanation, but fate was not always on my side, and things always seemed to go wrong at the worst moment. For example, the Ministers and senior Civil Servants in the Department of Transport went on retreat one weekend to a residential conference centre in Woking. The idea was to have a frank, confidential, review of the policies of the Department. That Saturday the press chose to make a joke out of one of our research projects. It was a study of traffic lights that could be operated by farmers to allow cows to cross busy main roads for milking (there are quite a lot of them now). The papers thought it funny. There were cartoons of elegant cattle pressing buttons and of be-smocked yokels with pitchforks holding up the M1. 'Cows ...' said Norman Fowler, with irritated contempt. I felt myself sunk in a very deep country pancake indeed. As for Kenneth Clarke, the special thing I learned about him that weekend was that he is an enthusiastic and unscrupulous player of croquet, even under floodlights at 10 p.m. The tough unscrupulousness under a charming exterior was probably just right when he became Chancellor of the Exchequer.

MINIS led to changes in how the DOE research programme worked. By 1981 we had transferred to the 'customer' policy directorates the responsibility for evaluating their needs, developing their proposed programmes *and* getting Ministerial approval for them *before* their contractors were commissioned to do the work. Ministers came directly into the decision loop. It did make for more critical probing of need and uncertainty, but it left the Chief Scientist with even less to do.

There were diversions, most of them as a hang-over from my past work in Antarctica and the Central Unit. In 1979 I was asked by a former colleague in the Scott Polar Research Institute, Hilda Richardson, to give a keynote address on the world environment to Soroptimists International of which she was then President – '2000 professional women and you', as Lizzie put it. When she learned that the meeting was in Hawaii she came along with enthusiasm, and we used some of our holiday time to visit the marvellous island of Maui (then scarcely scathed by the tourist boom), with its magnificent endemic silversword plants glimpsed through the mists on the rim of the great caldera of Haleakala. I was delighted to meet my old plant friend from Gough and Chile, *Sophora*, high on the Hawaiian mountains. We drove around the active lavas on the south side of the Big

The World Environment reviewed! The three Editors of UNEP's volume answer questions. From left: Mohamed Kassas (Egypt); Martin Holdgate (United Kingdom) and Gilbert White (United States). Photograph: Steve Jackson, Nairobi.

Island. We made contact with the SERC scientist in charge of building the UK Infra Red Telescope on the crater rim of Mauna Kea, and drove up there with him, from sea level to 3900 metres, pausing for lunchtime acclimatization on the way. He had been working there for months, but had never trudged round the crater rim to the highest summit. We did it together, puffing up the loose cinders.

Despite the return to a Whitehall desk, Cambridge remained home and both Lizzie and I got very used to long waits at the station as unreliable trains contended with leaves on the line, signal failures and the wrong kind of snow. Clearly the system was in an advanced stage of decomposition. But we couldn't move because David was in mid-school and from around 1982 we had another responsibility – Mulumba.

It had all started two years earlier at a parents' evening at the Perse. Lizzie found herself sitting alongside an African couple, and got into conversation. They were refugees from Uganda. Professor Matthias Semakula Kiwanuka had been Dean of the History Faculty at Makerere University – one of Africa's academic jewels – until Idi Amin asked him to write a new history of the country. There was no doubt about who was to be the great hero. Matthias chose exile – but getting himself, his wife Regina and five children

safely away was no easy matter. Regina ended up walking through the bush
for two days with their youngest, Mulumba. All went well and they were
now in Cambridge, but obviously a new job was paramount. Matthias found
it in Nigeria – and that posed a new dilemma since Mulumba was at King's
College Choir School. Would we have him to live with us during the
holidays? Of course – and that is how an engaging little Ugandan with an
outsize supply of charm found himself mimicking a Lancashire accent in
Blackpool and talking to black-faced sheep in Cumbria ('I thought they'd
like to see another black face!' he explained). The gender balance in our
household became even more lop-sided, with Lizzie surrounded by five
males (the fifth being our loving, dim-witted, Labrador, Hy).

Around 1980, UNEP's tentacles extended. Mostafa Tolba, Maurice
Strong's successor as Executive Director, was thinking about how to mark
the tenth anniversary of Stockholm in 1982. He decided to propose a 'Session
of Special Character' of the UNEP Governing Council. As background, he
commissioned a major review of what had happened to the world
environment in the decade, and I was asked to serve on the international
steering committee and to be one of three Editors of the volume. I wanted to
do it – but how could such a commitment be compatible with a full time job
in DOE and DTp? I persuaded my Permanent Secretaries that thanks to all
the cuts and reconstruction the job of Director General of Research was no
longer full time. They agreed I could devote some six weeks (or perhaps two
months) to the UNEP tasks, provided that my salary was repaid to the
Department and the British taxpayer. With two old friends, Gilbert White of
the USA and Mohamed Kassas of Egypt, I attended meetings of the steering
committee, mostly in Geneva, pored over and re-wrote text, and spent many
days in Nairobi as the three-man editorial team converged on the final
version. We were due to present it to a Workshop in March 1981.

It was not a good time, because Father was very ill. He had been operated
on for colonic cancer in 1965, six months before retiring as Headmaster of
Arnold School. Despite the nuisance of a colostomy, he had made a good
recovery and embarked on an active retirement. At 79, he was up the ladder
painting our gutters in Cambridge. Then, suddenly, a new inoperable cancer
presented itself. He responded with detachment and dignity. Instructions
were given about the management of his affairs and about the kind of
funeral he wanted. 'Don't waste money on a gravestone,' he instructed.
'They are a confounded nuisance. I want to be cremated and scattered.
Don't mind where. Have a simple family funeral. If the School want a
Memorial Service afterwards, that's up to your Mother, you and them.' I
was told firmly to go ahead with the visit to Nairobi meanwhile. Lizzie
promised to see that I went.

On 11 March I was at Heathrow. I knew that Father was due to come home after a period in hospital, and hoped that the news implied a remission. I rang Mother.

'Bad news,' she said bluntly. 'Dad died about half an hour ago.'

He died in his own bed, with a glass of whisky at his elbow, and Mother and his sister Evelyn nearby. The school he had led for twenty-eight years lined the avenue as his coffin was driven past. He had his own way about the arrangements – and as I had been instructed, I went off to Nairobi just a week late.

But when the job was over, and the big volume duly presented, the Permanent Secretaries remembered that I had time on my hands. So they began to load other responsibilities onto me. 'Martin, Peter Scott-Malden is retiring. We want you to look after the Countryside Directorate . . .' That was in 1981. 'Martin, with the slimming of the research programme, we think there is no need for a full time Deputy Secretary to direct research in DOE. We would like you to devote half your time to policy work. We're giving you the Air, Noise and Wastes Directorate and your old Central Directorate on Environmental Pollution.' I became Richard Chilver revisited. And so it went on. I began to feel rather like a racehorse, being given more weight. But it did add to my interest and enjoyment, and it did mean a lot more work directly for and with Ministers.

The breadth of this expanding portfolio makes writing about it extremely difficult. Every week brought a confusion of themes – science issues, conservation issues, pollution issues, waste disposal issues, radioactive concerns, and at the end of my time in DOE, water policy issues as well. And international demands jostled with national ones. The only way I can hope to make sense of them in the remainder of this Chapter is to take them theme by theme, treating the whole period between 1982 and my departure from DOE in 1988 as one block of time.

So let me start by getting my polar past finally disposed of. This was a period of intense debate over what should be done to regulate the use of Antarctic minerals. Brian Roberts had seen it all coming years before, and had proposed that an international Convention be negotiated to control mineral exploration and protect the environment from damage during any subsequent exploitation. He argued that this had to be done before discoveries piled on the economic pressure. In 1977 I had been 'loaned' by DOE to the Foreign and Commonwealth Office to chair an expert group on the subject, held in conjunction with an Antarctic Treaty meeting in London. In 1979 we convened a broader and less formal group at the Rockefeller Institute's lovely conference centre at Bellagio, on Lago di Como. Here, at 'the point that divides the winds' and looks up-lake to the

Antarctic conference at Estación Teniente Marsh in 1982.
Bunny Fuchs, pipe in hand, in discussion with Finn Sollie.

mountains, Pliny the Younger had had his villa. Here we debated, especially, the ecological impacts of mineral exploration and exploitation in the far south.

These early meetings established four main points. First, no significant deposits of oil or ore were known to exist anywhere in Antarctica. Second, by analogy with other southern continents, such deposits were none the less likely to be there – although with 98 per cent of the continent covered by ice, orefields on land were likely to be deeply buried. In the Ross Sea there were three sedimentary basins that looked as if they could contain oil or gas fields, but vast tabular icebergs floated across them in summer and in winter the whole area was closed by pack. So – as the third consensus point – exploration and exploitation would be technically difficult and exceedingly costly and only likely to be attractive if world oil and mineral prices rose because more accessible deposits were exhausted. Finally, most scientists and almost everyone else who treasured Antarctica as the world's greatest wilderness recoiled at the mess, pollution and disturbance that mineral industries would bring.

But the debate about the future of the Antarctic remained lively. The Chileans decided that it should be carried forward at a Conference they proposed to hold *in* the Antarctic, at their station Eduardo Frei on King

George Island in the South Shetland group, in 1982. I was asked to give a paper on environmental issues.

We (the party included Bunny Fuchs, George Knox, Gordon Robin, Ray Adie and about fifty others) met at Santiago. The city had changed a lot since George and I were there twenty years before. Gone were the clear airs and views of the mountains. Smog ruled, even from the top of the Cerro San Cristobal, 300 metres above the plain. We flew to Punta Arenas (and George and I peered through broken clouds to look for old haunts as we went). We were loaded into a Hercules, and headed out over Cape Horn (with a good view of Isla Navarino), and bumped down on a snowy runway at Frei. It was October, and too early in the spring for much plant life to be visible, but there were plenty of seals and birds. We visited several bases, including one on the Antarctic mainland, and it was wonderful to be there again.

Bunny Fuchs was undoubtedly the star of the show. Nobody could have guessed that he was already 75 years old. He exuded energetic youthfulness. The 25th Anniversary of the Crossing of Antarctica was celebrated by his giving a lecture and showing a film. He brooded over the meeting: his remarks were infrequent but to the point, and they often pulled loquacious diplomats down to the bedrock of common sense.

A little over a year later I was asked to review the Use and Abuse of Polar Environmental Resources for a workshop at the Pacific Science Congress in Dunedin, New Zealand. Rather at the last moment, they also asked for a more general address on the state of the world environment, based on the big UNEP review volume. Lizzie and I decided to take our main annual holiday in the southern rather than the northern summer. We flew to Sydney, had a day's sightseeing, and went on across the Tasman Sea, watching the long white wall of the Southern Alps heave up over the rim of the ocean and resolve itself into snow and cloud-capped mountains. In Christchurch, we stayed with George and Dorothea Knox and I visited the Botanic Gardens with Eric Godley. Nigel and Margaret Wace joined us for a journey over Arthur's Pass and down the west coast of the South Island past the Franz Josef and Fox Glaciers, which like those in Southern Chile come down almost to sea level in latitude 44 South. We pushed into green, wet, southern beech forests (with tree ferns). I sensed in reverse the excitement the New Zealanders had felt when they first saw the forests of southern Chile, and saw how similar life was in these sundered fragments of bygone Gondwanaland.

In Dunedin we met Willy Kuschel and Bill Watters. We had dinner with Father's cousin, Professor Will Morrell, an authority on colonial history in the Pacific. And we went with a zoologist, John Darby, to the dramatic beaches of the Otago Peninsula, where we visited the only mainland colony of Royal albatross, saw Yellow-eyed penguins (on which John was doing research), were chased by a quarrelsome young Hooker's Sea lion bull and watched Fur seals playing in the surf just like humans – paddling out, picking up an incoming swell, riding the breaking crest, and swimming back for more. And so, out of the green, cool moisture to a hot dry Canberra, and first sights of Platypus and Spiny anteater (*Echidna*) at the nature reserve of Tidbinbilla. It made me nostalgic again for the old life as a biogeographer and ecologist at the bottom end of the world.

Not to be outdone by the Chileans, the United States convened a further conference *on* Antarctica *in* Antarctica in January 1985. 'Get yourself to Christchurch, New Zealand,' they said. 'We'll do the rest.' The party gathered at the US Antarctic Research Program facility at Christchurch airport for kitting out. To my surprise it included another old Arnold School boy, Ken Croasdale, now based in Canada as an oil industry engineer. Eight hours drone this time, in a Hercules with service webbing seats (but with a Portaloo strapped in the cargo hold, because ladies were present). It was slow because the aircraft had to be equipped with skis, and they added immensely to the drag. The last hour was relieved by wonderful views of the mountains of Queen Victoria Land – the same ranges that led Ross, Scott and Shackleton to their landfall in McMurdo Sound. We set down and refuelled under the gentle, steaming volcanic cone of Mount Erebus. There were eight C-130 Hercules aircraft in a row on the Ross Ice Shelf at Williams Field. One had bent propellors, having dropped a ski into an unexpected crack in the ice.

The Americans had warned us that the meeting was to be in a field camp with 'arduous conditions' and we had had to get medical chits of fitness. The camp, which they called 'South Beardmore Camp' was not actually on the Beardmore Glacier at all, but on a parallel ice stream, the Lennox King. We found five Jamesway huts (well-insulated, plastic-covered versions of the wartime Nissan hut) in a row on the ice. They were warm (indeed we had to turn the heating stove in the men's sleeping hut down and wedge the door open with a climbing boot to make the fug bearable). There was hot and cold running water. There were showers and flush loos. There was a bar (which we had drained almost dry by the time discussions ended). The meeting hut was comfortable, with table and chairs. It was real luxury-on-ice.

We were there four days. We made one local excursion, walking across the glacier to the nearest rock outcrops two miles away. For the Lennox King hereabouts is over twenty miles wide, smooth and snow covered, and such crevasses as exist are well filled or bridged. We were near its eastern flank,

The southernmost cricket game in the world. Geoff Larminie of BP hits out under the midnight sun, amid the Transantarctic Mountains.

where the Transantarctic mountains lift in cliffs and ice to Mount Kirkpatrick, 3500 metres high. On the other side of the glacier, flat-lying bands of rock rose to a great tableland of comparable height. And the sun shone right through the 24 hours, wheeling to a low point above the Polar Plateau, which we could just glimpse to southward.

Geoff Larminie of BP and Arthur Watts of the Foreign Office decreed a game of cricket. The Beardmore Casuals took on the Gondwanaland Occasionals – both teams with a core of players from Australia, New Zealand and the UK but with non-cricketing nations enlisted freely as well. I had sprained my wrist, by slipping when trying to pass from one hut to another in carpet slippers – easy enough had I not overlooked a small patch of smooth ice. So I umpired. The pitch was the ski-way of a C-130 (surely the heaviest roller ever used in the game!). The wickets were inked on a flat plank. The bails were cans of beer. The ball was soft (a hard one would have buried itself in the snow). Two overs were allowed per batsman. The temperature was about minus ten degrees and the umpire's beer froze during the game. Gondwanaland won – but although the *Guinness Book of Records* accepted it as the southernmost game of cricket ever played, they declined to include it in their volume, judging it a 'unique feat' rather than a competitive event. Perhaps they felt it just wasn't cricket.

But the jolly to end all jollies came when after three excellent and productive days our hosts decided to show us the South Pole. Two C-130s duly droned in, and soon we were airborne over the massive complex of mountains, crossing to look down on the Beardmore Glacier itself. Here Scott and Shackleton had forced their way to the Polar Plateau. It was an immense tangle of crevasses that brought their tales of hair-raising escape home vividly. Then, the last rock outcrops sank into the rising ice and a vast expanse of flat whiteness droned by. 'Great God,' Scott had written, 'this is an awful place.' We banked, lost height gently and bumped along the snow runway at South Pole station, almost 3000 metres above sea level.

What a contrast with Amundsen's and Scott's arrivals in December 1911 and January 1912! Scott got there after 76 days on the journey, and 69 camps. He found a bleak, featureless snow plateau marked only by the snow cairns, ski-tracks and tent left by his predecessor. He noted the details: 9,500 feet above the sea, temperature minus 22 degrees, and 800 miles of solid sledge-dragging as the road home. We droned in by comfortable, warm, aircraft to find the place humming with humanity.

The first call was on the Station itself. You enter down a ramp like that at Tutankhamun's tomb. Ahead, a geodetic dome rises above the general level of the plateau. Over the opening a big sign reads UNITED STATES WELCOMES YOU TO THE SOUTH POLE. Inside there are three two-storey huts, and on either side long arms of arched corrugated metal shield a gymnasium, stores, a vehicle shed and immense foam neoprene fuel tanks. All the fuel and supplies are ferried in by air during the short summer 'open season'. Nearby there are small laboratories. We visited one undertaking atmospheric measurements, and they had a Dobson spectrophotometer for measuring ozone density overhead. 'Any sign of ozone depletion?' I asked. 'No,' came the reply. It transpired that the team did not arrive until after Christmas, by which time the spring ozone hole had closed up.

There are three markers for the South Pole. One is the Station itself, maybe half a kilometre from the pivot of the Earth's rotation. The second is the Ceremonial Pole, which is a hundred metres or so from the station and runway. This is used for visiting statesmen. It is surrounded by the flags of the Antarctic Treaty nations, and marked by a red and yellow striped barber's pole topped by a glass sphere, flanked (at least when we were there) by an inflated plastic penguin wearing a muffler. A further few hundred metres away lies the simpler board that marks the real Pole. It has to be moved periodically to keep it in the right place, for the ice cap is in slow motion. We walked out to it. A Korean diplomat was photographed as the first of his nation to reach this uttermost point of the Earth. Ken Croasdale and I got ourselves photographed, because we were the first Old Arnoldians to go

Ken Croasdale and Martin Holdgate, both of Arnold School, at the ceremonial South Pole in January 1985.

there and to have two simultaneous old school 'firsts' was especially unusual. There is a ring of empty oil drums around the Pole so we walked around the world in ninety seconds. And so back for food, hot tea, briefings and back into the aircraft to the camp, the final sessions and home. I don't know what it all cost, but I hope it helped to make diplomats understand what the Antarctic environment is really like. It may have helped to stiffen resistance to possible mineral industries.

Back to the DOE. When I became Deputy Secretary for countryside and conservation in 1981, I walked straight into two pieces of legislation. A Zoos Licensing Bill was going through Parliament, and a wide-ranging Wildlife and Countryside Bill followed on its heels. The former provided for the compulsory inspection of all wild animal and bird collections open to the public. The inspection was to be by qualified vets, drawn from a panel appointed by the Minister. It was designed to get rid of over-crowded, badly-caged zoos, and enforce standards based on modern regard for animal welfare. As a zoologist and Fellow of the Zoological Society of London I welcomed it. In the years that followed, the British Zoos community wanted similar measures applied throughout Europe, where some inhumane zoos were giving the whole business a bad name. A draft Community Directive based on the UK law was prepared but was abandoned – partly at the instigation of British Ministers – on the grounds that this was something each nation should decide for itself. Subsidiarity, which meant only having things of genuine European concern decided at Community level, was one of Margaret Thatcher's articles of faith, and zoos licensing was a ready sacrifice on the altar of principle. It was not until 1999 that the EU adopted a Directive which demands that all zoos are inspected and licensed, meet high standards of animal welfare, and contribute to animal conservation and public education. Those that fail can be closed down.

I have been a Fellow of the Zoological Society of London since 1968. Although the Society was one of Solly Zuckerman's three parallel careers (the Department of Anatomy at Birmingham and the role of Scientific Adviser to Government being the other two), it did not cross my official Whitehall horizon until early in 1982. By then, Solly (now Lord Zuckerman) had become President of the ZSL and he was determined to use the opportunity of a sympathetic Secretary of State in the shape of Michael Heseltine to win Government support for a national institution which was under financial stress. Falling visitor numbers and the rising costs of maintaining animals, buildings and scientific research combined to point the way to crisis. Unlike most zoos in the capital cities of the world, London Zoo received no money at all from Government. In contrast the Natural History Museum and the Royal Botanic Gardens at Kew were government-funded. Solly declared the situation anomalous and demanded a grant.

Michael Heseltine's fellow-Ministers were far from keen. Before anything was decided they demanded a fact-finding investigation. Roger (Lord) Chorley, who had been my contemporary at Cambridge and was a partner in Cooper and Lybrand, was chosen to take a hard look at the costs, income and potential of the Society in general and London Zoo in particular. I was told I had to sit alongside him and watch the Government's interests. Solly summoned me to lunch at his home at Burnham Thorpe, on the north Norfolk coast. I had a very good meal, a walk round his fields and a clear indication of where he considered my duty lay. In the midst of the discussion he decided that the Secretary of the Zoological Society, Professor John Phillips, must be a member of the study team. He rang him up and told him so. 'I'll fix it with the Secretary of State,' said Solly as I was leaving. He did.

The study showed that Ministers were right to be cautious. Although Solly had done some remarkable things in his long tenure first as Secretary and then as President, his achievements had been more in securing capital funds for new buildings, including two admirable research institutes, than in raising endowments or revenue. In fact, London Zoo was in a mess. Its site was (and still is) cramped, occupying only 36 acres in a corner of Regent's Park. Many of its buildings were unattractive both to the animals they housed and to the people who came to visit them. Paddocks were too small. There was nowhere for people to sit comfortably under cover and watch animals moving, feeding and interacting. It was a fair step from the nearest tube station (and that was the antiquated and unsalubrious Camden Town). The car park nearby was not run by the Zoo. And although the financial health of the Zoological Society depended largely on takings at the gate, we felt that it had very little idea about how to market itself. We advised that it needed a Director General who would tighten the management, control costs and promote the London and Whipsnade zoos as the attractions they ought to be. We also urged that the research institute should be grant-aided through the Research Councils. In the end (and I telescope here many years of interaction) money was transferred to allow the Institute of Zoology to be supported through the Advisory Board for the Research Councils, and Ministers approved a once-and-for-all capital grant of £10 million intended as an endowment. It did not work, and further crises followed in the 1990s.

The Wild Life and Countryside Bill (which became an Act on 30 October 1981) was a major tidying-up measure but its most important feature was that it greatly strengthened the law regarding Sites of Special Scientific Interest. Way back when I worked for the Nature Conservancy, an SSSI was simply an area of importance to conservation, identified by the Conservancy and notified to the local planning authority. The latter was expected to keep the conservation interest in mind when deciding any applications for development that would change the character of the site. The Conservancy incurred no obligation to do anything energetic to safeguard it – indeed it was not obliged even to tell the landowner it had been notified, though this was almost invariably done. Only the highest tier of conservation areas, those declared National Nature Reserves, had any real protection.

But the new Act changed all that. The owners of SSSIs had to be notified. Agreements to manage the land for conservation could be negotiated with owners (and paid for). If an owner started doing something that threatened the interest of the site, the NCC could seek an Order from the Minister that stopped the action (with penalties for breach). While an SSSI could be altered (and not a few main highways have sliced through them, and continue to do so), the constraints became much more serious.

The question of how absolute the protection given to SSSIs should be is almost unanswerable – or rather, the answer depends on where you sit. Green nature-lovers believe that protection should be complete. The argument goes that very little of the surface of the United Kingdom is in even a remotely semi-natural state. Almost all our ancient 'wildwood' has gone. Most of our fens have been drained, bogs cut, lowland heaths wooded or planted with villas, and chalk grasslands blitzed into monotony by nitrogenous fertilizers if they haven't been ploughed to take advantage of the EU cereals subsidies. So the remaining patches are precious heritage, and once gone will never come back. That was the heart of the Cow Green argument.

Most people would agree with the presumption that the heritage should be protected. But all land in Britain belongs to somebody. It is hard to deny an owner the right to make the best living from his or her property. It is impossible to demand that no change can ever be accepted. If the community as a whole really must have a mine, hospital, reservoir, airfield, rail link or even motorway, and the only possible location involves an SSSI, the site may have to be sacrificed. The argument often comes down to the costs, benefits and less tangible aesthetic values on each side. And this means debate and judgement. Debate about the real value of the wild heritage (something commonly got wrong in economic equations). Debate about whether its essential features can be replicated in a new 'wild area' somewhere else. Debate in public inquiries. Judgement there and by Ministers. For very often the argument ends up on a Minister's desk, and she or he has to take a decision that is bound to be unpopular with somebody.

In the early 1980s, there were two conservation issues on which Ministers found it easy to be popular – albeit at some cost in terms of scientific rigour. The first was the great public row over the killing of baby seals on the Canadian ice, north of Newfoundland and in the Gulf of St Lawrence. Some of the killers were indigenous Inuits, while others were Newfoundland and Nova Scotia fishermen (people who were, I think, known as 'blue-noses' for obvious reasons a century or so ago). The seals were killed soon after moulting from their woolly birth pelt to their smoother first juvenile coat. The killing was done with a club – which looks inhumane, but actually isn't because the animals usually square up to face the approaching sealer, a seal's skull is fragile and a hefty blow with a lead-loaded club smashes the brain and causes instant death. But it makes messy television, especially because the mothers can be filmed writhing around, with eyes watering in the cold Arctic air. All this was distasteful, especially to comfortable, urban, European society and a ban on import of these sealskins into the European Union was demanded.

Ministers came under pressure – both ways. A delegation of Canadians toured Europe to put their case. Conservationists were asked whether the harvest threatened the species – and answered ambiguously (my personal view was and is that the honest answer was 'no' – the seal stocks numbered millions and a sustainable crop could have been taken, adjusted from year to year following census information). But the political pressure was such that it was easiest to agree a ban. Public opinion in Europe wanted it, and the European Ministers answered to their electorate, not to that in Canada. People in simulated sealskin jumpsuits gyrated up and down outside the Berlaymont building in Brussels as we gathered for a European Environment Council. A monster petition was deposited in the Council chamber. Brigitte Bardot appeared in the newspapers cuddling an equally adorable seal. The ban was agreed.

This was my first international visit with William Waldegrave. He had come to the DOE from the Department of Education and Science as a Parliamentary Under Secretary in 1983, only a few days before he had to go to his first Council in Brussels. The whole delegation went over together in a small plane. He has published his version of the exchange that took place on the way.

'Martin Holdgate was to go with me, to keep me calm,' he said. 'Alas! He signally failed to do so!'

Why? Because I noticed, as we crossed the Channel, that the Minster had laid his brief aside and was calming himself by reading *Handley Cross*, a minor countryside classic by the Victorian writer, Surtees. He was chortling away. Now I had been brought up on Surtees, and I recognized the cartoon he was giggling over. If I remember correctly, it was a John Leech drawing of Mr Jorrocks, hero of the tale, having a difference of opinion with his horse. I leaned across and quoted the caption.

'Come h'up, I say, you ugly Beast!'

The Minister was not calmed, although I don't think he took it personally. But he soon became very much at home with the 'green environment' portfolio. And banning sealskin imports certainly went down well with most voters. It was a good example of a situation where the science was questionable but public values were decisive.

The other example of an issue where it was easy to be popular came up a little later. There was an outcry over the death of swans from eating too many lead weights, then used in great quantity by anglers. And angling is reputedly our most popular outdoor sport. If all the people who sit from time to time under green brollies on cold river banks were put end to end, they would, so the story goes, stretch from the source of the Thames to Greenwich and back again. Anyway, there seemed little doubt that it was the weights that were doing for the swans. The angling fraternity was resistant to change, not least because the substitutes (which included blobs of tungsten dust, cemented in a resin) were more expensive. A popular campaign – Save Our Swans – was decreed. The *Daily Mirror* seemed the perfect vehicle. We went to lunch with Robert Maxwell.

That was, indeed, memorable. Arriving by Ministerial car at the offices, we were escorted to the penthouse suite, where an immense, suave and genial Maxwell greeted the Minister effusively and his principal adviser (me) with the measured treatment appropriate to a second class citizen. We sat at luncheon with Maxwell at the head, William Waldegrave on his right, me on his left and an entourage of *Mirror* editors at the far end. They were quite senior chaps, but it was soon apparent that Nursery Rules applied. They only spoke when spoken to. Robert Maxwell conducted a dialogue with William, who from time to time referred a question to me. That was acceptable. But then – horror of horrors – I ventured to volunteer a remark. It was greeted with cool, slightly pained, politeness – conveying the message that Properly Trained Subordinates Do Not Do That Sort Of Thing . . . But the *Mirror* did run the campaign, and there was a swift movement to phase out lead weights. The swan population in southern England has never been more mutely booming.

The main business of promoting the conservation of nature and of outstanding landscapes was delegated – quite rightly – to the Nature Conservancy Council and the Countryside Commission, the latter having counterparts in Wales and Scotland. Issues only came to DOE when a Minister had to rule – as when there was controversy over a site. There was an early ruckus on the Somerset Levels where angry farmers hanged effigies of the then Chairman of NCC, Sir Ralph Verney, and the then Minister, Tom King, because they had combined to obstruct drainage of ancient and species-rich wet meadows, denying the owners lucrative EEC cereals subsidies. Road schemes erupted periodically, with Twyford Down as the most notorious. But the most awkward issues were in Scotland, one to do with proposed afforestation on Creag Megaidh and the other with proposed peat cutting at Duich Moss on Islay. Both sites were SSSI, and the latter was famous among bird-people as a major wintering haunt of White-fronted geese from Greenland. Maybe that and the sheep-dip was what gave the peat, and hence malts like Laphroaig, their special flavour?

Should the whisky distillers be permitted to cut peat there? Would it harm the birds? Were there alternatives? In the end, after much acrimony (including the hasty departure of telly-botanist David Bellamy from an irate confrontation with the would-be peat-diggers of Islay), both sites were safeguarded for nature. But the argument raised an important procedural issue.

By then, in the swift-turning kaleidoscope of Ministerial change, Nicholas Ridley had become Secretary of State for the Environment. He was concerned about the curious anomaly that all other planning decisions in Scotland went to the Secretary of State for Scotland – yet because the Nature Conservancy Council was a Great Britain body, these vexed cases north of the Border, on which feelings ran high, were decided in London. Scottish landowners complained that the NCC had far too many bright, young English ecologists with no real understanding of rural life. They found them fussy and bureaucratic. Mr Ridley sympathized, and felt that the whole set-up was inappropriate.

'Malcolm Rifkind takes all the other land use decisions in Scotland,' he proclaimed,'yet I get these controversial cases referred to me. It's wrong. They should be decided in a Scottish context.' It was impossible to disagree – but how could the problem be solved? One option (and I still think it was the right one for the time) would have been to make the NCC more of a federal body, strengthening its Scottish and Welsh Committees and referring conservation policies and specific cases in those two countries to the respective territorial Ministers. Nick Ridley seemed willing to consider that option, but for some reason the then Chairman of the NCC, William Wilkinson, and his colleagues did not come up with a plan the Secretary of State felt able to accept. He therefore decided that the Nature Conservancy Council should be split into separate national bodies for Scotland, Wales and England. It was the end of the road for the Huxley and Tansley vision of a nation-wide Ecological Service.

The destruction of the NCC made Nicholas Ridley something of an ogre in the conservation world. People saw him as an assertive, choleric politician and thought he would be beastly to deal with. Nothing could be further from the truth. He was easy to argue with. He listened. He had an artistic sensitivity (he was a good watercolourist who would have liked to be an architect, following his grandfather, Lutyens, but had become a civil engineer instead). He was unfailingly courteous. He was interested in the policy issues behind a case. He had a very deep regard for the liberty of the subject and hated needless regulation and bureaucracy (hence his objection to the expansion of European Community directives into fields that seemed to him to have nothing to do with the Common Market). The main down-side was that he chain-smoked virtually the whole time (which, I fear, killed him in the end) and drank incessant cups of Marsham Street coffee – not the greatest brew on earth. Long meetings with him had their environ-mental disbenefits. But I liked him, and know that many others who worked for him in the DOE did so too.

When my responsibilities broadened to take in the Directorates dealing with pollution, I picked up another hot issue – radioactivity in the environment. We had two distinct kinds of radioactive headache – accidents and errors that led to the contamination of the environment, and the lack of a coherent policy for the safe disposal of wastes. There was added tension because every publicised accident – however trivial it appeared to the industry and their medical advisers – made a news story that worried people deeply. Events overseas like the leakage of radiation at Three Mile Island in the USA and later the Chernobyl disaster, gave all things nuclear a bad name, in Britain and almost everywhere else.

Divisions of responsibility are never easy, and this issue was bedevilled by them. The Secretary of State for the Environment was responsible for making sure that nuclear wastes and emissions did not cause a hazard in the environment. Industry, Energy and Employment Ministers were responsible for overseeing the operation of nuclear power stations, the economic production of electricity, and the safety of the work force. The managers of the installations themselves, and the Central Electricity Generating Board under which they then came, were of course responsible for day to day operations. We were advised on wastes by an independent Radioactive Wastes Management Advisory Committee, RWMAC.

Radioactive waste is an inevitable product of many modern activities – including radiation therapy in hospitals – but the nuclear power industry is its main source. An especially thorny problem arose over what to do with fuel rods from power stations when they had emitted most of their useful energy. One option was simply to store them, properly contained, while the radioactivity decayed to the point of safety – but this meant secure containment for centuries. It was also technically difficult because the fuel rods used in our older power stations contain reactive uranium in a casing of reactive magnesium and 'go off' if they are just left in a stack somewhere. Another option was to reprocess them, sending the uranium round again – and streaming off the plutonium, some of which was then needed for nuclear weapons and more of which would be needed as fuel if the fast breeder reactor came to fruition. Britain had opted to reprocess, and it was done at Sellafield in Cumbria.

Sellafield was old (it was originally a research site, linked to the Calder Hall nuclear power station which was Britain's first, opened by the Queen in 1956). It had grown like Topsy: higgledy-piggledy. It had been the scene of the disastrous Windscale fire in 1957, which blew a mass of radioisotopes into the air and contaminated a broad swathe of the western Lake District. That incident was none the easier to get away from when it emerged that it had been comprehensively hushed-up: the change of name to Sellafield was partly a PR job, to shed the bad image of Windscale. By the early 1980s the plant was a jumble of excellent modern buildings and inadequate older ones. I remember watching how spent fuel rods from the Magnox power stations were handled following their unloading from special rail containers (whose safety was another public concern, despite a spectacular test train crash arranged by the CEGB from which the container emerged unscathed). The cans containing the rods were slid into a deep water tank, and workers with long tongs, standing on a gantry above, swung them into a device that sliced them open and passed the contents on their way to dissolution and reprocessing. It was, we were assured, safe enough – but there were the workers, standing open-legged with only a metre or two of radiation-absorbing water between the rods and their genitals . . .

And there were lots of old pipes that dripped ominously (they contained nothing worse than water, but they looked messy). There were three tanks that held effluent which was discharged into the Irish Sea down a long pipe – and events showed that the wrong kind of liquid could get into those tanks. Once there it had to be shed to the sea, because there was no provision for a return flow. There were patches of ground flagged 'Contaminated – Keep Off'. Michael Heseltine stirred things up properly on his first visit, when he was observed to be making notes as he walked round. They took him into the meeting room for a discussion, expecting the usual easy technical questions from an impressed layman. One of them told me afterwards how it went.

'Well, Secretary of State, what did you think?'

'I thought it was dreadful. Here is a list of ten things I noted that I consider unacceptable on any well-run industrial site, never mind as sensitive a one as this . . .'

There were endless minor problems, partly because of the age of the site but even more because (so it seemed to me), CEGB, the site management and the work force were still riding on the wave of past acclaim. And they had gained that familiarity with the work that begot acceptance of the problems and contempt for lay and public views. They were genuinely hurt when what seemed to them minor incidents caused public uproar and Ministerial reproof. On two occasions radioactive effluent that should not have gone to sea was discharged by error (William Waldegrave and I found ourselves walking the grey shores of the Irish Sea while men with radiation counters measured the consequences). It was not that great harm was done, but that the image of what had begun in high hope as a masterpiece of modern technology, offering limitless cheap power, was corroded. Moreover, it was true that over the years about a tonne of plutonium had found its way to the sediments of the Irish Sea – a point latched onto by Greenpeace who made periodic and well-publicised attempts to bung the pipe up. Although in the period between 1970 and 1985 emissions were enormously reduced, the public – and international publics in Ireland and Scandinavia – continued to see Sellafield as an abomination. And it remained a fact that it was (and is) the largest discharger of radioactive materials to the sea in the whole western world.

All this spilled over to the waste disposal side. The dump at Drigg, where low-level waste went, was no more than a series of open trenches looking like any other local tip. Intermediate waste was stored in old wartime bunkers. Once sea dumping ceased to be an option alternatives became urgent. RWMAC gave clear (and critical) advice on how to improve disposal at Drigg. But what should we do with the really hot stuff – the high-level waste from reprocessing, which contained materials that would be intensely radioactive for hundreds of years? And what should be done with the intermediate waste that really could not be buried in a shallow trench?

You can argue that these things should have been thought about before the industry was permitted to expand. They had been – but in an atmosphere of much greater technical euphoria than prevailed in the early 1980s. By that date nobody wanted a radioactive dump anywhere near their back yard. NIMBY was succeeded by BANANA – Build Absolutely Nothing Anywhere Near Anybody. The search for a safe place to deposit high and intermediate level waste was long, tortuous, and full of culs de sac. It is still going on.

It seemed clear that the hot stuff had to be solidified. There were two methods. An Australian Professor advocated Synroc – a kind of artificial basalt – which would be hard, very heat resistant, relatively safe to handle, and rather expensive. The alternative was vitrification in glass blocks, themselves sealed in metal containers. Rival British and French systems were examined. In the end, Ministers accepted the French one. But the hot blocks clearly had to be stored for at least fifty years to allow enough radioactive decay for them to cool to room temperature. That did take some of the heat off the search for a disposal site – which almost everyone assumed should be a deep mine in a hard, unfissured, waterproof rock.

But where? The Geological Survey was asked to provide a list of twelve sites in different rock formations. These would then be explored by drilling. Granite masses in Cheviot or Galloway? Deep clays in the Midlands? Salt or anhydrite deposits in Cheshire or Teesside? Shales in Scotland? The first site, at Dounreay in Sutherland, near to a nuclear site, was duly drilled and found unsuitable. Cheviot came next. So did a rising tide of public alarm – not least from the defenders of the National Park. There were demonstrations. The Home Secretary, Willie Whitelaw, told Tom King, then the responsible Minister of State in DOE, that the police were worried about the safety of the drilling teams. The programme stopped. Public alarm also stopped the disposal of drums of intermediate waste in the old anhydrite mine at Billingham on Teesside, ideal though it appeared on technical grounds.

Sometime around 1985, Walter Marshall, Lord Marshall of Goring, Chairman of the CEGB, had a Brilliant Idea. Why not find someone who owned a really big backyard (obviously over the right kind of rock), who needed money for a Stately Home, and who would accept a waste disposal site in return for substantial funding? He even had a volunteer. The place was code-named Site X. The idea had certain deficiencies, not least that planning permission would be required, and the local authority and other residents around the big private backyard might not share the enthusiasms of the landowner. It did not get very far. I summed it up in a flippant limerick:

> The Noble Lord Marshall of Goring,
> Was greatly in favour of storing
> Intractable waste
> In a Very Safe Place.
> But he wouldn't say where – which was boring.

Not very poetic, but I sent it to that connoisseur of light verse, Kenneth Baker, who was briefly our Secretary of State in 1985-86. He professed himself amused. I'm not sure that he would have been as happy with my next one, though, because he featured in it.

It happened after Cabinet. He came back in a jaunty mood and joined other Ministers and senior officials for a round-up. But he started with a jocular complaint. 'The staircase at Number Ten is lined with Cabinet group photos,' he remarked. 'And I'm not in any of them. Yet I've lived through two ranges of high-level changes – that sounds like a line of verse – and I think it's time I got my photograph!'

We turned to serious matters. But I tried to follow his poetic notion:

> Said Ken, with a snort and a glare,
> 'There's no Cabinet group on my stair!
> I've lived through two ranges,
> Of high-level changes.
> And I want to be snapped – while I'm there . . .

I sent it to Robin Young, then his Private Secretary. It probably never got into the Red Box. Private Secretaries are partly there as filters.

The Chernobyl incident in May 1986 really jarred the public and saw the start of a new and highly critical approach to nuclear power. By chance, I was visiting the Chairman of the National Radiological Protection Board (and of the Royal Commission on Environmental Pollution), Sir Richard

Southwood, at Harwell when the first reports came in. The cloud that had swung south over Italy and then north towards Britain had arrived over Lowestoft. It was raining. Radioactive materials were coming down. The prediction was that the cloud would continue north-west and that serious pollution was likely in the hills. It was right. Snowdonia, the Lake District and Galloway were the worst affected areas. But we really had very little idea of how serious the impact would be. The NRPB was satisfied that there would be no direct hazard to human health because the polluted air mass would pass so quickly. There was little problem with water supplies because whatever reached the reservoirs of Cumbria or North Wales would be so greatly diluted. But what would happen in the upland ecosystem?

John Jeffers swung ITE into action, on his own initiative, amid cool, or even hostile, reactions from his supposed research customers. And, as so often happens, prediction proved wrong. Government experts had thought that the deposited radioactive materials would be washed out of the grasslands quite fast. They weren't. The radioactive caesium isotopes, which have a half-life of as much as 30 years, stuck in the peaty soils and went round again and again in the soil-grass-sheep-soil cycle. Levels in sheep rose to the point where the meat was unsaleable. On some hill farms the ban was to last for over ten years. The need for basic research and the value of long-term monitoring were demonstrated. Meanwhile there was a massive public revulsion. Before Chernobyl, 37 per cent of people in Britain, 44 per cent in Germany and 32 per cent in Finland opposed the building of nuclear power stations. Afterwards the figures were 44 per cent, 82 per cent and 64 per cent respectively.

Alternative policies began to be pressed. Greenpeace had long argued that it was wrong to reprocess spent fuel rods – the world was awash with cheap uranium, the fast breeder reactor no longer seemed a practical proposition and nobody ought to want to extract weapons-grade plutonium. Stop reprocessing. Abandon THORP, the Thermal Oxide Reprocessing Plant which Sellafield wanted to build. Store the spent fuel. Best of all, Stop Nuclear Power. The tide of opinion swung slowly. After an exhausting public inquiry, THORP was built and is now in operation. But there is still no clear solution to waste disposal. Constructing underground stores shielded by masses of impermeable rock still seems the best answer – but such places are hard to find. In 1986 William Waldegrave and I visited the Canadian research site at Whiteshell, north of Winnipeg. It seemed perfect in theory – a granite boss intruded into ancient crustal rocks. But underground it was fissured and dripped water. Nobody was confident that a better site could be found in the more complex geology of the United

Kingdom. A few years later plans to excavate an experimental mine gallery under Sellafield to see whether it would be suitable for high and intermediate level waste were vetoed by John Gummer when he, in turn, became Secretary of State. Some Minister, sometime, really will have to get to grips with this problem – especially if we want to consider nuclear power, which emits no 'greenhouse gases', as part of the mix of energy sources for the future.

When I picked up the pollution portfolio again in the early 1980s, I found that several old friends from a decade earlier were still around. Among them were lead, the 'ozone hole', acid rain and climate change.

Lead was at the heart of one of the longest-running pollution sagas of the period. Everyone knew it was a poison, but everyone also knew that it is a common element in soil, plants, food and water. People always have some of it in their bodies. The trouble starts if we get too much – as used to happen quite often to workers in the lead industry, but less frequently in everyday life. In the 1970s questions began to be asked about the safety of everyday exposures, especially to the tetra-ethyl lead which was added to petrol to make engines run without 'knocking'. Professor Derek Bryce-Smith, a chemist from the University of Reading, argued for a ban on these lead additives.

As I have explained, this argument was rejected in the 1970 White Paper, but a few years later it began to heat up again. We in the Central Unit organized a review, which we published in our new *Pollution Papers* series in 1974. We were strongly influenced by the Government's medical advisers, headed by Professor Pat Lawther of the Medical Research Council. They emphasized that it was the body's total uptake of lead from all sources that mattered – and that the average person got far more from food and water than from breathing in petrol and exhaust fumes. Serious health problems still existed in places like Glasgow, where acid water from mountain reservoirs corroded old lead pipes and cisterns. Children could still pick up too much if they nibbled flakes of old paint, which could contain 40 per cent lead. But Pat Lawther was confident that petrol was not a hazard. None the less, the Government was uneasy and agreed to stop the permitted lead content of petrol rising any higher, and then to start a programme of phased reduction

As time went by, it became clear that this was not satisfying anybody. New research showed that the lead levels in the blood of people away from industrial contamination – the 'natural background levels' – were much lower than Pat and his colleagues had thought. The implication was that our blood lead levels were unnaturally high. Studies around a smelter in the Isle of Dogs showed a lot of lead in dust (and on worker's clothes and in their homes). Lead in roadside dust in inner cities also reached disturbing concentrations. Industry continued to argue that lead 'anti-knock' was a simple, cheap and safe way of making cars run smoothly, but Ministers sensed trouble ahead. Moreover, there was increasing awareness of the need to clean up other pollution in exhaust gases, and the proven way of doing this was to use catalytic converters (which lead would poison). Taking the two strands together, getting lead out of petrol began to look sensible – many years after Peter Walker had told me it was his first objective as a new Minister.

The Government needed authoritative advice. It is always easier to change a long-defended policy if you have new evidence to call on. The Royal Commission came providentially to the rescue. In September 1981 they had finished a study of oil pollution at sea and began to plan their next investigation. As usual, they consulted widely and the Chairman, Professor Dick Southwood, came into the Department for a chat. Somehow – and I do not recall how – we seized on the notion that lead in the environment might be a good subject, illustrating as it did a whole series of interlocking environmental, chemical, medical and policy issues. Ministers – who could have asked the Commission to advise on the issue, but far preferred the choice to be spontaneous – were delighted.

The Royal Commission took the subject away, and reported in April 1983. They recognised the many sources of the lead in your and my bodies. Without saying that present exposures were dangerous, they advised that measures should be taken to reduce human dispersion of lead wherever possible. That conclusion led to a raft of practical ideas – including phasing out lead additives in petrol. 'We can find no compelling arguments for the retention of leaded petrol except as an interim measure to enable the majority of cars' (which couldn't run on unleaded) 'to be phased out.' Ministers accepted the recommendation with alacrity, almost before the Report was cool on the news-stands. Like Saving Our Swans, it was a 'win-win' announcement.

We began to get concerned about ozone depletion around the time of the Stockholm Conference, though Sherwood and Molina's worry was over the impact of more and more aircraft flying in the stratosphere. In contrast, chlorofluorocarbons (CFCs), then used widely as aerosol propellants and in refrigerators, had been seen as 'wonder chemicals' with no environmental vices. I remember a homily on the subject from Dr Phil Harvey of ICI, at their Runcorn plant where more chlorine was made (and more mercury emitted to the environment) than anywhere else in Britain. 'They're wonderful substances!' he enthused. 'Enormously useful in industry! And so inert that they have no impact on anything on the ground. They simply diffuse up into the stratosphere, where the sun's rays break the molecules down into simple inorganic radicals . . .'

Unfortunately, around 1974 people began to realise that one of those simple radicals – chlorine – could react with ozone and strip off one of its three oxygen atoms, leaving ordinary oxygen which does not block ultra-violet radiation from the sun. There were calls for action to ban CFCs. And because the destruction was the collective consequence of emissions from every industrialised country, the action had to be worldwide. Industry demanded that everyone moved together, so that control bore fairly on all. And they argued for no controls until the science was certain. Proof did not arrive until 1984 when my old colleague Dr Joe Farman of the British Antarctic Survey published the first scientific paper demonstrating a massive decline in the amount of ozone over part of Antarctica in the southern spring months of October and November.

There was surprise at Joe's results, obtained using old-fashioned ground-based instruments, because sophisticated American satellites had noticed nothing. Then they found that their computers had rejected the information because it deviated more than ten per cent from the yearly average. As the Antarctic ozone hole widened and attracted blacker headlines, people became alarmed that the result would be an upsurge in skin cancer, especially among golden Australians on the golden beaches of New South Wales. Mostafa Tolba of UNEP swung into action. The International Convention on the Protection of the Ozone Layer was agreed in Vienna in 1985, to be followed in 1987 by the Montreal Protocol which set a timetable for getting rid of CFCs. In 1990 this was beefed-up further in London. But all this was not exactly politics-free. The USA pushed hard for an early ban – reputedly as soon as DuPont signalled that they could market substitutes. The UK opposed – allegedly until ICI gave the signal that they could, too. Now almost every Government is on the side of the angels – but the devils soon swung back into action with a growing international black market in the banned substances.

Acid Rain was another long-running saga. The Swedish study, presented in Stockholm, was followed by a lot of scientific argument about the causes of the fishless rivers and lakes it reported. Fingers began to point at Britain, for we were the biggest emitter of acid sulphur oxides in western Europe. The UK Government was unmoved. An International Convention on Long-Range Trans-Boundary Air Pollution was negotiated under the UN Economic Commission for Europe in 1979, but it did little more than agree to share information and support research. This suited the CEGB, but not the aggrieved Nordics. Then came a shock. Germany, regarded as an ally of Britain and France in resisting action, suddenly changed tack and supported the call for a mandatory 30 per cent reduction in sulphur emissions. Leslie

Reed (by then Chief Alkali and Clean Air Inspector, in succession to Frank Ireland) and I saw the reason when we were invited on a fact-finding visit to Germany.

We gathered in Munich and Frontier Police helicopters took us over the Bavarian forest and along the wooded hills that form the border with what is now the Czech Republic (but was then, of course, Czechoslovakia, and firmly within the Eastern Block). High on the Fichtelgebirge, at around 800 metres, we saw stands of dead and dying spruce trees. We visited others on the ground. The cause was not obvious. Some trees had magnesium deficiency while others had heavy insect infestations and yet others had foliage that looked as if it had been damaged directly by air pollution. It seemed likely that the direct damage was due to acid fumes spilling over the border from Czechoslovakia, where there was a lot of dirty industry powered by sulphurous brown coal. Oxidants produced from chemical reactions involving car exhausts in the Munich basin may also have played a part. The magnesium deficiency may have arisen because the deposited acidity upset the soil chemistry, while the insects may have made whoopee in the weakened trees. Whatever the details, the cause for alarm was obvious. Forests have a deep cultural significance in Germany, going back to the remote and folk-remembered past, but amplified by Goethe and expressed in today's love of walking in the woods.

So Germany demanded action. But the British Government was resistant. It would cost a lot of money. Our emissions were already falling from their mid-1970s peak. Was there proof? There seemed no way we could be contributing to the problems on the eastern German frontier. Were we liable in international law when our emissions obviously mingled with others (even though we did provide about 80 per cent of what came down on the granite of southern Norway)? And surely it couldn't just be acidification – there had to be more complicated interactions? The most plausible explanation was that acid sulphate accumulated in the soil and led to the release of aluminium, which poisoned tree roots and the fungi that live in essential symbiosis with them. When this toxic aluminium was washed out into rivers and lakes, it killed fish and other aquatic life too. The Department of the Environment was convinced of this explanation quite early, especially after William Waldegrave and I visited Norway and Sweden and saw some of the research on the bare, acid uplands, visited clear, almost lifeless lakes and heard first-hand of a catastrophic decline in salmon fisheries. But the Prime Minister and Cabinet were unmoved, and there was predictable Treasury omniscience and obstruction.

What do I mean by that? In my experience the British Treasury is a culture within a culture. It is staffed by highly intelligent Civil Servants who give the impression of suffering acutely from the Not Invented Here syndrome. Their position as advisers to the Chancellor and Cabinet on all financial matters gives them a duty to question whether what other departments want to spend money on is really necessary. So far so good. But I noticed from time to time that Treasury officials would decide to attack the underlying science or information. 'Can you prove that the acid rain in Norway comes from Britain?' 'Surely the damage is trivial in proportion to the cost of redesigning all our power stations?' 'Why should we take responsibility for what happens in another country?' 'We do not consider that the science is good enough to justify the public expenditure.' The answers to the three questions (at that time) were: 'yes', 'no', and 'because we accepted an obligation to do so at Stockholm'. As to the final statement – there were no qualified scientists in the Treasury.

The international climate heated up. I was sent as UK delegate to a meeting in Munich at which I had to make a speech explaining why, although we recognized the seriousness of the concern, we could not join the '30% Club' – partly because the baseline date of 1980 took no heed of the reductions we had achieved before then, and partly because we disliked arbitrary percentage targets. William Waldegrave should have made the speech, but was held back in London to answer Parliamentary Questions on the Arts, because the Minister, Lord Gowrie, sat in the Upper House. The campaign for the Elgin marbles was being pressed by Melina Mercouri, Greek Minister for Culture. 'Keep your marbles, Willie,' teased Nicholas Ridley as our man left a Departmental meeting to respond. *The Times* commiserated with 'the unfortunate official' forced in Munich to produce what artistic verisimilitude I could to cloak a bald and unconvincing narrative. William Waldegrave appeared next day and did some good corridor diplomacy, but it was obvious we were on a hiding to nothing. We were not helped by Yuri Israel, the Russian delegate, who promised that the USSR would reduce movement of sulphur oxide across their western border by at least 30 per cent – relying on 'our abundant natural gas and modern nuclear power stations' (this was before one of the latter blew up at Chernobyl).

It was about this time that I ventured into verse on the theme of 'Disgruntled Diplomacy'.

> Distinguished Delegates!' I hear him say
> 'I do not think the statement made just now
> By the distinguished spokesman for UK
> Is quite correct. It does not take account
> Of lifeless rivers and translucent lakes

Caused by the impact of the acid rain
Spread from his country.'

So – he means I lied
Or was, at least, selective with the truth!
And now he comes with raven wings a-beat
To pick some scanty morsel of a bone
Of tactical advantage. Yet he knows
As I know, and the whole encircled row
Of faces known through long and weary years
In this grey Tower of Babel know he knows,
What my position truly is, as I
Know his, and both of us the reasons why!

Most delegations have a grievance primed
Awaiting but the trigger to deliver.
The Nordics have their plaint on Acid Rain.
Spain windmill-tilts at ocean dumps of waste.
Jordan is stung to fury by the news
That Israel has a planned Med-Dead canal.
Iran berates Iraq: Iraq, Iran
While far away impartial rivers roll
Their mingled blood to the polluted sea.
The tales are stacked like records in a row
Awaiting but the lever arm below.

Shall I call my attacker to withdraw?
Tell him my Government does not accept
That Walter Marshall's sulphur is malign?
Tell him that science is working on it still
And should it prove his dying fish are caused
By the effulgent fumes of British power
We will take action? No, there is no point.
He did not speak for me, but for his Press.
'Britain attacked on Acid Rain again.'
Give them a story that they want to hear
Muster the votes – election time is near!

What's that? The Chairman thinks we should adjourn.
He hopes we'll join him for a drink or two
Or three or four. And so another day
Of speaking for the peoples of the world
Is ended. And for all that we have said
There grow no trees the more, die no less dead.

I wrote it at UNEP, sitting next to Charles Caccia, former Canadian Environment Minister. 'I never knew you were such a cynic,' he said. But I fear that many negotiators will find echoes of experience in these – for me – unusually bitter lines. There must be a better way to do international business.

I was in Nairobi, attending the UNEP Governing Council in 1985 and staying in the old-world comfort of the Muthaiga Club. Urgent telephone call. Sir Peter Harrop, Second Permanent Secretary in DOE. 'We want you to come home. The Prime Minister is convening a scientific teach-in on acid rain at Chequers on Sunday. We want you to explain the impact of acid rain on trees. Sir Hermann Bondi, Chairman of NERC, will cover fresh waters and Sir John Mason, Director General of the Met Office, will deal with the atmospheric chemistry. It'll be important – will settle what our policy is for the next few years.'

Chequers is a lovely house, and the atmosphere was warm and relaxed. Denis Thatcher greeted those arriving, showed them to the loo in a most courteous manner, and acted as friendly host. But the day was a serious one. Margaret Thatcher was unusual among Prime Ministers in many respects – and one of them was that she was a trained research chemist. She therefore understood – and was well able to question – the scientific details of the acid rain story. The outcome? No immediate change in policy, but strong support for a co-operative research programme between the Royal Society in Britain and the Norwegian and Swedish Academies of Science. The project was led by John Mason in his capacity as Vice President of the Royal Society. The green lobby and Norwegian public opinion attacked it as prevarication. It did mean delay. But it cracked the problem. John Mason, formerly a stern critic of the environmental arguments, became convinced that if acid emissions were cut back depositions would decline and this in turn would reduce the releases of acidity and of toxic aluminium from the soil to fresh waters. The UK agreed to fit flue gas desulphurization equipment to three new power stations and to take other measures to curb acidity. Although we never signed up as members of the '30% Club', we met its targets. Later, we committed ourselves, with the rest of the European Union, to an 80 per cent reduction in sulphur emissions by 2000. The target was achieved. We would have attracted far less criticism, and spent no more money, had we signed up to the 30% Club at the outset.

By the mid-1980s, from being an environmental leader, the United Kingdom was drifting down-league to unenviable castigation as 'the dirty man of Europe'. The volume of European Directives on environmental issues proliferated. Those in Whitehall who had thought they could be accommodated without much change to established British law and practice

– and that we could see off new measures we did not like by a blend of superior wisdom, negotiation and, if necessary, veto – were proved wrong. One of the most absurd controversies was over bathing beaches.

The European Commission published proposals for quality standards for bathing waters in 1974. The British thought that the science was shaky and the standards dubious, but agreed that something did need to be done to clean up the filthy, overcrowded beaches in the land-locked and polluted Mediterranean. The DOE Water Directorate did not think the measure was needed in Britain, because our coasts were swept by strong tides and currents, and because it was believed that bacteria in human sewage did not survive in the sea. But Ministers were advised that we could comply with the Directive by simply notifying the Commission of a token list of bathing beaches which we knew met the standards. This was done. Brighton, Bournemouth, Southend and Blackpool were not among the twenty-seven coastal sites 'where bathing is traditionally practised by a large number of bathers'.

I was only involved in this argument peripherally, as the Deputy Secretary responsible for CDEP (the Central Directorate on Environmental Protection) as CUEP had become. The Water Directorate handled water matters, and they were not part of my command. But I recall meetings with William Waldegrave soon after he took over the environmental portfolio at which he was very clear that our national position was untenable, and insisted that we notify all significant bathing beaches – even though this would mean spending a lot of money on cleaning them up. It happened in the end, but the rearguard action did us no good.

Nor did an attempted scientific rearguard action in which Eric Ashby, now Lord Ashby, figured centrally. The House of Lords Select Committee on European Community matters believed that the scientific basis for the Commission's proposals was often severely defective. I felt the same, having attended a few 'expert' meetings in Brussels in which the expertise was far from evident. The Commission appeared to rely heavy on scientists from the Joint Research Centre at Ispra in Italy, and many of them had started in the field of nuclear physics and had scanty environmental credentials. Eric Ashby persuaded the Royal Society to convene a meeting of representatives of the various European academies of science to discuss how to improve the quality and credibility of the scientific advice the Commission received. The notion was that we might follow the lead of the World Health Organization and get each national Academy, working with national Governments, to list a panel of respected experts in various spheres on whom the Commission might call. But the first meeting was poorly attended, and a second one in France was worse. The initiative soon fizzled out. The implication was that the European scientific community was far less critical of the Commission than we were.

Gradually, our European commitments became mainstream. A number of us became familiar with the meeting rooms in Brussels and Luxembourg, where the Environment Ministers met in Council every six months, to debate (and from time to time approve) new Directives and other Community measures. The United Kingdom was usually represented by the DOE Minister of State holding the environment protection portfolio – in my time, Tom King, William Waldegrave and John (Lord) Belstead. Meetings commenced at around 10 a.m., but got very little done before the Ministers adjourned for a lengthy private discussion over lunch. In early afternoon, serious negotiation got under way – and often dragged on and on. I did not attend all the Environment Councils, but remember only one – presided over by Tom King – which completed its business by 8 p.m., allowing us to go out for dinner. It was much more usual to be locked in courteous but apparently irreconcilable debate well after midnight.

There were, of course, lighter moments. Once, when the Italian Minister had to slip out to the loo, his senior official tried his hand at clarification. 'Now that my Minister is out of the room,' we heard him say, courtesy of the English interpretation, 'I will tell you what the position of my Government really is . . .'

The Commission stage-managed the Councils, and were the source of all the proposals before them. They also had a technique for giving the *coup de grâce* to interminable overnight sessions. At about 1 or even 2 in the morning, they wheeled on the Brussels Blockbusters. These were baguettes filled with ham, washed down with tumblers well filled with strong whisky. The tone of the debate warmed after that, leading to compromises which (as in the Paris Convention) had strong elements of verbal fudge. We generally got away in the darkness before dawn to snatch a bit of sleep before catching the plane home.

The steady swell of European and national regulation brought with it the need for proper enforcement at home. Our machinery was fragmented. Years before, when the Health and Safety Inspectorate was established in 1975, the Alkali and Clean Air Inspectorate had been transferred to it. We in DOE now believed that we needed an integrated pollution prevention system. The Royal Commission agreed. It had criticised the transfer of 'the Alks' to HSE in 1976, arguing instead for the creation of 'HUMPI', Her Majesty's Pollution Inspectorate. In 1984 it returned to the charge. This time, Ministers were disposed to listen. 'The Alks' were swept back from HSE, and merged with the Radiochemical Inspectorate and a number of other groups to create Her Majesty's Inspectorate of Pollution, HMIP. The new body, led by a senior Under Secretary, Brian Ponsford, became a welcome component of my wing of the DOE. Now it is part of the Environment Agency.

The international responsibilities that went with CDEP also brought me back into UNEP. My return began with the Session of Special Character in 1982, when I wore two hats – as UK Delegate and as co-Editor of the big book on *The World Environment, 1972-1982*. Keen to raise the standing of UNEP, Mostafa Tolba urged Ministers to attend (in the early years, very few had been seen at the Governing Council). Mobutu Sese Seko of Zaire swung into the hall surrounded by an impressive guard of gun-toting henchmen. Tom King, as Minister of State in DOE, led our team and produced a quite different touch of novelty when the time came for his speech.

He began tamely enough.

'I want to begin by saying how delighted I am to be back in this beautiful country of Kenya . . .'

He hesitated.

'. . . and if the interpreters will forgive me . . .'

He switched into Kiswahili, and delivered two sentences for the benefit of our East African hosts. It went down a treat. They didn't know he had learned it as an officer in the King's African Rifles, on National Service at the time of the Mau Mau uprising – or that (as he discovered when looking at a group photograph when waiting to see his Ministerial counterpart), he had personally locked up several members of the current Kenyan Cabinet . . .

A year later, I was elected President of the Governing Council. And, by a curious turn of fate, the Argentine Ambassador was a Vice President. Our countries were not 'on speakers' – we had severed diplomatic relations after the Falklands war. But international office neutralizes your nationality (at least in theory). There was much consultation of Foreign Office protocol before the way was cleared for me to attend the Argentine official reception – the first British official to enter their Ambassador's residence for over a year. The gesture, in its tiny way, helped to restore bridges, and the process advanced further when members of our respective delegations, who had known one another for years, discovered that both had suffered family losses in the conflict. They talked quietly and sadly together in the corridor.

The job of the President of the Governing Council is to sit in the Chair and steer the debate. Mostafa Tolba and his team provided excellent briefs, and the job can be a very simple and formal one. They even wrote your speeches for you (if you let them). But I didn't let them prepare my main address, delivered towards the end of the proceedings. Even Mostafa didn't know what I was going to say (and this upset him, for he liked to manage the stage). I decided to have a go at the way we used our time. I took the texts of forty speeches made in the main plenary session and worked out (by simple measurement of column inches) how much time had been devoted to what issue. About 15 per cent had gone on fulsome compliments to the President, Bureau and Executive Director. 'We are flattered,' I said, 'but we could have done with less.' I suggested that a third of the time had been spent on boasting about national actions that were not germane to the agenda of the meeting and an equivalent amount had duplicated debate in the Committees where the real action was taken. Only 8 per cent had gone on discussing how we were to get the money to do the many things that delegates wanted. I suggested that the Governing Council should review the efficiency of its own working. It went down quite well, although it took Mostafa some time to forgive me the suspense. But he did ask me to chair a staff conference on how to increase UNEP's efficiency, and then once more to be a joint editor of the next big volume on *The World Environment* which covered the whole period 1972-1992, so it all came right in the end.

Departmental officials do not have much to do with Prime Ministers. Their job is to support their own Secretary of State and Ministers, who in turn deal with the PM. But there are exceptions – when a Prime Minister wants to get into an issue in depth and calls for the officials with direct knowledge and responsibility. As Margaret Thatcher did on acid rain, and later on climate change. And did one day on football.

It was a cause of some mirth among family and friends that I, who was a rabbit at games at school and preferred climbing hills to all other outdoor activities, should be the Deputy Secretary for Sport. But personal history would never determine what an official gets in his or her portfolio: Civil Servants are expected to be able to master a broad brief. And many Civil Servants thought sport was a bit of an odd-ball. A prolonged media campaign in the 1950s and 1960s had led to the designation of a Minister for Sport in the second Wilson Government – Denis Howell, once a football referee. British fortunes did not improve overnight, but having a Minister at least showed recognition of the importance of the subject. And the Minister demonstrated his powers when he also had responsibility for drought in the 1976 summer: he visited the stricken areas and the heavens opened. Perhaps he would cause a similar shower of gold medals? Anyway, when sport landed on my desk in 1981, Neil Macfarlane was the Minister. He was supported directly by an Assistant Secretary who did know about sport, David Teasdale, and he got expert advice from the Sports Council. My role was just to watch over all, and be there when needed.

One Saturday in June 1985, our son David called out from the study, where he had been watching TV.

'Dad, you're responsible for sport, aren't you? You'd better come and watch this!'

'This' was the extremely ugly riot at the Heysel Stadium in Brussels where Liverpool was playing Juventus in the European Cup Final. As we soon discovered, it led to thirty-eight deaths, numerous arrests and the exclusion of English football teams from competition in mainland Europe. It was made worse for me by the knowledge that Neil Macfarlane had sent a message to his Belgian counterpart only two days previously, expressing concern over reports that tickets might be on sale at the ground and that restaurants and wine bars were to be open before the game. He feared that it would be all too easy for boozed-up Brits to get in and make trouble. The Belgian Minister had replied haughtily that all was under control.

The telephone rang. The Prime Minister wanted an explanation. 'Please come to Number 10 at 0900 on Monday with the officials who know about football. The Minister for Sport, the junior Home Office Minister, Giles Shaw, and a Foreign Office Minister, will also be there . . .'

David Teasdale was on leave. Obviously he needed to be contacted. The Resident Clerk at DOE (an official who stays in the Department overnight and at weekends as a line of urgent communication) had a contact address, and tried it. No Teasdale. He was somewhere in the Isles of Greece. That left me and James Warnock, the Principal in the Branch, who had only been in the Division for two weeks.

We briefed ourselves and were grilled by the PM, who had already expressed national regret and personal outrage and announced that England was withdrawing from all European football competitions (a pre-emptive move, getting out before we were booted into touch). Her concern was over how football clubs could control their supporters. Admission of club members only? Membership cards? Electronic membership cards read at the gate? All-ticket matches? What else? There were repeated meetings with the football authorities during the following two weeks. I will not go into detail. What impressed me was the speed with which Margaret Thatcher, who started off knowing next to nothing about football, mastered the subject and asked such probing questions that she made the old men of the Football Association and League look ignorant. It sounded as if she was producing ideas they had never thought of. Perhaps she was.

For most of her time in office, Margaret Thatcher was not thought of as an environmentalist. But Sir Crispin Tickell, then UK Ambassador to the United Nations and himself well informed about how human outpourings of 'greenhouse gases' might change the climate, stimulated her interest in this topic. In 1987 she convened a 'teach in' at Number 11 Downing Street, the Chancellor's residence, attended by about half the Cabinet and a galaxy of scientists and industrialists. She started briskly, by telling the Ministers that they were there to listen, and should keep quiet as three experts, Tom Wigley, climatologist from the University of East Anglia, Crispin Tickell and Sir Robin Nicholson, industrialist and former Chief Scientific Adviser to the Government, gave presentations.

The message is now familiar. The Earth is habitable because certain gases that occur naturally in the atmosphere – water vapour and carbon dioxide – let in the radiation coming from the sun but trap the longer-wavelength radiation that would otherwise be reflected back into space. It's called 'the greenhouse effect' because that's what the glass of a greenhouse does. It means our planet is about 30 degrees Celsius warmer than it would otherwise be – and this, in turn, is obviously crucial for life. But humanity has been upsetting the system. We have burned a lot of coal, oil and gas which are 'fossil' fuels – laid down in the rocks by long-dead plants and marine life. We are therefore putting a surge of carbon dioxide into the atmosphere – and we are also releasing methane, nitrous oxide and CFCs, which are all 'greenhouse gases'. By the early 1980s most climatologists and ecologists were worrying that the result would be a warming of the Earth by between 1 and 4 degrees Celsius by the latter part of the twenty-first century – and that sea level would rise, because of the melting of glaciers and the expansion of the warmer ocean. Rainfall might become more torrential, and storms more violent. All this would be serious – for even a 1 degree rise in mean temperature would shift the zones of tolerance of plants, including crops and forest trees, over a hundred kilometres towards the poles or 130 metres up the mountains. And there seemed no easy way to halt the process: fossil fuel energy drove the world economy.

After the three presentations, a panel of scientists, economists and industrialists discussed the findings and what they might mean. We were given a good lunch, and I had to sum up. There was no dramatic change in British policy after the meeting, but I think it did help to make Margaret Thatcher more aware of the importance of world environmental issues. The increasing British commitment to action against greenhouse gases was strengthened when Sir John Houghton, Director General of the Meteorological Office, was appointed to chair the most influential of three expert groups under the Intergovernmental Panel on Climate Change. In 1989 the Prime Minister gave further evidence of her environmental conversion in a forceful speech at a Royal Society dinner.

But I have leaped forward. By 1986 I had a broad and interesting portfolio of duties, covering action against pollution in all its forms, at home and abroad, along with countryside and sport and my residual role as Chief Scientist in DOE and Chief Scientific Adviser in the Department of

Transport. We had created Her Majesty's Inspectorate of Pollution. But that year my load of responsibilities gained another weighty burden.

Peter Harrop had retired. His post as second Permanent Secretary was suppressed by the Treasury. Sir Terry Heiser, the latest of the six heads of DOE I served under, called me in.

'Martin, we're having to do some reorganization following Peter's retirement. We think you really can shed most of the research responsibilities, since you have such a good deputy in David Fisk. We want you to take water and water privatization. From Monday. We can't make you up to Second Permanent Secretary but we will promote you to "tweeny".'

'Tweeny?' There is (or was) an arrangement whereby senior Deputy Secretaries who carry more than normal responsibility get paid at an Upper Intermediate Pay Point halfway between Deputy and Permanent Secretary. Money without the status of the higher grade. Anyway, there it was. I got immersed in water.

The real problem was not with the routine policy, which meant a lot of contact with the regional Water Authorities, and was largely handled by a very capable Under Secretary, John Gunn, but with privatization. Ministers had established a tight timetable. John Patten was the Minister of State in charge and he had weekly meetings with his team of senior advisers, including people from the City helping to prepare for flotation. But first, of course, the policy had to be settled.

The new water companies were to be sold on the basis of a prospectus. That had to indicate fairly to would-be buyers what they were getting for their money. Government had to come clean about the standards for water quality or sewage treatment that might be demanded by Ministers, or emerge from negotiations in Brussels. Ministers would risk legal action if they sold the water industry without divulging any new and costly demands that they knew were on the way. So privatisation did impose some constraints on environmental policy.

Originally, the idea had been to sell off the regional water authorities as entities responsible for the whole water cycle in the ten major regions of the country. This would have meant that the new private companies would have been responsible for the cleanliness of rivers, their amenity, conservation and recreational use, and also water supply, wastewater treatment and sewage disposal. But Nicholas Ridley had decided that the conservation of amenity, river quality and recreation were 'public goods' that had to stay in the public sector. The privatised companies were to be utilities, selling water to consumers, managing reservoirs, and treating waste water to the standards required by a public 'watchdog', the National Rivers Authority. That made good sense – a public body was charged with the public good, and commercial bodies dealt with the commercial aspects. So it was settled, and remains, except that the NRA has merged with the Pollution Inspectorate as part of the Environment Agency.

By early 1987 it was evident that I had reached my career ceiling in the Civil Service. I was clearly not going to be a Permanent Secretary. I was 56. I had a very large rag-bag of responsibilities. The job was interesting, but the prospect was for four years of the same before retirement at age 60. I went off to Nairobi again, to lead the UK delegation to the UNEP Governing Council. Wolfgang Burhenne, German lawyer and long-standing colleague, approached me at a drinks party by the pool at the Norfolk Hotel.

'Martin, Kenton Miller is leaving his post as Director General of IUCN. The Headquarters is likely to move to the Netherlands. I am a member of the Search Committee for a new DG. Would you be interested in the job?'

I hesitated. IUCN? International Union for Conservation of Nature and Natural Resources. The oldest federation of nature and environment conservation bodies in the world, and now also much concerned with law, education, and environmentally sound development. I had been to one of its major conferences in Ottawa in 1986. I knew several people who had been closely associated with it, including Max Nicholson, Peter Scott, Maurice Strong, Lee Talbot, Mohamed Kassas and Wolfgang himself, who chaired its Commission on Environmental Policy and Law. I knew it was a highly respected body. I also knew it was in financial difficulties. But it might be a new and refreshing challenge.

'I might be,' I said. 'I'll have to talk it over with Lizzie.'

CHAPTER EIGHT

Back to Nature

IT WAS THE third time I had been asked about IUCN. On both previous occasions, family or career had stood in the way. This time I took it seriously. I had reached my Whitehall summit. The next three years looked like providing the same kind of work, and then retirement. The atmosphere of cuts, constraints and privatization and Ministers' apparent belief that the public service was a necessary evil, to be minimized rather than cherished, was slowly but surely reducing the standards and the pride of what had been the world's most professional, impartial and able administrative machine. Why not accept parachute, launch and pull rip-cord? I had a long talk with Lizzie.

'It's an international outfit that spearheads the protection of species and national parks, but it has a much wider range of environmental interests as well,' I explained. 'It was clear at that meeting William Waldegrave and I went to in Canada in 1986 that they were becoming concerned with social aspects of conservation and sustainable development. And they say the Headquarters will be moved to the Hague. The Dutch Government is offering a free building. That's handy for Amsterdam airport – direct flights to Cambridge – only an hour and a half from home. We could get back to see our mothers easily, any weekend . . .'

Our mothers were 89 and 87 respectively, in middling health, and living in residential care in Cambridge. We needed to be in regular touch, but they were well looked after. Robert and David were also independent, being about to graduate from Newcastle and Leicester Universities, and Mulumba was no longer our responsibility. We would have to be in Cambridge quite often, but we reckoned that if we were going to 'go international' there would be no better time. I told Wolfgang Burhenne that I was definitely interested. Naturally, though, there would be things to explore.

Suddenly, in September, a telegram arrived in the Department. COUNCIL APPROVED YOUR APPOINTMENT AS DIRECTOR GENERAL IUCN CONGRATULATIONS AND WELCOME = SWAMINATHAN. Dr Monkombu Swaminathan, a world-famous Indian scientist, was President of IUCN.

This could be described as jumping the gun. I had not been to visit the headquarters of IUCN at Gland in Switzerland. I had not accepted any formal offer. I had not told Sir Terry Heiser, the DOE Permanent Secretary, that I was even considering a move. And the telegram arrived just when we were up to our necks in the North Sea. A Ministerial Conference on the future of that productive but polluted tract of water was to be held in December, and I was leading the preparations. Dr Swaminathan's telegram meant that I had to break the news of my possible defection at once. Terry Heiser was not enthusiastic. But he understood – especially when he realized that this job offered the prospect of continuing after I was 60. Post-retirement employment is a preoccupation with senior Civil Servants as they advance through their 50s. But all this was in the air until Lizzie and I had actually been to Geneva to look at IUCN. I sent cautionary letters to Dr Swaminathan and to Dr José Furtado, a member of the Search Committee based at the Commonwealth Secretariat in London, who had been charged with agreeing terms with me.

IUCN, the International Union for Conservation of Nature and Natural Resources, was founded in 1948 through the initiative of Julian Huxley, then Director General of UNESCO, with the support of the Ligue Suisse pour la Conservation de la Nature and the Government of France (which convened the founding meeting at Fontainebleau). It was designed as a kind of United Nations for Nature – with membership open to States, Government Agencies and Non-Governmental Organizations. Its mission was to be a champion for nature at a time when post-war reconstruction in the developed countries and rapid economic growth in the newly-independent former colonies would clearly expose wildlife and wilderness to new pressures. Like the ecological service that Huxley and Tansley had envisaged in Britain, it was to apply ecological knowledge to the conservation and wise use of natural resources. Max Nicholson, although not a founder member, had been a very active supporter in the early days.

The Union was governed by a General Assembly of all the members, which met every three years. The GA, like its United Nations counterpart, debated the big issues and passed resolutions. In between sessions, the Union was governed by its Council, and run by its Director General and Secretariat. Perhaps its most famous features, however, were its Commissions. Sir Peter Scott had built up the Species Survival Commission, which prepared action plans to save threatened animals and plants. SSC was (and still is) the world's largest network of experts on the conservation of individual species. In my time it had some 5,000 members, organised in about a hundred specialist groups (it is bigger now). Under the strong leadership first of Gren Lucas of Kew and then of George Rabb, Curator of Brookfield Zoo at Chicago, and with expert staff inputs from Steve Edwards and Simon Stuart, SSC broadened its scope and deepened its professional skills, branching into captive breeding and other conservation techniques. It knew more than any other body about saving the world's rarest and most endangered animals.

The Commission on National Parks and Protected Areas led the action in IUCN's other traditional heartland area, and here Hal Eidsvik of Canada and Adrian Phillips of the British Countryside Commission were prominent. CNPPA was a kind of forum for the world's 'parks people,' and they used it to exchange knowledge of how to conserve outstanding landscapes and habitats. Other Commissions brought together specialists in environmental law, education, ecology and environmental planning. In parallel with this voluntary effort, the members of the Secretariat ran programmes on forests, wetlands, marine environments and deserts. There were close links with WWF, familiar as the World Wildlife Fund but for some arcane reason recently re-named World Wide Fund for Nature. IUCN was greatly respected as the international forum for conservation – and despaired of, because somehow it had never become the force its founders dreamed of.

The Union was based in the little town of Gland, near the shore of Lac Léman – the lake of Geneva. An unprepossessing town, with a core of a few older houses, most of them once farms, and a rapidly spreading fringe of light industry and apartments. The IUCN Secretariat was housed in two buildings. The larger was a grey structure with white windows, boasting the label 'WORLD CONSERVATION CENTRE'. Overflow staff were housed in a red-painted modern industrial structure across the road. 'The White House and the Kremlin' said someone facetiously. Both were shared with WWF. Kenton Miller, the current IUCN Director General, had his office in the Kremlin. Charles de Haes, Director General of WWF, ruled the White House. There were rumours of a Cold War between them.

When we went for our exploratory visit, we found ourselves drawn into a staff conference, followed by dinner in a nearby village inn. There were only about fifty people there, but they were obviously highly dedicated. Their enthusiasm for what they were doing reminded Lizzie of the Antarctic Survey, and this made her positive at once. But it seemed a very small concern. 'Running this'll be like falling off a log,' I told her. 'I should have some time to do some science, think about world conservation, and maybe write a book or two...' We went for a drive up a snaking road through beech forests to the little resort of St Cergue in the Jura mountains, and looked across the lake to a vast panorama of Alps. We explored the little town of Nyon, founded by Julius Caesar in person. We took the train and walked round Geneva. We were greatly attracted by what we saw – though of course, at that stage, we still expected that we would be master-minding a move to the Netherlands rather than staying in Switzerland. 'It'd be good living here, though,' said Lizzie. 'But in any case it feels the right job for you!'

We decided to accept. Terry Heiser said firmly that in that case I should retire from the Civil Service at the end of January 1988. Kenton Miller was not due to leave IUCN until April, but this would allow overlap and our attendance at the General Assembly to be held in February in Costa Rica. 'You can't do two jobs at once,' said Terry, 'and once you go to the Costa Rica meeting, your mind will be on the new job, not the one here. Better to make a clean break.'

Meanwhile, there was work to do – especially for the North Sea. I was chairing both a Scientific Working Group that was preparing a report on the state of the sea and a Policy Working Group that was drawing up the agenda and draft Declaration for the Ministers. Both groups were drawn from all the coastal countries around the North Sea and some whose territory barely touched it, like France. The Prince of Wales was to make the opening speech. The Conference would be presided over by Nicholas Ridley as the senior Minister for the host country, and Lord Belstead, as Minister of State on the environment protection side of DOE, would lead the UK delegation (William Waldegrave had by this time gone to a Ministerial post in the Foreign and Commonwealth Office).

I briefed Ministers on our scientific conclusions. There was a need to reduce the influx of toxic materials like heavy metals, most of which came down the rivers. The Rhine was the largest single source. There was a problem with nitrate and phosphate from farmland and sewers, for these were fertilizing the sea and causing 'red tides' – outbursts of red-tinted microscopic plants that could be poisonous to fish, shellfish and people. This problem was at its worst around Denmark. There was almost universal opposition to the continuing dumping of industrial wastes and sewage sludges in the North Sea – and here Britain was the principal offender. It seemed clear that the practice would have to cease. And beyond that, there was widespread demand for adoption of 'the precautionary principle' – the principle that if something had the potential to cause harm to the environment, its input should be minimized or stopped altogether.

Britain was not ready for general acceptance of the precautionary principle, which had taken shape in Germany, although the decision to move to unleaded petrol ahead of scientific proof of its impact on health was really an example of it. The Treasury was predictably negative about any new policies that imposed costs – as phasing out the dumping of sewage sludge, and stopping the tipping of colliery waste on the Durham coast clearly would. But unless we gave way on dumping the Conference would fail and the UK would once again be castigated as the 'dirty man of Europe'. Ministers decided they had to comply. They would also emphasize the need for internationally-coordinated research and monitoring. The international scientific group agreed with this, but it had to be presented carefully. Britain was often accused of urging better science as means of procrastination. We needed to appear not only as the champion of science and rational analysis, but as committed to the environmental action that science indicated. The tone of the Conference would be all-important.

The keynote speech would set that tone. I was summoned, together with Jeremy Eppel, the Principal in charge of organizing the meeting, to brief the Prince of Wales at Highgrove.

We were ushered into the drawing room on the first floor. Prince Charles appeared, with Jimmy Saville who was advising him on the style and delivery of his speeches. We gave them the same presentation of the facts that we had given Ministers. The Prince was keen.

'The sea is tremendously important to me,' he said. 'Ever since I was in the Navy and commanded that ship. I would like to use this speech really to move action forward. I can't say anything that disagrees with the Government's position, but I can highlight the issues and try to get the Conference off to a positive start. And I do need to say something fairly memorable. But no carbuncles, please . . .'

We chatted about the state of the North Sea. There was a problem with debris – much of it plastic waste from ships – that washed up at the tide-line and never decayed. The phrase 'ribbon of filth' dropped into the conversation, and subsequently into the speech itself. I explained about the precautionary principle. HRH thought it was obvious common sense. Jimmy Saville was adamant that the speech had to be lively. We agreed that it should strike a note that all the delegations found harmonious. It should be a keynote speech for the Conference as a whole: Ministers would make the points specific to the UK. I promised some notes on where I thought the consensus might lie. The Prince ended with a touch of philosophy. 'I think I can use my position to do some good,' he said. 'I can raise issues and make sure they are talked about. I can ask questions. That's how I see myself contributing.'

We went away. I did send several pages of ideas. A number of paragraphs did find their way into the speech. It struck a positive note, and launched the meeting on its way to success. It got the precautionary principle established as a central strand of European Community environmental policy. It was greeted with a kind of amazed delight by most of the European delegations. 'I never thought to hear a speech like that in Britain,' said one. 'I wish we had a Prince who understood the environment so well,' said several others.

Unfortunately it was a much better speech than Nick Ridley's or John Belstead's, whose drafts had been diluted and 'sanitised' in the process of interdepartmental clearance. As Jonathan Dimbleby records in his biography of the Prince of Wales, I got blamed for helping him to upstage Ministers. Perhaps it was just as well that I was going.

I went back to Geneva soon after the North Sea Conference. For the question of IUCN's location loomed large. Switzerland had countered the Dutch offer. 'Stay here, and we'll give you a new Headquarters too,' they announced. I joined a Working Group that went to look at three possible buildings in the Hague. We were warmly welcomed by Donald Kuenen, former Rector of the University of Leiden and also former IUCN President. The offices were good, and we could have managed there very well. But there was some haggling over tax allowances: in Switzerland IUCN was permitted to retain the income tax it deducted from its staff, while the Dutch did not see their way to making the same concessions. The balance was a difficult one. The Netherlands would be cheaper, and Amsterdam was an ideal airport for worldwide travel. Taxation would be higher. Residence permits and house purchase for European Community citizens would be easier. The upheaval of moving would be considerable, and we would be bound to lose a lot of Swiss staff, or staff married to Swiss. Some people looked sadly at the prospect of exchanging the wonderful mountain environment for the damp pastures and wind-whipped dunes beside the grey, cold, North Sea. In the end we recommended that IUCN stay in Switzerland. However, the decision would need confirmation by the General Assembly in Costa Rica in February.

27 January 1988. Retirement party at DOE. Well over a hundred colleagues, saying the customary nice things. Nick Ridley said a few kind words and William Waldegrave came back from the Foreign and Common- wealth Office to make a very generous speech. And so it was over. Eighteen years since I joined the Central Unit – nearly half my professional life. What had I achieved? In the scientific world such a question is easier to answer because most of the achievements are set down in published research papers, and you can evaluate their influence by the frequency with which they are cited by others. Another measure of success is expressed in the achievements of the people you have trained. It is much harder in Whitehall, because policy edges forward incrementally, as a result of a vast number of interactions. The most I could claim was to have helped make the national and global environment just a little bit cleaner and safer. Anyway, that phase of my life was over now.

A few days later, Lizzie and I flew to Costa Rica. Politics began in the air, for Raymond Junod, a member of the Conseil d'État of the Canton of Vaud,

Goodbye DOE! Martin Holdgate's farewell photograph on the roof of the North Tower, 2 Marsham Street, January 1988. © The Times.

the state of the Swiss Confederation in which IUCN was based, was on the plane and began to explain his incomprehension over the need for any further debate about the Headquarters location. It was a good test of my barely-adequate French. We swung into San José, were spirited through the entry formalities by Fiona Hanson, a tirelessly efficient IUCN secretary, and found ourselves in the Hotel Cariari where the General Assembly was centred. About 800 people were converging from over a hundred countries. Prince Philip, International President of WWF and IUCN Vice President, had his suite just along the corridor.

It was a most enjoyable event. Partly, I suspect, because as Heir Apparent I had no responsibilities – and was welcomed as a possible saviour. For it soon became evident that IUCN was in a financial mess.

To explain why, I should say a bit about how it is funded. The money comes three ways. First, the members pay dues (in Swiss francs). These however only account for around 10 per cent of the total income. Second, some money is donated – WWF traditionally gave a million Swiss francs a year, but announced in Costa Rica that it was halving it. Third, money is provided for specific programmes and projects, especially by Development Aid agencies. In 1988 IUCN was getting its best contracts from the Nordic countries, the Netherlands, Switzerland and Germany. These contracts supported programmes like those on tropical forests and wetlands, and had caused IUCN to set up a growing series of Regional and Country offices in developing countries – including a tiny unit in Costa Rica. But the expansion of contract work also brought tensions, for as that side of the programme grew the proportionate share of work done through the Commissions declined, and this upset some members. A small part of the contract income could be siphoned off to help pay for the central management of the organization and its voluntary networks, but these had, for the most part, to be paid for out of 'unrestricted' money like dues and donations, and these funds were in shortest supply.

Bodies like IUCN are very vulnerable to changes in cash flow. Imagine that a crisis in Ruritania leads to the collapse of the currency or Government cuts, or both. Suddenly the inflow to IUCN is slashed. But it takes time to cut the salary bill, or to save money on travel. So there is continual risk of a deficit. In 1987 it had been compounded by an accounting error which led money to be wrongly classified as an accumulated 'unrestricted' bank balance when it was actually restricted project money received in advance. Moreover the financial management service was run jointly with WWF International – but the two bodies had quite different needs. IUCN had to be able to monitor short-term changes in cash flow. WWF had about 50 million Swiss francs in the bank, available for whatever programmes their Executive Committee decided.

That in turn led to jealousy. Many of our people believed that WWF had really been created as IUCN's fund-raising arm. They got cross when WWF cut its donations or mounted competing initiatives. But the history was more complicated. True, WWF was the brain-child of Peter Scott, Max Nicholson and others, who *were* closely associated with IUCN and saw the need to raise funds for it. But they had a wider vision, sensing that the time was ripe for a public appeal to save vanishing wildlife – tied especially to spectacular species like tigers or rhinos or birds of paradise. They expected that many of the initiatives the Fund supported would be pursued through IUCN. But they never saw the relationship as an exclusive one, and as WWF grew stronger it naturally determined its own priorities. If IUCN was to be the preferred channel for WWF money, it had to market itself, especially by proving that it could deliver real conservation goods. It had not always done so.

All this was new to me in Costa Rica. But I sat in on various meetings of the Council as the budget was slashed and Mike Cockerell, the Assistant Director General (Management), proposed new figures. Mike was a British engineer who had worked in the Hong Kong administration and the Battelle Institute in Switzerland. He had developed a new financial management system for IUCN, which was to be the secret of success in the years ahead. He was tough, and at times a bit dictatorial – which put staff backs up. But it was obvious that he was highly competent. I saw that he would be a key figure in the team.

I also saw that we would have to give priority to a new working partnership with WWF. Prince Philip had made that pretty plain when I had sought an audience with him in London before I actually took the job on. He spoke bluntly about some of the IUCN officers, Council members and management. 'You should get rid of that bloody man, to start with...' was one injunction. It so happened – for a variety of reasons – that the bloody man went. This, no doubt, was reckoned positively to my account. But I heard the same kind of harsh language from the IUCN camp, much of it directed at the WWF Director General, Charles de Haes. A Belgian by birth, Charles had been trained as a manager in the private sector, especially under the entrepreneur and businessman Anton Rupert, in South Africa. He had been at the helm of WWF for much of its existence. He had a strong personality and a quick mind – and was intolerant of those he regarded as fools. He clearly thought that IUCN had more than its fair share of incompetents.

The squabbling was harmful. The more the two organizations fell out, the weaker conservation would be. I think that once Charles de Haes and I achieved a measure of mutual understanding and respect, we both set out to heal the rifts. Prince Philip helped a good deal. He was an IUCN Vice President for my first three years as Director General, and came to two of the three General Assemblies during my period of office (he only missed the third because IUCN was following WWF in meeting in Argentina, and it was felt that two British Royal visits in one year might jar political sensitivities). Before long, Charles de Haes and his deputy, Henner Ehringhaus, were meeting Mike Cockerell and me regularly for a chat over lunch, and we started dropping into one another's offices when there were problems to discuss.

But this was far ahead. My memory of the Costa Rica General Assembly is of the friendliness of the event, and of its relaxed atmosphere despite the financial tensions. There were good professional workshops (I found myself discussing Antarctic conservation in one of them). There were invaluable personal contacts (which is what many people came for). Old friends like Lee and Marty Talbot and Gerardo Budowski (the first Director General of IUCN and a colleague on the IBP CT Committee years ago) mingled with new colleagues. It was a wonderful opportunity to see IUCN staff in action. There were field trips (we went up an active volcano named Poas in driving mist, and found several plants typical of the cooler south, including a big

Gunnera like the Chilean *pangue* and a little orange-berried *Nertera* like the one that grows on Tristan). We had a formal welcome from President Oscar Arias in the lovely theatre in down-town San José, after which everyone, including the President and the Duke of Edinburgh, walked to a reception through streets guarded by nothing more formidable than Boy Scouts with staves. And Prince Philip entertained about forty of us to a splendid dinner aboard *Britannia* which was in port on the Pacific coast of Costa Rica, ready to take him on a visit to the Galápagos islands.

It was dark as the dinner ended – a warm, moist, tropical night with lights reflected in puddles on the quayside. We stood at the ship's rails and watched the Royal Marines beat Retreat, their white uniforms wheeling and marching with exact precision. Oscar and Margarita Arias said their farewells, spent a few minutes chatting to the spectators behind the rope barriers, and drove away. The General Assembly wound to its close. We left feeling happy about the future.

We moved to Switzerland in April 1988. We took the easy way when it came to a home. We simply took over the lease of the house in the village of Gingins where Kenton and Sue Miller had been living. A modern, end-of-terrace house on four floors, the basement containing the fall-out shelter obligatory in Switzerland in case the nuclear balloon went up outside. The house looked south-east over an old orchard, to a glimpse of the lake and the high Alps beyond. We could sit on our little paved terrace on a fine summer evening and sip our gin and tonic as the rose tints spread on the peak of Mont Blanc and its attendant summits: the Dent du Midi, the Grandes Jorasses and the Aiguille Verte.

Gingins (our English friends found the name easy to remember, with or without tonic and a twist of lemon) lies at the foot of the Jura, about 500 metres above sea level. Its fields run up to the base of a forested escarpment, which culminates in the crest of the Dôle, 1677 metres high. We soon found that the forests were criss-crossed by delightful tracks, popular among weekend walkers, while the high pastures were wonderfully rich in flowers. As the snow melted in spring, so crocuses appeared at its margins; later came the brilliant little blue gentians and orchids, and in high summer tall yellow-flowered gentians, spearing from amidst the long grass, munched by golden-brown cows tinkling with bells.

Life in Switzerland suited us. We enjoyed the ordered, dependable society in which things happened when they were supposed to happen, and where services were good and the environment beautiful. Oh – I know that like all societies it had its other side. It was fine if you had a good income and a conformist nature. It was not good for rebels or the poor. Officially the latter did not exist – but in reality problems with homeless and jobless youth, aggravated by drugs, were emerging in Zurich and Geneva in our time. There was even crime. When we arrived, people often did not bother to lock their houses when they went out. By the time we left, everybody did.

IUCN decided to stay in Switzerland because we were well-established there, because our staff liked it, because we were offered fine facilities, and because any of our Council or members could come to visit us regardless of nationality. The same, of course, would have been true in the Netherlands – but was not so in all countries. We had members in Israel and South Africa. They could not travel to countries that did not recognize their Governments, or accept the legitimacy of their passports. Some of our members from the developing world liked Switzerland for another reason – it had no colonial past.

Some of us, unused to a federal state, did find aspects of its government strange. Switzerland has a three-level system: Commune, Canton and Confederation. You live in a commune, or district, which sanctions your residence, to which you pay certain taxes and within which a lot of local decisions are taken. The communes are grouped into Cantons which are the real States of the Confederation, and dominate much of its governance: the Federal level deals only with the highest and most nationwide affairs.

This three-layered politics was destined to have a big influence on the location of our new headquarters. No sooner had we returned from Costa Rica, with a happy Raymond Junod reporting to the Canton de Vaud that the General Assembly had ratified the decision to stay in his home country, than debate began. The Vaudois Government had a policy of locating new state-sponsored development in the north of their territory, around the old Roman spa of Yverdon-les-Bains on the lake of Neuchâtel. In Swiss terms it made sense – it created new employment, drew population away from the zone of townships along the lake of Geneva, and was quite handy for internal communications with Berne and Zurich. But for an international organization like ours it made no sense. We were shown a site – a good site – overlooking the lake at Yverdon. We said we wanted to stay near to Geneva, and close to WWF in Gland.

Geneva itself, of course, was out of the question. It was a separate state. We were in Vaud, and Vaud had promised to help finance the new building. In Vaud we would remain. The commune of Gland was happy for us to stay. We looked at a splendid big house with remarkable Art Deco fittings, standing in wooded grounds by the lake. The principal bedroom looked ideal as Director General's office. It had an en suite bathroom, with green marble slabs surrounding a bath into which one descended in Roman fashion.

'That's great!' I said. 'I'll make that my personal think tank. I'll appoint a

The opening of the new IUCN Headquarters. The Syndic of Gland plants a ceremonial tree! Photograph: Studio Berger, Nyon, for IUCN.

group of attendants – we'll call them the Companions of the Bath – to wait upon me and record my wise words . . .' I was suspected of rather poor British humour. The deal fell through.

We did end up in Gland, but it took two years to agree on the site and arrangements. Annoyed by our rejection of Yverdon, the Canton of Vaud said they'd only contribute 5 million francs. Their public works department estimated the cost of meeting our needs at 35 million. The Confederation simply would not make up that difference. Minister Walter Gyger, the senior Federal Civil Servant in Berne concerned with our affairs, telephoned me.

'What do you really need?' he demanded. 'Could you buy a building? What about the one you're in – could you buy it from WWF, and let them move?'

Mike Cockerell had the building valued – between 7 and 8 million francs. But it did not really meet our needs – it had no good meeting rooms and no space for our library. We looked at what else was on the market. The Syndic (Town Clerk) of Gland was helpful. Gyger came to the rescue.

'If Gland will donate a site, and Vaud will pay 5 million francs, we'll find twelve. That makes 17 million. If we simply give you the money, will you organize a competition between at least three architects and then take responsibility for putting the building up?'

This was what any Director General would hail as the dream solution. I closed hastily. We invited architects. One was so enthused by the notion of building a temple of science and conservation that he wildly exceeded his brief and designed a building that would indeed have been most impressive – but which simply broke all the planning rules for the site and would probably have bust the budget as well. That left two designs. One was for a long rectangular building that reminded me of an English railway station. The other was for a well-lit, airy, structure, partly open-plan and partly with individual offices, with good meeting facilities and a prospect of light and greenery in the interior. We chose the latter. The deal was tied up before we met in Perth, Western Australia, for our General Assembly in 1990 and the building was occupied in 1992. It works well. I am proud to have seen it through to completion in my time as Director General.

But this, too, is to leap far into the future. We arrived. We started to find out about basic facts of life like how to buy a car (you had to have your residence permit first, and for that you had to have a chest X-ray and bill of clean health from a clinic in Geneva). There were things like opening bank accounts, finding a doctor and dentist, finding which shops and supermarkets sold what, and where everything else was. Lizzie flung herself into it all with obvious enjoyment. She joined the International Women's Club of Nyon and before long found herself chairing its Charity Committee and helping to organize an immensely successful fund-raising Bazaar. We became friendly with our neighbours in Pré de la Ferme, which proved an international village. Rolf and Rita Buser and their two boys, German-speaking Swiss, on one side. Donald and Pat Prater, English, on the other. By curious coincidence, Donald, a scholar in German and writer of biographies, had studied at the Sorbonne at the same time as Robert's father, Hartmut, just before the war.

For me, the need was to get to know everyone in IUCN and to work out how to develop the programme 'within available resources' (to use a phrase endlessly repeated by Mostafa Tolba of UNEP when his Governing Council tried to tell him to do things they weren't willing to fund). Here, I was helped immensely by Mike Cockerell and his scientific 'oppo' Jeff McNeely, by my superb Personal Assistant, Estelle Viguet, and by the IUCN Personnel Officer, Christine Bühler. But of course, as I got into the job, problems became evident. It was clearly going to be nowhere near as easy as falling off the proverbial log. Indeed, in October 1988 I wrote a rude diatribe about the woes of IUCN entitled SIX MONTHS OF GLANDULAR FEVER and sent it to the staff. I was disturbed by the lack of team spirit, by internal rivalries, and by an inward looking attitude that seemed to me ill suited to an organization created to achieve world conservation.

IUCN's 40th Anniversary. The participants in the special conference pose on the Escalier des Adieux at Fontainebleau. Yolanda Kakabadse (later to be President) and Monkombu Swaminathan flank Martin Holdgate in the front row. Photograph: Inez Forbes, UNESCO.

Getting out to see our members was clearly an important part of the job. In 1988 I found myself in Brussels, the Hague, Washington DC, New York, Nairobi (followed by a visit to field projects in Kenya and Tanzania), Dar es Salaam, Helsinki, Stockholm, Oslo, Copenhagen and Paris – as well as London.

The Paris visits were special. For 1988 was the 40th anniversary of the founding of IUCN. When I arrived I discovered that, probably as a result of the financial crisis, the Council had not made any plans for marking the event. My senior French colleague, Frédéric Briand, thought this was wrong. He saw the anniversary as a great opportunity to emphasize that IUCN valued its links with the French-speaking world (something in doubt because of the anglophone domination of the Secretariat and Council). So we swung into action. We arranged a special number of our *Bulletin*, written largely in French and translated into English rather than the habitual other way about. Frédéric persuaded UNESCO, one of our co-founders, to lay on a special evening Gala, and José Carreras and Barbara Hendricks gave their time to sing for us without charge. It was one of Carreras' first public engagements since his recovery from a tussle with cancer, which made it especially generous and welcome. In fact all seemed fine until I found that I had to go on stage and deliver a speech in French in front of about a thousand people, headed by the Foreign Minister of France. Happily, Frédéric wrote it and rehearsed me, and the subterfuge worked. 'I never knew you spoke such good French,' said Charles de Haes. He soon discovered the truth.

On the serious side, the Government of France, our other co-founder with UNESCO and the Ligue Suisse, supported a meeting at Fontainebleau, in the very hall where the Union was created, and convened a special commemorative gathering in the Conference Centre in the Avenue Kléber, where we were addressed by the Premier, Michel Rocard. To cap it all, we were allowed to share a reception at the Muséum National d'Histoire Naturelle with a group dedicated to saving the wild bears of the Pyrenees – I'm not sure about the symbolism. At that event, I had to present a special message – somewhat presumptuously entitled the 'Declaration de Fontainebleau' – to President Mitterand. It all helped to make the point that IUCN was energetic, had ideas, and valued its links with the French-speaking world.

Most of the visits in the northern countries were for fund-raising, to take part in Conferences, to give lectures, or a combination of all three. One of the Conferences took me back to London early in 1989, I suspect at the instigation of Fiona McConnell, head of the international division of the Central Directorate on Environmental Protection. I was to be Rapporteur of a Conference Margaret Thatcher was convening to strengthen the targets for getting rid of the ozone-destroying CFCs. The Prime Minister welcomed everyone, Nick Ridley sat in the chair, President Moi of Kenya gave an opening address, and Mostafa Tolba was in great form (cheered by Mrs Thatcher's public announcement that she was doubling the UK's contribution to UNEP!). In one sense it was a bit of a re-run of the North Sea Conference, for after a reception in the Egyptian Gallery of the British Museum, where Mostafa could be seen in rapt contemplation of treasures from his homeland, the Prince of Wales gave a spirited after-dinner address under the shadow of an Armenian mausoleum from the fourth century BC. But HRH once again upset Nick Ridley by departing from his text and speaking with deep sincerity about his own environmental beliefs. The Secretary of State's irritation was evident at the planning session next morning. 'What are we going to do about that bloody Prince?' he demanded. He calmed down when it became clear that a lot of us agreed with what the Prince had said.

IUCN's most loyal supporters were in the Nordic countries and the Netherlands (despite their unhappiness over the Headquarters). It was important for the Director General to go there, meet their Ministers, talk to senior officials and persuade them to go on supporting our programmes. But most of the interesting action was on the ground in the developing countries, and it was this that took me to East Africa in August 1988.

Lizzie came too, for this was to be partly a safari. We flew into Nairobi, to be met by Rob Malpas, head of the IUCN East Africa Office which was the largest of our presences in the developing world at the time (the others were in Costa Rica and Pakistan). Rob was a zoologist and a first-class manager of field projects. He was less happy in Ministerial offices, or in the arcane political world of the UN. But it helped that I knew Mostafa Tolba and many of the senior UNEP staff very well, and that the Minister we had to deal with was George Muhoho, who had played a prominent part in Kenya's delegations to the Stockholm PrepComs.

George was an enigmatic fellow. Indeed he had metamorphosed down the years. I first knew him as a slim, young, Catholic priest. His status as a diplomat with obvious influence at home seemed strange until it was reported that he was President Kenyatta's brother in law – brother to Mama Ngina, the ageing President's last wife. George's swift elevation as Ambassador to the Holy See (the Vatican) became less surprising – and indeed he was a clever and highly articulate man who would have succeeded in many situations. Time went by, and Jomo Kenyatta died – and George moved across to work for UNEP. The wheel spun again, and behold – he was Kenyan Ambassador to UNEP, dispensed of his Orders, married, and with a family. By the time he became Minister for Environment and Tourism the slim figure had broadened, but the charm, fluency and quickness of wit remained. You had to get up very early in the morning to get ahead of him.

Rob Malpas took us to the office we rented – on the edge of town, in a modern building that belonged to an association of local airways. It stood amid well-kept lawns, with fringes of garden, in the midst of dereliction. The way there was by rutted roads where the pools were hub-deep after the rains. The spaces between were of scanty, ungrazed, grassland, dotted with half-built structures. From our upper floor you looked out across the Nairobi National Park, whose fence was only a few hundred metres away. Rob's is the only office desk from which I have seen three wild Black rhinoceros, accompanied by ostrich, giraffe, wildebeeste and gazelles. 'The rhinos come up here to be away from the tourists,' he said. 'They don't seem to mind the aircraft.' That end of the Park was under the flight path to the international airport, and big planes whistled overhead quite often. The rhinos did not give a snort.

We had a spare weekend. 'I've fixed for you to go to Governors' Camp,' said Rob. 'You can see the country and wildlife on Saturday, and Iain and Oria Douglas-Hamilton will come down and give you a fly-round on Sunday morning. I'll turn up for lunch and drive you on to the Serengeti.'

We flew to the Masai Mara in a DC3 – lovingly maintained, with the original 1930s-style decor. Governors' was a tented camp – but what tents! Big sleeping tents with real beds, and an en suite loo and washroom. Lizzie was a bit jumpy. 'Will there be snakes?' was her predictable question. 'Of course, lots of them!' said I. Silly thing to say. Every time she needed to go to the loo, I was sent in front with a torch, like the man with a red flag in front of an early car, to make sure that no hostile reptiles lurked behind the throne. Indeed wildlife was all around. Elephants browsed on the far bank of the little river as we ate lunch, and at night chomping noises outside suggested the presence of a hungry hippo. We went for evening and morning drives in an open-topped Land Rover and saw more elephants, lionesses with families of cubs on a recent kill, one rhino and calf guarded by a Ranger in a Land Rover and ringed by tourists, and the familiar East African assemblage of gazelles, giraffe, hartebeeste, buffalo, zebra and much else.

Iain Douglas-Hamilton flew in after breakfast on Sunday. Iain is an internationally-respected authority on elephants, and the author of a highly-readable book about his family life among them, in the Lake Manyara National Park in Tanzania. He also had the reputation of being an exciting pilot to fly with. Rob had briefed him. 'Elizabeth Holdgate has never been up in a small aircraft,' he warned. 'Please treat her gently – straight and level, no dives or tight banking!' Iain promised to be good.

He was – to start with. We took off and flew sedately at about six hundred metres, with the Masai Mara park spread out around us. Then – 'Elephants! Do you mind if we go down and take a look at them?' Then – 'Look!' It was the wildebeeste migration, coming north from the Serengeti plains. Thousands of wildebeeste, in a long, dark brown ribbon like an army of ants. It was too much for sedateness. Down Iain went, to fly parallel with the column and about fifty metres up. It was a spectacular sight, and Lizzie did not seem to turn a hair – or an abdominal muscle. Iain relaxed. We made a wide sweep over the escarpment to the west, and encroaching grainlands to the north. 'That belongs to the President's son,' said Oria, pointing to a big new farm with a shiny corrugated iron roof.

We turned south towards the Serengeti and made a sweep into Tanzania.

This is the greatest wildlife area remaining in East Africa. Most of it is grass plains, undulating gently and rising occasionally into low ridges capped by rocky outcrops. There is an escarpment on the west, with Lake Victoria beyond it. To the east the land rises towards volcanic peaks, several of which

The wildebeest migration, as seen from Iain Douglas-Hamilton's aircraft.

surround the immense caldera of Ngorongoro. The whole area is the home of big populations of wildebeeste and other antelopes (wildebeeste are really antelopes though they look like small brown cattle with shaggy dark manes). There are many zebra, hartebeeste, gazelles and buffalo. Many of these animals migrate with the season, and as the grazing waxes and wanes. But the whole is one system, and the vast Serengeti National Park in Tanzania – almost 1.5 million hectares in extent – is inseparable from the 150,000 hectare Masai Mara National Reserve in Kenya: animals make nothing of arbitrary international frontiers.

Iain turned back. Then he reverted to type. Vultures were wheeling to one side, dropping towards an invisible kill. Most pilots of single-engined aircraft give these big birds a wide berth. They are the most dangerous things in the sky, because if you hit one you are almost certain to crash. But Iain was different. 'Vultures!' he said. 'Something must have died down there. Let's go and see what it is! Keep an eye open for birds, Oria!' And down we went – happily hitting no members of the queue for MacZebra's, but not quite certain as to what was on the menu that day.

Rob rolled in to Governors' later than planned – he had hit rain, and the track traversed black cotton soil that gets immensely slippery when wet. He had spun off once or twice and had to take it slowly. By the time we got away it was clear that we were going to have to drive in the dark for a few hours. We left the Mara through an incredible monument to futility – an immense gateway, standing in the midst of nowhere, straddling the road but easy to by-pass on either side. We were told that it was the product of a World Bank grant to Kenyan National Parks. Then we turned south and began to come across the wildebeeste – and their watchers.

There was a little grassy knoll on the right hand side of the road. On its top were six lions, sitting in a row like very good children at Sunday School, all looking expectantly over the crest. Down below a Japanese family was busy photographing. The lions looked suitably attentive. But they weren't interested in the Japanese. Beyond them, coming ever nearer, was a massive herd of wildebeeste. Uncounted suppers on the hoof were drifting unsuspectingly towards the lions, who only had to wait. Unfortunately we couldn't stay and see what happened next.

We entered Tanzania at a very minor crossing south of Keekorok where they had run out of official immigration forms – so we had to write our own on pages torn from a notebook. It took time, but was very good-humoured. Then on, across darkening plains, and among patches of scrub. We paused for 'comfort stations'. As Lizzie got back into the Land Rover she muttered, 'Bet there's a lion just round the corner.' There wasn't – only a cheetah which lolloped carelessly along the road ahead. A herd of buffalo stampeded across. At last – yes, there were more lions. Then, round a corner, we came on a vehicle with a man lying under it tinkering with the engine. He seemed more alarmed about us than the lions, and declined help, beyond asking for directions to the nearest safari lodge. And so to Seronera, and supper with Markus Borner of the Frankfurt Zoological Society, IUCN's partner in a major study of the management of the Serengeti and Ngorongoro.

Markus flew us on next day, after a meeting with Serengeti officers and a quick drive to look for leopards among a ridge of abrupt rock 'koppies'. Lizzie liked his style of pilotage. He flew about a hundred metres up, so that she could see the ground clearly, and spot whatever moved there. 'It's like being on top of a very grand double-decker bus!' she said. But slowly he climbed as we approached the Ngorongoro crater, slipping over the rim at about 2,500 metres to open up an immense view of the interior, which is one of the most spectacular wildlife habitats in the world. We looked out across a great caldera – a basin formed by the collapse of the central parts of a volcano – about thirty kilometres across and six or seven hundred metres deep. A large soda-lake with a white fringe of salt-flats glinted in the distance.

Markus determined on a quick fly-round. Cutting his engine, he glided down until he was level with the tops of Lerai Forest, a big patch of fever trees (a kind of acacia) near the southern corner of the crater. There were elephants there. But he was on the hunt for rhino. Once upon a time hundreds of Black rhinoceros roamed Ngorongoro, giving it one of the densest rhino populations in the world. By 1988 poaching had knocked the numbers down to only around thirty. They were still under grave threat from those foolish men who think that ground rhino horn will make *them* more horny, or those vain people in the Arab world who treasure rhino-horn dagger hilts as a badge of rank. It was hard to blame the poachers, though, for they could make more money by one act of slaughter than they could earn lawfully in several years. It was much easier to blame the middle-men, who creamed off most of the money while leaving the poacher on the ground to take the risk of long imprisonment or even of being killed in a shoot-out with park rangers.

Markus found three rhino in his swoop-about, before climbing up slowly in the warm, thin, air to approach the airstrip on the caldera rim. As at Chepu thirty years before, somebody had to drive along the runway to clear it of animals – in this case zebra – before we could land. And so to the hotel, perched on the lip of the crater and with a marvellous view over it. We spent two days there, meeting the Chairman of the Ngorongoro Conservation Area Authority, Mrs Esther Malacela, the Director, Juma Kayera and our own staff member, Scott Perkin, who was preparing a management plan. We had ample time to drive around and admire the diverse wild life, picnicking beside the Land Rover in warm sunshine and watching a herd of buffalo grazing a few hundred metres away. It all looked very safe and peaceful – and clearly was, for as we drove on we came upon four very well-fed and sleepy lions, tummies uppermost, snoozing in the sunshine. I was allowed to go for a walk to examine the scrub forests on the eastern rim of the crater, guarded by a ranger with an ancient rifle. I went carefully, for that weapon seemed more dangerous than any wildlife we might encounter!

Ngorongoro poses the kinds of problem you will find in many parts of the developing world. It is, unquestionably, magnificent scenery, and it still supports a profusion of wild animals. In a day there you are virtually certain to see elephants, hippos, lions, buffalo, zebra and wildebeeste, and you have a good chance of seeing a rhino as well. The only big and spectacular beasts you won't see are giraffes, for there aren't any in the caldera. You can even see an amazing amount in long-range telescopic safaris from the hotel terrace, beer in hand. But the hotel and staff houses are in the wrong place by today's standards, which dictate that such installations should be on the edge of a National Park, not plumb in its centre. If people live in the middle of wild life they will inevitably come into contact and possible conflict, as we saw on the road from the airstrip when we met an agitated man waving to

slow us down, as an equally agitated young elephant summoned up courage
to cross the road. Old male buffalo of questionable temperament were
grazing along the hotel driveway. Scott Perkin's lawn was regularly nibbled
by zebra, and one night he had to spend an hour sitting in his car, waiting
for an elephant which had found out how to detach a loose connecting pipe
on his water tank to finish its leisurely drink and amble away from the back
door.

But the real problem is the interaction between wildlife and tourism on
the one hand and local people on the other. This has been a vexed issue ever
since 1872, when Yellowstone was established by the United States
Congress as the world's first National Park. Such parks were the vision of
the great Scottish American naturalist, John Muir, who saw in the
wilderness the noblest manifestations of God. The American philosophy
was well summarized by President John F. Kennedy in his welcome to the
First World Conference on National Parks, organized by IUCN and held in
Seattle in June 1962. 'National Parks,' he wrote, 'are places where we can
find release from the tensions of an increasingly industrialized civilization,
where we can have personal contact with the natural environment which
sustains us.' Secretary of the Interior, Stewart Udall, was more apocalyptic.
'With few exceptions the places of superior scenic beauty, the unspoiled
landscapes, the spacious refuges for wild life, the nature parks and nature
reserves of significant size that our generation saves will be all that is
preserved. We are the architects that must design the remaining temples . . .
The opportunities diminish with each passing year . . . With each day that
passes the natural world shrinks . . . Nature-islands of solitude and repose
are an indispensable ingredient of modern civilization. Save for homesites,
park lands are the highest human uses to which land may be put.'

Very well – but the American vision of a National Park was one of
wilderness, of lands without people, where bears, wolves, moose, deer,
buffaloes and eagles ruled. But such a vision could only be made real
because, even as late as 1880, much of the United States was relatively
empty. What people did not realize was that much of the emptiness was
artificial. For at the time of European contact in 1492, there were probably
some 80 million people in the two Americas. Their numbers fell
dramatically in the two following centuries, owing largely to the diseases the
Europeans brought. The native American peoples were scattered and broken
tribes, dwindling like the Alacaluf, even before conflicts over land led to
their dispossession by settlers pushing westward.

So, when IUCN began its work on National Parks the predominant
vision was that 'real' parks were uninhabited. Indeed the term 'National
Park' is restricted by IUCN to Category II in the six categories of protected

area it recognizes, namely areas established 'to protect outstanding natural or scenic areas of national or international significance for scientific, educational and recreational use. These are relatively large areas not materially affected by human activity where extractive resource uses are not allowed.' On this definition the British 'National Parks' are not correctly named – they are 'Category V' 'Protected landscapes or seascapes', established 'to maintain nationally significant landscapes which are characteristic of the harmonious interaction of man and land while providing opportunities for public enjoyment through recreation and tourism within the normal life style and economic activity of these areas.'

The problem is that the Category II model simply does not work in many parts of the world. People have lived for thousands of years even in areas that appear as wild as the Serengeti, Ngorongoro, the Kalahari desert, Kakadu in western Australia, the Karakoram Himalayas, or the deep Amazonian forests. Some of these wild places are sacred to ancient cultures. The depopulation of such areas in pursuit of the American National Parks concept – and this has happened – inevitably breeds conflict. Many people now see it as morally wrong. The future of the great National Parks has to be built on partnership between the local people, the tourist industry, and the wildlife and scenery on which both depend.

Ngorongoro used to be inhabited. Indeed, two European settlers started a farm in the caldera in the 1920s. Today, nobody is permitted to live there. The springs and pools below the western slopes are, however, a vital resource. Every day you will see a straggle of cattle and Masai herdsmen plodding down the dusty tracks to these springs, but they must all plod back by nightfall. The caldera is a human exclusion zone. That may be necessary, if tourist revenues are to be sustained, but it fuels resentment.

Further resentment was evident in 1988 because the Ngorongoro Conservation Area Authority, the biggest employer in Loliondo District, with over 400 staff, had only five local Masai on its books. Worse, hardly any of the revenues from tourism were going into helping the local people. Yet they had an agreement that in return for not living in the caldera or cultivating land to supplement the produce of their herds, they would get veterinary services and boreholes to enhance water supplies. This was not happening, and calf mortality from disease was appallingly high. While human numbers had risen from about 10,000 to 25,000 in the past twenty years, livestock numbers had remained static. Many families had fewer than the six and a half cows statistically necessary to support them, and so were forced to make illegal cultivations or to buy grain from outside the area – selling animals they could not spare in order to pay for it. The whole situation was evidently volatile, and M.S. ole Parkipuny, the dynamic local

MP, predicted conflict if the income from tourism and conservation was not shared more equitably.

We saw the human problems and the potential for a new relationship when we drove to the north, to the Masai village of Nainokanoka under a big volcano called Olmoti, itself about 3000 metres high. We bumped along the track, raising clouds of red dust as we went. Once the caldera rim was left behind, the country was a swell of treeless grassland – and much of the grassland was coarse tussocks of fire-resistant *Imperata*. It was not much use to cattle, or indeed anything else, except in the first flush following a burn. The land was poor, and made worse by misuse. And another manifestation of unsustainability came slowly into view over a low ridge.

A Masai man appeared. Not unusual. But he was actually carrying a hefty tree branch. Astonishing. Man does women's work, carrying firewood! Social revolution in the Crater Highlands? No – in a moment normality returned as three women trudged in his wake, bowed under massive bundles of branches. Clearly a husband was showing them the way, and graciously condescending to carry a branch that was too big to cut up and add to the bundles.

But the scenery was exciting and tourism could be the key to strengthening the local economy and helping people to use the land more sustainably. Foot safaris could take more adventurous visitors to the craters of Olmoti and Embagai, where there is a good deal of wild life, and perhaps (if a frontier crossing were permitted) toward the highly active volcano of Oldoinyo Lengai, just across in Kenya. Another obvious area for exploration is the famous Olduvai Gorge, west of Ngorongoro but still within the Conservation Area, where Louis and Mary Leakey found early human remains. Simple, but clean and secure camps would be needed, and they could follow the pattern of a traditional *boma*, with two-person huts, central feeding and washing facilities and loos, all within a stout thorn fence. Local Masai, taught English, would find a natural outlet as guides and guards. They would then find that there was money in wild life – money, for example, in offering a photographer the thrill of stalking an elephant on foot. This in turn would alter attitudes to habitats, and less burning should allow the return of mixed vegetation with more scrub.

We tried to tie together what had been learned in three years' work in Ngorongoro at a three-day workshop Rob Malpas arranged in December 1989 in a hotel complete with palm trees and a coral beach, just north of Dar-es-Salaam, the capital of Tanzania. I found myself steering a group of about forty people including the Chairman of a Commission of Inquiry into the Conservation Area, the District Commissioner and the Area Commissioner for the whole Arusha region. What came out? First that

Ngorongoro had to be managed as a multi-purpose area for the benefit of local people, wildlife and tourism. Second, much more needed to be done to employ local people, and to improve food security for the Masai. There had to be better links between the Conservation Area Authority and the District Council. Government had recognized the importance of Ngorongoro by nominating it as a World Heritage site and needed to ensure that it continued to merit that status. It was all common sense, but rather bureaucratic and reminiscent of Whitehall (the Area Commissioner, Mr Mwingira, had a dry humour, great skill with words and an approach to administration that marked him as the very model of a modern Civil Servant). I am not sure how much difference all the talking made on the ground.

But striking the balance between the protection of wildlife – for its own sake and as the foundation of lucrative tourist industries – and recognising the right of local people (many of whom are desperately poor) to use the natural resources their ancestors have depended on for centuries, is at the heart of Africa's conservation challenge. In Ngorongoro and its neighbourhood the conflict is less intense because the Masai co-exist with wildlife and do not hunt (though they kill lions that attack their cattle). In other areas the establishment of National Parks turned meat-eaters into poachers. Bakari Mbano, working for IUCN in the land adjoining the Serengeti, has urged that this should change. He asked the local communities how many of each species they used to kill, and suggested that licensing the taking of that kind of number would make people guardians of wildlife rather than its adversaries.

Bakari's proposals may have been influenced by his knowledge of the CAMPFIRE project in Zimbabwe, then heralded as one of Africa's success stories. The project was based on research that had shown that wild animals like antelopes and buffalo, grazing unimproved African rangelands, could provide more meat than if the land was converted to cattle ranches. CAMPFIRE gave local communities the power to manage and use their wildlife and benefit from the proceeds. They killed wild animals, but at sustainable levels. The meat was distributed in the villages, while horns, skins and other products were either sold directly to tourists or used in craft industries. The communities also sold the right to shoot elephants, antelopes, zebras and giraffe to safari hunters, who paid large sums to kill animals that would have otherwise been shot by local rangers as part of the management programme. As the project developed, further revenues came in from photographic safaris. The scheme was controlled by elected local committees, so that local people had real 'ownership' of it. The revenues have gone into schools, corn mills, water supplies, clinics and drought relief.

It has demonstrated that wildlife can be conserved, outside protected areas, if it is allowed to be used in a sustainable way – but that this will only work if the local communities are at the heart of the process.

Such ideas horrify many people whose ideal is of undisturbed wild life feeding and breeding peacefully in National Parks that are the nearest place on Earth to the Garden of Eden. Yes, and in an ideal world I agree with them. But we live in a world – and especially an Africa – where human populations are growing and pressures on land are intensifying the whole time. Go to the Aberdares National Park in Kenya if you want to see the new frontier. When the Queen came to the throne she was watching wildlife at Treetops, in the Aberdares Forest. Now that viewing lodge is almost on the edge of cultivation. A two and a half metre high electrified fence stretches for over 35 kilometres, to prevent conflict between people on the farm side and the elephants, buffalo, wild pig and baboons that abound on the wild side. The African future is either of coexistence between people and wild species, which means people using wild species in the areas around the Parks, or the conversion of the Parks to fenced islands in a sea of human use. If that happens nothing bigger than a fox has much chance of survival outside – and they under the persecution their relatives have long endured in western Europe, which settled its wilderness centuries ago.

The Species Survival Commission took these kind of issue seriously, and a project led by a Secretariat member, Steve Edwards, defined the guiding principles for the sustainable use of wildlife. But the very notion jarred the emotions of people who felt that wildlife was sacred, and that our job was to save tigers and elephants from marauding humans. This view was strongest in rich countries with a so-called Anglo-Saxon culture. It was, perhaps, at its most vociferous in Australia, where people tend to express themselves on any issue just that bit more strongly than the case warrants. In my nastier moments I spoke of some of their views as manifestations of insular intellectual endemism – only to be pulled up by an Australian who demanded to know why I used the insulting word 'intellectual'?

Such conflicts reared their head several times within CITES, the Convention on International Trade in Endangered Species. This was originally adopted to stop the wildlife trade pushing sought-after animals and plants to extinction. It works by allocating species threatened by trade to one of three lists – Appendix I, where trade is either totally forbidden or sanctioned only under exceptional circumstances, Appendix II where trade is permitted but has to be tightly regulated, and Appendix III which lists species whose trade is subject to special national controls. IUCN (drawing on the Species Survival Commission) and the World Conservation Monitoring Centre in Cambridge acted as expert advisers on the status of species: WWF and IUCN also operated a world-wide network called TRAFFIC which recorded what trade was going on in various regions. Between us, we tried to provide factual information and the best possible scientific advice to the Conferences of Parties to the Convention.

But it wasn't plain sailing, and we were thumped pretty badly by the African elephant. Despite press reports, this is by far the commoner of the two species of elephant alive today, for the habitats of wild Asian elephants are much more restricted and under much greater pressure from people. But the fact remains that in the 1970s there were about a million and a quarter elephants in Africa and by 1988 the total had dropped to under 700,000. Poaching for ivory was the main cause, and markets in Japan, Taiwan and other rich Asian countries were the main driving force.

There was a lot of publicity and popular concern. Governments in countries that depended on wild life for tourism were driven to near desperation by the poaching – which was taking rhinos for their horns at the same time. But what to do? In many countries there just was not the money to patrol National Parks in sufficient force to deter poachers. Moreover, when WWF did assist by financing armed patrols, riding in helicopters, and when Parks services adopted a 'shoot first' policy, a lot of the flak ricocheted back at WWF. We in IUCN worked with WWF to set up a joint expert group which suggested that the best course was to close the markets by making international trade in elephant products illegal under CITES. Its findings were not unanimous, because some argued that destroying the economic value of a wildlife resource would threaten it because local people would have no incentive for its conservation. But WWF, with other conservation bodies, decided to call for a ban on the ivory trade. Charles de Haes asked me to join them.

I agreed to do so, after hastily consulting our President and Council, but I found myself in a dilemma. Like WWF, we had always said that we were not opposed to the sustainable cropping of living resources, provided that this was compatible with long-term conservation. In some countries the elephant populations were large and growing. Zimbabwe and Botswana both had about 55,000 and they were increasing by some 2,500 a year, threatening local cultivation and at times of drought exerting a massive pressure on vulnerable habitats. The authorities there – including several IUCN members – said they had to cull their populations, so why should they not be allowed to market the resulting ivory and leather, as well as sell the meat for local consumption? Other people, including the powerful and well-known Director of Wildlife Conservation in Kenya, Richard Leakey, argued that so long as there was a legal ivory market, criminals would infiltrate it. It all came to a head at Lausanne, where CITES met in 1989.

The arguments got quite vicious, partly because of the emotions elephants arouse (and indeed, I think they are the wild animal I myself feel most emotional about, and most enjoy watching). An ivory ban was agreed – and a member of the French delegation leaped to his feet in delight, and blew a whistle, inviting a rebuke from the Swiss Chairman for conduct unbecoming in a reputable scientist and national representative. There was, however, provision for expert review if countries requested it – and IUCN was clearly going to be a central player in that review.

In 1992 we met again in Kyoto, Japan, and I found myself in the hot seat as Chair of the relevant Committee (which meant I had only one day in two weeks to admire the temples and other fine buildings of that ancient capital). Conflict was inevitable because the southern African countries had tabled a proposal which would have allowed them to trade elephant products other than ivory. Kenya, led by Richard Leakey, opposed. Leakey was a staunch champion of the ban and had persuaded President Moi to burn the Kenyan stockpile of tusks, in a flamboyant gesture that hit the world's headlines. Rowan Martin of Zimbabwe argued that Zimbabwe had to control its elephants and was being denied the right to derive revenues that could be ploughed back into conservation. The two needled one another in the debate, and although the bigotry and hostility that had plagued the Lausanne meeting was absent, there were too many occasions when scientific evidence took second place to emotional judgement, or to playing to the press gallery. The ban on international trade in elephant products stayed in place. The Zimbabweans began to question the intellectual honesty and practical usefulness of CITES itself.

The second international agreement with which IUCN was closely concerned was the Ramsar Convention on the Conservation of Wetlands of International Importance Especially as Waterfowl Habitat. That title makes such an impossible acronym that the Convention is always known by the name of the town in Iran where it was originally negotiated – at a time when Iran was at the forefront of international nature conservation. From the beginning, IUCN was responsible for providing its Secretariat, although we operated an arms-length relationship very like that between the Department of the Environment and the Secretariat of the Royal Commission on Environmental Pollution, with the Secretary General of the Convention, Dan Navid, accounting directly to his intergovernmental Steering Committee. But when the Ramsar Conference of Parties met, the Director General of IUCN was expected to go along, and this took me along the lake of Geneva to Montreux in 1989, and then back to Japan, to Kushiro, in 1993.

Kushiro is in the far north of Japan, on the island of Hokkaido. The city is undistinguished architecturally, but the nearby wetlands are superb, and celebrated as the breeding grounds of the Japanese crane, with a stately minuet for its courtship dance. Sadly, we gathered too late for the spectacle, and indeed for much of the time chill mists blew in from the cold offshore sea and even shut the airport from time to time. For me, the meeting demanded little more than a welcoming message to the opening session, participation in a few workshops, a visit to a few wetlands, and a lot of valuable discussions in the corridors. It was timely, however, because we were striving to build closer links in Japan, and ultimately secure their State membership. This meant some fairly intensive discussions in Tokyo, on the way back from Kushiro. One of the sensitivities was over whaling – for IUCN's General Assembly had passed resolutions criticising Japan's so-called scientific whaling for Minke whale in the Antarctic, and the Fisheries Department argued that the country should not join such a misguided organisation. It took a lot of skilled diplomacy by our Council member (and member of the Japanese Diet) Akiko Domoto, and the encouragement of Ambassador Nobutoshi Akao of the Foreign Ministry, to calm them down.

One thing anyone concerned with conservation soon learns is that it is hopeless unless it is rooted in long-term consensus and security. This was brought home to me in May 1989 when I went to visit Garamba in what was then Zaire. I went for a party, to celebrate the 50th anniversary of this, the oldest of Zaire's National Parks, established in 1938. It was world-famous because it is (or was) the home of the last population on Earth of the northern sub-species of White rhino ('white' being a corruption of the Afrikaans word 'weit' or 'wide', describing the lip which is broad for grazing, in contrast to the hooked, browsing, upper lip of the slightly darker-grey 'Black' rhino). Once there had been hundreds of White rhino in Garamba, alongside three thousand or more elephants, ten thousand buffalo and a lot of other species including the only giraffes in any Zairois National Park. But Garamba lies right up in the corner of Congo, against the Sudan frontier where after years of civil war, automatic weapons were commoner than toothbrushes. And if that was not enough, gold prospectors were encroaching on the southern edge of the Park, along the river, and thought nothing of trading in poached rhino horn when they could get it. By the early 1980s the Park rhino population was down to 22. In 1988 there were about 30, slowly increasing but still terribly vulnerable.

The Park was managed by the IZCN – Institut Zairois pour la Conservation de la Nature – whose Director, Mankoto ma Mbelele, was on our Council. IUCN, together with WWF and the Frankfurt Zoological Society, was running a project with two goals. First, we were supporting a study by a biologist, Kes Hillman Smith, of the rhino and other key species. Second, we were helping the IZCN prepare a Park management plan that

would give the rhino the best possible chance of survival. An aircraft
stationed at the Park Headquarters and piloted by Charlie Mackie was used
both for finding rhinos and for deterring poachers – who were quite likely
to take a pot-shot at it as it flew over. WWF had poured a lot of money into
these tasks and helped finance the rangers, who had in turn set up a look-out
post on a prominent hill near the middle of the Park. But while armed strife
raged on the border, all was at risk – a risk compounded by political
instability in Zaire itself and a far from peaceful situation in the north-west
of nearby Uganda.

In 1989 it was quicker and easier to get to Garamba from Nairobi rather
than go to Kinshasa and fly across the whole breadth of the immense Congo
basin. Hugh Lamprey, Head of WWF in East Africa, agreed to fly Rob
Malpas, Ian Grimwood, doyen of Kenyan conservationists, and me in his
elderly but lovingly maintained single-engined plane. We droned slowly
across the eastern bays of Lake Victoria and past Entebbe, Uganda's principal
international airport, and so across forests and cultivated lands to Lake
Mobutu Sese Seko (formerly Lake Albert, and before that, no doubt, known
by some ancient name to which one day it will return). We touched down
on a Sunday at the little town of Bunia to fuel and complete entry
formalities – which went surprisingly swiftly, since only one rather sleepy
official was on duty. And so across a great swathe of forest, northward.

Hugh was a good pilot, but his chart locker seemed surprisingly empty.
The only map of Zaire I could find was an Esso Road Atlas, so I tried to
follow our route on that – a difficult job as there were hardly any roads, and
what there were vanished much of the time under the forest canopy. 'It's
actually very easy,' said Hugh. 'We just fly north, and where the forest stops
there's a river. Beyond the river, there's grassland. That's Garamba. The strip
is by the Park Headquarters just south of the river.'

It was just as well he was right, for we ran into a line of thunderstorms,
dodged through a gap, and found the land below blotted out by cloud and
rain. However, the river and the green plains duly showed up, and after a
brief circuit of the wrong airstrip we found our destination, its name,
Gangala, picked out in white stones. We bumped down – and I suddenly
found that we had the VIP treatment, complete with guard of honour. Ian
Grimwood being a Major, I turned to him for guidance on the inspection
process, and before long we were bumping into Park headquarters, to find
that the VVIPs from Kinshasa had still to arrive – in a DC3, which, they
calculated, could just about get in and out on the short runway.

They gave me VIP quarters – a white-painted round hut like a cheese,
one quarter walled off as a bathroom with basin and loo. The water was cold
and not ideal for drinking as it came out of a nearby pool into which the

Elephant-back safari at Garamba. Rob Malpas and Hugh Lamprey clamber aboard.

drains also seemed to run. The roof was thatch, which made the mosquito net dual-purpose: to keep biting flies at bay and to catch any creepy-crawlies that dropped from above during the night. I checked for snakes and scorpions almost as thoroughly as if Lizzie had been there, but the only intruder I met was a charming little green frog that goggled at me from its perch on the loo cistern. Rob, Ian and Hugh, meanwhile, went off to stay with Charlie Mackie and with Kes Hillman Smith and her husband Fraser, who lived in comfortable, if basic, houses on the edge of the river.

We had a good look round the Park on the day after our arrival. Hugh and Rob had an elephant-back safari – a unique experience in Africa, where they tell you that their native elephants are untameable. Garamba is the proof otherwise. In Belgian colonial days they decided to domesticate a number of forest elephants – a form rather smaller and with lighter tusks than the giants of the East African savannah – to haul logs and do other useful work. Mahouts were imported from India and about fifty females were duly trained. Four elderly ladies were still alive in 1988 and they provided for Rob's and Hugh's tour – which demonstrated ecotourist potential by fording the river close by a herd of hippos who seemed untroubled. We were introduced to four little elephants that had just been caught, as the next generation of trainees.

Meanwhile Ian Grimwood and I drove out with Kes and Fraser Smith in the hope of finding rhino. We were disappointed, even though Kes knew more about their habits and likely locations than anyone else, and regularly walked up to them, no doubt keeping a watchful eye out for buffalo and lions as she did so. (The following day Charlie Mackie took several of us on an early morning flight and we did see two of the beasts – almost ten per cent of the world population – in half an hour.) We evicted three young buffalo from our chosen picnic site on a little hill with a wide view over the Park, and sat down on some logs to watch nature wander about us – and then took a walk to within a hundred metres or so of three youngish elephants, which I photographed rather badly from the top of a termite mound. And so back, to find that the DC3 was in, and suits had to be donned to greet the Commissaire d'État (Minister) for Environment and Conservation, the Governor of the Region of Haut-Zaire, Mankoto, and other dignitaries.

The ceremonial began with the unveiling of a monument com-memorating both the 50th anniversary of the Park and its recent designation as a World Heritage Site. The little stone pillar bearing the plaque stood beside a round shelter and above a bend in the river, from which several hundred hippopotamus watched curiously. We heard that the construction of the monument had been accompanied by tragedy, for one of the three men who had built it had been snatched by a lion as the group sat together by their camp fire. When the lion was shot, it proved old, and sick, and no doubt driven desperate enough by hunger to pounce on a handy human. But this did not deter the dedication ceremony. The Master of Ceremonies called us to order and proclaimed the National Anthem. The gathering burst into song. So did the hippos – and I can almost swear that they were bellowing 'Mo-boo-too, Mo-boo-too.' But the Presidential name *did* sound rather like a hippo's roar.

We had speeches (my bad French again rendered grammatical by Frédéric Briand), and I gave an award to Mankoto on behalf of the Chairman of the Commission on National Parks, Hal Eidsvik. The Minister chaired a meeting about the future of the project, which was under strain because of tension between WWF and the other partners (resolved in the end by making it solely WWF's show). We had a feast, eating some goats that had appeared, bleating loudly, in the morning and had been butchered rather messily on the grass beside the main street soon after. And we departed, to find wide-awake officials at Bunia waiting for us and intent on extracting all the US dollars we carried in various taxes and charges they hadn't been ready with on Sunday. I left with a strong memory of how hard it was to safeguard an endangered species in a vast park, under-staffed, and ringed by well-armed and hostile potential poachers. It is even harder when the country itself is vast and almost ungovernable. Since our visit, Bunia has been in the news as the scene of massacres, but Kes and Fraser Smith have continued their work, flying from Nairobi when things in the Congo seem calm. I am assured that the tiny remnant of Northern White rhino is still hanging on.

IUCN found itself involved in the aftermath of other wars. For example, as Vietnam returned to peace, people wanted to know whether the mighty Kouprey, a massive wild ox only discovered and named by science in the 1920s, had survived. It had never been common, and the conflict had raged in some of its known habitats. IUCN worked in partnership with a distinguished Vietnamese scientist, Vo Quy, in an attempt to find and count Kouprey, and if possible catch a group to breed in captivity and raise young for release in new, safe wild areas. The field teams found footprints. They never saw an animal. But only a few years later another party headed by WWF's man in the region, John Mackinnon, found two quite new species – a primitive bovid looking like something halfway between a small cattle beast and an antelope, with long, straight-back horns like an oryx (they named it *Pseudoryx*) and a new kind of giant muntjac deer. Those mountainous, wet, south-east Asian forests are the likeliest place on Earth to make further dramatic wildlife discoveries.

From time to time recent experiences were drawn together in special gatherings. The biggest of these in my time at IUCN took place in February 1992, when we gathered in Caracas, capital of Venezuela, for the Fourth World Congress on National Parks and Protected Areas. Such Congresses are held every ten years, and this one attracted nearly two thousand 'parks people' from 133 countries. There was a bit of nervousness over the arrangements. We went to Venezuela because the Government – a State Member – had invited us (IUCN takes its major meetings around the world at the invitation of host countries, who agree to provide facilities, logistic support and a guarantee of free access for all our members regardless of nationality). But about two weeks before the Congress was due to open there was an attempted coup against the unpopular President, Carlos Andres Perez. Order was restored, and despite moans of uncertainty from some Foreign Offices, we went ahead – in what proved to be a narrow window of stability, for there was another coup a few weeks after we had gone, and President Perez was deposed!

Lizzie and I arrived at Caracas to experience VIP treatment in unfamiliar form. We were taken to an official car and whisked down the highway by a driver and guard. Traffic became congested. We heard a police warning siren and looked around for its source. Then it dawned – it was us! Our cheery young escorts loved the sound, and the sense of status it gave – though it has to be admitted that the other drivers took rather less notice than they would have done in Europe, maybe because they heard that noise too often, from too many cars. We then found that the two young men had been assigned as personal bodyguards for the whole meeting. When I was to walk across the highway to the meeting hall, right next to our hotel, I was supposed to call them and fall in for protection. I am afraid I did not take it as seriously as they did, and Lizzie was a bit uncomfy at the idea of going around in the company of a young man with a gun and a belt full of bullets. But they were very nice, and I think they enjoyed their assignment to these rather odd foreigners. It was a bit of a holiday for them.

The Congress did the usual things. It heard speeches, including a fine piece of eloquence from Sir Shridath ('Sonny') Ramphal, former Secretary General of the Commonwealth, who took over as IUCN's President from Dr Swaminathan in 1990. It adopted a high-sounding Declaration, full of sentiments like:

> 'We Recognize that:
>   nature has intrinsic worth and warrants respect regardless of its usefulness to people;
>   the future of human societies depends on people living in peace among themselves and in harmony with nature;
>   development depends on the maintenance of the biodiversity and productivity of life on Earth . . .'

But it was also a practical affair, with technical workshops on all manner of aspects of parks policy. The Congress adopted an Action Plan with 23 practical recommendations. It led on to new guidelines and a handbook or two. And, most important of all, it sent over 1500 professionals away with new ideas and new contacts.

There were the usual awkward moments. One came when we were putting final touches to the Declaration, and a number of non-governmental people, who had not been involved in the drafting process and felt annoyed at their exclusion, came to the microphones and proposed all manner of changes. That was solved by listening and accepting the proposals that clearly fitted in. The final alarm came in the closing ceremony. President Carlos Andres Perez was in a jumpy mood. His Protocol people cut the speeches short (and, yes, I was annoyed when my own Director General's address fell victim to their unease, but if you invite Heads of State, especially insecure ones, to your meetings you are in their henchmen's hands). As he was leaving there was a shout of protest from the crowd. It was just peaceful protest, but the security men were taking no chances. They gathered behind and around the President and rushed him out of the building – it looked like a rugger scrum getting down and charging with the ball for the line. The atmosphere was electric enough for none of us to be surprised when the successful coup was reported, along with charges of corruption against the deposed President.

The important thing about the Caracas Congress was that it put protected areas in context. Summing up the meeting (after the President had gone), I said I thought we had learned three things. First, that protected areas are important, because they not only safeguard places of great spiritual and inspirational value but protect resources vital to all of us. Second, that protected areas are about people as well as nature – the people who live in them and the people who come from afar, to wonder and delight. Third, that parks alone are not enough: they have to be set within landscapes that are used wisely and sustainably, guided by strategies for sustainable development.

Sustainable development? The term entered world eco-speak in 1987, in the report of the World Commission on Environment and Development, usually referred to as 'the Brundtland Commission' after its Chair, the Norwegian Prime Minister, Gro Harlem Brundtland. It was defined by them as 'development that meets the needs of the present without compromising the ability of future generations to meet their own needs'.

But the concept is older than the World Commission. Way back in 1980, IUCN led in the preparation of a World Conservation Strategy, published in partnership with UNEP and WWF, whose sub-title was 'living resource conservation for sustainable development'. Its message is summed up in one sentence in its introduction:

> Human beings, in their quest for economic development and enjoyment of the riches of nature, must come to terms with the reality of resource limitation and the carrying capacity of ecosystems, and must take account of the needs of future generations.

Very well, but how? The vision clearly needed to be brought down to earth, and National Conservation Strategies were advocated as plans for achieving development without destroying the environmental foundation on which human societies depend. In 1982, very much at Maurice Strong's instigation, IUCN set up a Conservation for Development Centre under Mike Cockerell's leadership, and one of its chief tasks was to help developing countries prepare national strategies. By the time I arrived, Bangladesh, Botswana, Costa Rica, Jordan, Kenya, Mauritania, Nepal, Pakistan, St Lucia, Togo, Zambia and Zimbabwe had either completed or were well advanced with this work. In Botswana they had taken the process right down to the grass roots, having meetings in all districts and many villages to consider what the people in those areas wanted.

But the Governments of the world, even if many were State Members of IUCN, were not content to leave so important an initiative in the hands of what was, technically, regarded as a non-governmental organization. In the 1980s UNEP saw itself as the natural champion of what was then called 'ecodevelopment'. In 1983 Japan came to the Governing Council with an offer to fund a Commission of eminent independent people who would draw up 'a global agenda for change' and prepare long-term strategies for achieving sustainable development by the year 2000. Japan was so sure that its initiative would be welcomed that its Government announced it publicly before the Governing Council met.

They were rebuffed. Some delegations – especially that of the then USSR – strongly disliked the notion of a group of independents telling Governments how to behave. They wanted an intergovernmental agenda that would lead to a consensus (which, of course, meant that they could veto unpalatable statements about the communist system and the planned economy). The inevitable compromise created two parallel initiatives. The World Commission on Environment and Development was established under Mrs Brundtland, and an intergovernmental process led by UNEP produced an Environmental Perspective to the Year 2000 and Beyond. Almost everyone has now heard of the Brundtland Commission and their book *Our Common Future*. Nobody has heard of what we somewhat futuristically styled 'EP2K+'. But long after Brundtland reported in 1987 the debate rumbled on. What really was 'sustainable development' other than a statement of the obvious? How could it be done? How could we safeguard living diversity and keep space for nature, as the human tide rose and broke with ever greater force on the shores of a beleaguered world?

The answers were not made any easier to find because the Brundtland Commission produced a fudge. They stressed that sustainable development meant meeting the needs of the present without compromising the ability of future generations to meet their own needs. But they went on to say that the essential needs of the world's poor should have over-riding priority, and that what limited the environment's ability to meet present and future needs was inadequate technology and social organization. This implied that the environment posed no limits on humanity that could not be managed away. But any ecologist or farmer knows that the environment does impose limits, even though we can, and do, adjust them by science and technology, which have vastly improved crop yields and livestock production. The Club of Rome was right that in the end human populations do have to come into a sustainable relationship with the environment, and this demands a difficult balancing act. Moreover, it has to be an act that works in real communities on the ground, listening to their needs and drawing on their experience.

The emergence of 'sustainable development' as a dominant theme transformed IUCN's work. Although the Union remained very active in its traditional heartland of species survival and protected areas, much of the money we received was for projects that set out to bring human communities into sustainable harmony with nature. These projects spanned Africa, West and East Asia, and parts of Latin America. They were a major focus of our work in my time in Gland.

CHAPTER NINE

Caring for the Earth

IUCN had projects at many levels, from poor rural villages to the capital cities where National Conservation Strategies were planned. In theory they should form a seamless robe, for the national strategies could only be implemented locally, and were no use unless they reflected environmental and social reality on the ground.

Robert Chambers – the same Robert invalided from Gough Island way back in 1955 – has devoted most of his professional life to solving problems of rural poverty, especially in India. By the 1980s he had emerged as a champion of village wisdom, and his message is simple (I paraphrase):

'Up-end your thinking. See that simple is often best. Stay in villages and listen to the people. Learn from them. Learn with them. Help them to do their own analyses. Encourage diversity. Put people before things. Put poor people first of all.'

Lizzie and I saw this kind of approach in action in 1988, after we left Ngorongoro. The villages were in the Eastern Usambaras, a little-known and rather minor mountain range rising some 1250 metres above the Tanzanian coastal plain near the little town of Tanga. We drove from the airfield past miles of derelict sisal plantations – once prosperous as a source of rope fibre, before polypropylene and other plastics took over. We bounced up through forests to Amani, where the IUCN project was based. And the place took us by surprise!

Amani was built in the period of German colonial administration, before the 1914-18 War. It was planned as a small hill station on the Indian model, to allow heated officials to rest and cool down away from the humid coastlands. It was built solidly and squarely in stone, with houses for residents and visitors, a hospital, a Club House and a Guest House (where we stayed). The ruins of a beer garden and restaurant crowned a hilltop, with wide views over the countryside (they would have been wider before the forest reclaimed its own). There was a research station and a superb botanical garden, with a collection of many native plants.

The Usambaras are important because the forests that formerly clothed them, and still remain in several substantial patches, are diverse and contain a number of plants found nowhere else in the world. Our familiar house plant, the 'African violet,' *Sanctipaulia,* was discovered there. IUCN became involved because there were fears that clearance would destroy the remaining forests and exterminate the unique species they contained, some of which might well be important sources of drugs. It is often forgotten that nearly half the medicines we use have their origins in wild plants. The indigenous inhabitants of tropical forests rely on dozens of species that pharmaceutical science has not studied. Some may be very important – like the little Rosy periwinkle, which has provided an important treatment for childhood leukaemia.

But how can the pressure be taken off the forest? How can people be stopped from cutting patches where they can grow cardamon as a cash crop? How can we stop destructive logging? The IUCN project, which was financed by European aid agencies and done in partnership with the Tanzanian Ministry responsible for forests, agriculture and conservation, was based in thirteen villages. The plan was to help the people to find new and profitable ways of using the land that had already been cleared, so that they did not need to cut further into the forests. Under the leadership of a Dutch specialist, Nick Bech, and a Tanzanian project director, Joseph Lindi, IUCN appointed two coordinators in each village. The choice was made after talking to the village elders, but the coordinators were young men and women in their early twenties. We met them all at a party on the evening of our arrival. They were a lively and likeable bunch, and most of them would have been at University in a richer community. Two stood out because they were albinos – red-haired and pale skinned, and nicknamed '*msungo*' ('whitey'), although the label carried no slur. We were impressed by all of them. So we were with what we saw on the ground.

The east Usambaras had been developed as tea gardens in colonial times and there were still large plantations and a factory. But the economics were marginal. Some of the plantations had been handed over to the villagers, who made a meagre income by picking the young shoots and taking them to the factory. In the villages nursery gardens had been established for other plants that might be grown for cash. Trees had been planted for fuelwood. There were fish ponds as a source of protein. Sugar cane was being cultivated – we were given samples to chew. School children were using simple surveying rods to mark out the contours on steep slopes and narrow lines of grass and sugar cane was being planted to control erosion. The boundaries of the forest reserves had been defined by a swathe of cleared ground 10 metres wide, in which a double row of teak cuttings had been set. Nobody would be able to argue that they did not know that an area was a reserve. But the extraction of single trees for local use as timber, or even for sawing into baulks for export, was not absolutely forbidden – so long as simple pit saws were used to shape the logs. It is hard work and that sets a guard against over-use.

The project seemed to be succeeding, but there were two doubts in our minds. First, would the improved nutrition and living standards in the villages simply fuel a population explosion? Second, would the news spread and friends and relations from outside the project area start moving in? I am not too worried on the first count, for birth rates are falling in East Africa as, very slowly, health care and family planning spread, education strengthens and more opportunities are created for women. But the second problem could be real. The answer is to expand the project so that it becomes the universal approach throughout the western and eastern Usambaras – and indeed more widely. It is no good if all that we have is a scatter of successes in a sea of human misery.

Mount Elgon in Uganda is a far greater mountain than the Usambaras, an immense volcano sweeping up to over 4300 metres. The frontier between Uganda and Kenya bisects it, and in theory both halves are protected forests and game reserves. But the project we started there in 1988 had much in common with the one in Tanzania, as Rob Malpas and I saw when we visited it on our way home from Garamba. We found the Ugandan side of the mountain scarred by deforestation as high as the eye could roam. Banana plantations had been established where the map showed protected forest. Villages scrambled up the denuded slopes to high altitudes, and their land was tilled across rather than along the contours, making easy channels for water to erode the red soil. The villages were a jumble of ramshackle thatched huts, full of ill-nourished children, some with obvious signs of diarrhoea. Bananas appeared to be the staple food, and cooking depended on ever longer treks up to the remnant forests, high in the mists. We climbed as far as the first trees, rising above a fire-climax tussock grassland, and met two women trudging down under immense bundles of branches. Turning this disaster area back to sustainable land use looked an almost impossible task.

But Uganda was clearly a land in determined renewal. Idi Amin had only recently been overthrown, and the Museveni Government was new and nervous. Kampala was still in the early stages of reconstruction. On the roads, young men with automatic weapons still guarded numerous checkpoints (we found it useful to be in white-painted Suzuki vehicles with 'IUCN' in large letters on the doors, for this put us in the same category as a UN relief agency and waved us through block after block). Encouragingly the new Government was clearly taking a long-term view, recognizing that reconstruction depended on taking care of natural resources. The National Parks were being re-established as important bases for a new tourist industry (the Queen Elizabeth and Murchison Falls Parks had once been among the finest in Africa). The tiny and stressed remnants of the former's once healthy elephant population were slowly increasing and matriarchs were again emerging as group leaders. IUCN had been entrusted with a national wetlands survey, led by Paul Mafubi and a British botanist, Doug Taylor. Their aim was to suggest how the innumerable lakes and swamps might be used best – whether as reserves for biodiversity, sources of fish, regulators of water flow or potential land for drainage and cultivation. The Government was prepared to wait for the survey before deciding what to do with the land.

These were just a few among many community-level projects in many parts of Africa, including Senegal, Mali and Burkina Faso, where a massive Sahel project inspired by Mohamed Kassas during his Presidency was under way. At the other end of the scale, we were working on National Conservation Strategies, sometimes in the face of deep uncertainty. We had to pull out of Chad when civil strife erupted, and Per Ryden and I found ourselves in Addis Ababa at a meeting to plan a strategy for Ethiopia at a time of tension. The evil regime of Mengistu Haile Mariam was wobbling to its end, military repression was evident on the streets, and we heard rumours of the sadistic execution of a group of rebel officers. At the other end of Africa, work in Angola and Mozambique only became possible when civil wars died down and there was hope of reconstruction.

Our work in southern Africa was based on our expanding office in Harare, capital of Zimbabwe. Harare soon became one of my favourite African cities. In that period, Zimbabwe stood out as a prosperous, multi-racial modern African state where the descendants of former European colonists lived in harmony with the majority Shona and Ndebele people. The bitter conflicts of the past seemed to have died away, and although it was well known that much of the best land was in the hands of white farmers, their contribution to the economy was so great that the destructive redistribution of a later decade would have seemed an improbable nightmare. Zimbabwe was a leader in the conservation of some of Africa's rarest and most spectacular animals, and a pioneer in the sustainable use of wild species in the CAMPFIRE programme. On the one occasion I met President Robert Mugabe, he struck me as both clever and charismatic, and not the man to destroy the prosperity of his country through personal paranoia. Admittedly, he was on his best behaviour, both because he was welcoming a meeting of African leaders and because I was in company with Sonny Ramphal, who had done much to smooth the way to Zimbabwean independence during his time as Secretary General of the Commonwealth. Mugabe's admiration and gratitude were evident. In the early 1990s we saw Zimbabwe as a jewel in the crown of the new Africa, and a model for South Africa to follow. Our IUCN office, led by a charming and energetic

Zambian chieftain, India Musokotwane, worked closely with Zimbabwe's Environment Ministers, and particularly with the redoubtable Victoria Chitepo and her successor, Herbert Murerwa.

Lizzie and I saw the Zimbabwe environment first-hand in 1990. It started – as all my official visits did – with formal engagements in the capital city, where we also visited one of the world's most interesting botanical gardens. Here, patches of natural vegetation have been lovingly and skilfully reconstructed (which is easy for the dry *miombo* woodland, but harder for a rain forest, which needs constant sprinkling from tree-high standpipes). We were also taken to a little wilderness area – about 100 hectares in extent – where we walked in the company of two orphaned baby elephants, and among a few zebras, gazelles and many birds. The baby elephants were very friendly, but they had learned that humans often carry nuts and other tasty things. So as we walked we would be nudged by a gentle shoulder or prodded by a probing trunk. The trouble was that even though they were only little, they weighed a good half ton, and a gentle nudge had a hefty weight of muscle behind it!

We had a weekend to fill, and India Musokotwane suggested that we spent it in the National Park and World Heritage site at Victoria Falls. Everyone knows that this is one of the world's three greatest waterfalls, the others being Niagara and Iguaçu. Here, the Zambezi falls into a deep gorge and the spray rises high into the air. You can hear the echoing rumble of it for miles, and this earned it its ancient name, *Musi-oa-Tunya*, the thunder that smokes.

European children are taught how the Scottish missionary-explorer, David Livingstone, discovered that wonderful spectacle, and named it for his Queen. But he didn't really discover it, of course. *Musi-oa-Tunya* had been known and revered from time out of mind. And Livingstone didn't just stumble upon it as he wandered through the wilderness – he was shown it by India Musokotwane's several times great-grandfather, who was the local Chief. Livingstone simply discovered it for his own culture, and made the existence of this great wonder of the natural world known in Europe. It was really a bit of arrogance to impose Queen Victoria's name on it, but I'm sure Livingstone didn't see it that way. All dominant cultures have done the same. That is why great mountains in South America have Spanish names, or even English ones like the Cordillera Darwin and Monte Burney, and why the world's highest mountain is named after an English surveyor-general of India. But we have examples at home – in the mountains of Eryri that the English call Snowdon.

Imposed name or not, and even laced about with tarmac paths like a Blackpool park, Victoria Falls is a wonderful place. And we saw the tourist

The 'Loch Zambezi monster'. Elephants in line ahead swim the river.

industry at its best in an evening boat trip on the Zambezi. Our guide was a cheerful young Zimbabwean, with a joky patter and a large box full of wines and beers, for this was a supper cruise. He manoeuvred us close to a female crocodile atop her nest (many eggs are collected for crocodile ranches nearby, but one hatchling in ten is restored to the wild at a size when its survival is almost assured, thereby maintaining the population and giving wild life an economic value). We weaved our way warily among snorting hippos. And we got an excellent photograph of something that looked just like the Loch Ness Monster.

It happened like this. As we cruised, we saw a party of elephants gather on the Zambian bank. Seven of them plunged in and swam across. We motored towards them, stopping a hundred metres or so to one side of their course. Elephants swim deep, and most of the time all that you see are the shallow black bulges of their bobbing backs. But every now and then a trunk is raised and a breath taken. My Loch Zambezi Monster was photographed as they swam in line ahead and only the leader had its trunk up.

The elephants burst out of the river, and wandered up the bank and across a road. And this brought home how intermingled people and nature are in this place. There is a tourist trail by a big banyan tree, where Livingstone halted – and when we walked along it we met people who reported about fifty buffalo on the bank, not far round the corner. Our swimming elephants had made off in the direction of the new golf course at the aptly-named Elephant Hills Hotel which was being restored after severe damage in the struggle for independence. Hippos obviously move out at night to graze the riverside grasslands. There are crocs a-plenty. It seemed inevitable that one day a visiting golfer at Elephant Hills would meet a stroppy buffalo on the fifth green. On the Zambian shore we saw a party having a barbecue only a kilometre or so from where our elephants had crossed.

Daniel Rychner, our Man in Botswana, flew in that evening in a light plane he had chartered to take us down to Gaborone to launch the National Conservation Strategy for Botswana. It was a fascinating flight, starting with a sweep over the Falls and the narrow gorge into which the river drops. Then across the droughted countryside, over Hwange National Park, where big bands of elephants roamed among dusty and devastated trees. It reminded me of Tsavo in Kenya before the population crashed in 1975. And so over a vast salt lake and south to Tuli Hills.

There was no loo in the aircraft, so Daniel had thoughtfully arranged a comfort stop on the five hour journey. Tuli Lodge was chosen for several reasons. It was about halfway. It had interesting environmental problems. And it was a place where we could complete entry formalities into Botswana. We put down on a dusty strip flanked by a small wooden hut with 'Welcome to Botswana' in faint paintwork. The immigration staff bumped up in a Land Rover.

The land use problems were evident. We came to Tuli past industrialization – a big smelter at Selebe Pichwe, belching out fumes that the prevailing wind carried right over the settlement where the staff lived. And we saw another pressure – centre-pivot irrigation systems making round green patches of crop in a dry brown landscape. Heaven knows where they were pumping the water from, or how long it would last. At Tuli Lodge the scrub woodland was being blitzed by elephants. And there were cattle and lions in juxtaposition.

'This place is right by the Limpopo,' the lodge warden explained. 'It's dry at present, and when there is a drought the only water in this district is right here. That's why the elephants and other animals concentrate here – it's also the only safe habitat for them. But the cattle herders drive their stock in from Zimbabwe, across the bed of the river which is the frontier. And this is where George Adamson's lions were brought and released – we have about fifteen lions around, and they are bound to take cattle, which causes fresh conflict.' George Adamson, husband of Joy, and made famous in the film *Born Free*, had been murdered not long before. After the murder 'his' lions were found a safe home at Tuli. But we wondered how safe they would be, and for how long?

We arrived at Gaborone. It was very hot, but very dry. I paid my formal calls on the President, Dr Ketumile Masire, and his Vice President, Peter Mumsi, who was also Minister of Local Government and Lands, and hence of Conservation. We discussed the National Conservation Strategy which, in accordance with national custom, had been debated in every local community in the land. We launched it with speeches followed by a party. The toast was '*Pula*' – which means 'water,' a commodity so precious in this dry land that it is also the name of a unit of national currency. We saw what they meant when we were taken out in searing heat for a picnic, enlivened by a telescopic view of Cape vultures nesting on a beetling cliff. Lizzie nearly wilted.

The biggest NCS exercise IUCN was involved with in my time as Director General was in Pakistan. Our presence there had grown rapidly from a single part-time representative to a team of over forty, based in Karachi with outposts in the capital, Islamabad, Peshawur and (after my time) Quetta. The driving force was a remarkable young woman, Aban Marker Kabraji.

Pakistan has been described as a feudal society. The label fits the landowners best, but it is a society where a relatively small number of families do wield great influence. Aban's family were Parsees, well to do and well-educated (her father Kursheed Marker had been at Queens' Cambridge, her husband, Kairas Kabraji, at Trinity, and Aban herself at Queen Mary College, London). The family business was in pharmaceuticals, but Aban's uncle, Jamsheed Marker, was Pakistan's Ambassador to the UN. Aban presided over a well-equipped office in a block behind the Marker home, shared with a WWF office and that of Shirkat-Gah, a women's NGO. It was a little 'conservation campus', and on my first visit with Mark Hallé, who had succeeded Mike Cockerell as head of our field operations department, it was opened formally by the Governor of Sindh.

Aban was determined to show me around. We went to Lahore, and called upon our Regional Councillor and Vice President from Pakistan, Syed Babar Ali, who was also the national President of WWF. He presided over a firm that made packaging and cartons in a big modern factory – the largest of its kind in the country. We had time to be tourists and enjoy the Shalimar Gardens with their hundred fountains, created by that great builder and connoisseur of beauty, Shah Jehan. We went to the Palace and delighted in the brilliant mosaics of semi-precious stones, at the head of the elephant stairs where bejewelled beasts had once heaved their way slowly up a long ramp. We visited the great Mosque, with its immense forecourt. We wandered through the spice-scented, twisting alleyways of the Bazaar with myriad stalls and endless chatter as bargains were struck. We marvelled at the threads of interweaving traffic – elderly motorbuses, battered lorries, a diversity of cars, horse and bullock-drawn carts, mules, cycles, cycle-drawn rickshaws, and here and there a camel plodding along, nose held high in disdain at this clamorous mass of humanity all around.

But the real business was in Islamabad, where a young and highly articulate graduate, Syed Ayub Qutub (another Queensman), headed the team that was preparing and negotiating the text of the Strategy. Aban had persuaded the Deputy Chairman of the National Planning Commission to preside over an interdepartmental Steering Committee of officials drawn from all the key ministries. The set-up, in fact, closely resembled that established by Solly Zuckerman to negotiate the British White Paper on Environmental Pollution, back in 1970. The point was that if people from all the main Ministries were involved, they were also more or less forced to accept ownership of the results. The downside was that sharp statements and new visions tended to get blunted and blurred in the fog of officialdom. And bureaucracy in both Pakistan and India is an endemic remnant of the British Raj, surviving in all its clerical complexity while the British Civil Service has moved on.

National Conservation Strategies are no good if they are simply the product of erudite minds pontificating in capital cities. The real test is whether the NCS leads on to wise action for conservation and sustainable development on the ground. So I was always keen to visit grass-roots projects and IUCN had quite a few of them in Pakistan. In the slums of Karachi, at Orangi, where about a million descendants of Muslims displaced by the partition of the sub-continent lived in a warren of narrow streets, we were helping an urban renewal scheme by supplying trees. Planted in the courtyards of houses, they provided fruit, fodder and shade. In the Indus delta, where the great river loses itself in winding channels amid mud flats, the mangrove forest, important as a shelter for fish and valuable for fuelwood and fodder, had been destroyed by over-cutting and by the grazing of thousands of camels in summer. IUCN was leading a mangrove restoration scheme over hundreds of acres of flats, and the first year's sproutlings were already thrusting their narrow stems from the mud. But the most dramatic setting of any IUCN project I saw in all my six years was in the far north of the country.

We flew by helicopter to Gilgit and Hunza in the upper Indus valley. Leaving Islamabad in the early morning, we droned ever closer to the great mountains. For about twenty minutes the aircraft hummed slowly past the ice-covered flanks and serrated crest of Nanga Parbat, over eight thousand metres high and eighth highest mountain in the world, brooding like a frozen dinosaur above the green valleys of Kashmir. We wound along the gorges of the Upper Indus – cliffs and slopes dropping over two thousand metres to the twisting, turbulent river far below. As we dropped towards Gilgit we glimpsed the cluster of massive peaks around K2, second of Earth's summits, and had a fine, nearer, view of another great mountain, Rakaposhi.

At Gilgit, Aban, Mark Hallé and I were greeted by Shoaib Sultan Khan, head of the field programme of the Aga Khan Rural Support Programme, with whom we were working. Ismaili Muslims predominate in the population hereabouts, and the Aga Khan is their spiritual leader. The AKRSP was revitalising the life of over a thousand villages. Water was the key, for despite the vast mountain glaciers and permanent snowfields, this is a very arid country. Little rain falls in the valleys, which during summer depend on streams and rivers fed by the melting snows high above, and on springs bursting from the cliffs. There is very little pasture on the valley floors, and the grasslands high in the hills have been damaged by overgrazing. The forests that used to clothe the moister upper valleys have been cut for timber and fuel, further aggravating aridity and erosion.

The village we visited was high up the valley, past the old fort at Hunza, deep in a narrow cleft under spiring peaks that would have made even the Alps look like a miniature landscape. The AKRSP had surveyed the line for new water channels, tapping streams and springs to irrigate orchards. IUCN's contribution, led by a young Danish consultant named Michael Junkov, was to plant trees that would stabilise slopes and provide fuelwood and fruit (apricots were a staple, and could be seen spread to dry on the flat roofs of many of the whitewashed houses). The produce went to market, generating cash to repay the start-up loans made by the AKRSP and provide a capital foundation for new ventures. All members of the village communities were involved in the debate about what should be done at each stage – the men and women separately, in accordance with Islamic tradition. It was clear that things were beginning to move, and that as in the Usambaras, there was a prospect of greater prosperity, achieved with less damage to the environment.

Gilgit and Hunza are in the disputed territory of Kashmir, albeit in an area that is solidly Muslim in faith and has been administered by Pakistan since partition. Over the top of Nanga Parbat, the land drops to Srinagar and the area administered by India. This is not the place, nor am I qualified, to comment on the bitterly divisive politics which blight one of the world's loveliest places and bring tragedy to many of its inhabitants. But I heard a fine example of delicate diplomacy one lunch-time in Islamabad in 1992. I had been visiting the Pakistani Minister for Environment, Anwar Saifullah Khan. We had dropped in on a World Pheasant Conference (where I found

In the great mountains. Village women participants in an IUCN project above Hunza in the upper Indus valley.

my old Nature Conservancy colleague David Jenkins established as Secretary General), and opened the Sustainable Development Institute under the forceful leadership of Tariq Banuri, who had had a lot to do with the National Conservation Strategy but was a firebrand when it came to IUCN's record of balance between 'northern' and 'southern' political interests. We were due to see the Prime Minister. But he was otherwise engaged – Nelson Mandela, not yet President of South Africa, was in town. So Anwar swept me off to the President's lunch and I had the great pleasure of meeting Mandela – though there was no chance for more than the fewest of words. But at lunch Mandela was pressed by his host to use his good influence with India to win concessions in Kashmir. His reply was masterly.

'I have the greatest respect for Pakistan and for India, as great democracies,' he said. 'I am sure that if you approach your difficulties in the spirit of the democracy that you cherish, you will find a way...' Passed back to you, brother, and don't assume that because your guest is courteous and mild-mannered he is weak or politically naive...

Although IUCN was very active in Pakistan and also in Nepal, further along the Himalayas, we did little in India (although many distinguished Indian scientists, lawyers and conservationists have been deeply involved in the Union's work). I think one reason for this is that India is well-furnished with good scientists and feels that it does not need outside organizations to help run its conservation strategies or programmes of sustainable development. But WWF has been very active there, especially in projects to save threatened species like tigers and Asian rhinoceros. We saw the strength of their presence when I went with Aban Kabraji, Babar Ali and Kursheed Marker to Delhi for the opening of the new WWF Headquarters in India – a building donated by a charitable Indian Parsee, S.P. Godrej. Our own IUCN President, Monkombu Swaminathan, was prominently involved because he was also President of WWF-India.

It was amusing travelling to India with old hands like Babar and Aban. 'Make sure you get off the plane first,' they emphasized. 'You need to be at the head of the queue. The *babus* (clerks) at the desk still fill in all the forms manually. It can take five minutes a person. If you're at the back of a queue of fifty people you can be there several hours!' We disembarked pronto and sprinted for the immigration desks. It worked. And then – we met senior Indian conservationists. Pakistanis and Indians – all in their 60s – greeted one another like brothers. Kursheed Marker explained. 'We were all at school together at Dehra Dun, before partition. We know one another really well.'

The visit to WWF India produced two incidents that are amusing to look back on but were not equally funny at the time. Prince Philip was there, as President of WWF International, to thank Mr Godrej for his generous gift and inaugurate the Headquarters. At the reception afterwards I found Professor Gordon Conway, formerly head of the Imperial College Centre for Environmental Technology and at the time Ford Foundation Director in south-east Asia. He hadn't met the Prince. I presented him, thinking they would find a lot in common for Gordon is a distinguished practical ecologist with deep knowledge of the developing world. I turned back a few minutes later to hear sounds of altercation. They had begun to discuss the human population explosion and its implications for conservation. Prince Philip was arguing that Asia simply could not stand its current rates of human growth – and suggesting actions. Gordon (while agreeing with the first point) differed strongly over the means. 'Oh no, Sir, no Sir, no Sir!' went Gordon, finger wagging. 'Oh yes, sir, yes, sir, yes, sir!' went HRH. I hastily found another person to present. But neither of them seemed particularly upset afterwards.

The genuinely amusing happening was at Robin Pellew's expense (Robin was then Director of the World Conservation Monitoring Centre in Cambridge, but soon to take over as Director of WWF-UK). We were outside, in the grounds of the hotel where a Seminar to inaugurate the new HQ was being held. We stood in line to collect a buffet lunch, and retired to attack it, sitting on a low wall, plates on knee. We both had a mound of rice in the midst of which was a pool of vegetable curry topped by a chicken leg. Suddenly there was an incident such as I had only read of in *Plain Tales from the Raj*. A Black kite swooped in over Robin's shoulder, grabbed his chicken leg, and flew off. He behaved as a dedicated conservationist should.

West of Pakistan, we were also busy in the Arabian peninsula, and especially in Oman and Saudi Arabia. I went there with the head of our marine section, Danny Elder, to find a blend of new-style sustainable development work and older-style species conservation. In Saudi Arabia we had been surveying the coasts and shallow seas in partnership with the Monitoring and Environment Protection Agency (whose Director, and later President, the late Dr Abdulbar Al Gain, was an old colleague from UNEP days). The records in the Gulf proved invaluable during the Kuwait war, because they defined what the marine plant and animal life was like before it got plastered with oil. From this baseline the scale of the damage and the progress of recovery could both be measured – and the results, as with the *Torrey Canyon* long before, showed that while oil had a severe initial impact the scars healed as the years passed. We visited Abdulbar in Jeddah, mindful of the injunction not to attempt to take any alcohol into that fiercely prohibitionist country. At his luxurious home, in its walled compound, however, things were different. A trolley of bottles of whisky was trundled out to ease our desiccated tissues. Somebody said he got it from the airport, where contraband confiscated from foolish tourists was not all poured down the drain.

We were also working in partnership with the National Commission for Wildlife Conservation and Development in Riyadh. Its Director, Dr Abdulaziz Abuzinada, welcomed us warmly with coffee and fruit juices and a banquet in traditional mode, squatting on carpets to eat roast sheep under a starry sky. An IUCN consultant, Dr Graham Child from Zimbabwe, had prepared a comprehensive survey of national wildlife resources and this had led to plans to re-introduce species such as gazelles, Arabian oryx and ibex to wild habitats (the Zoological Society of London played a leading part in the action that followed). We went to look at a study area south of Riyadh, passing the 'Riyadh river' where the city's sewage outfall pours through the desert and supports lush vegetation and abundant birds. Out in the drylands, we drove and walked in temperatures of around 42 degrees Celsius in a spectacular wadi with springs and patchy vegetation, where we counted over forty reintroduced gazelles. They were obviously breeding well.

Saudi Arabia adjoins Oman, where IUCN was also busy. It is a very different country, scenically and socially. And I do not allude simply to its more liberal attitude to alcohol consumption by non-Muslims. I also found it more relaxed in other ways. We were warmly received by the Minister,

On the edge of sustainability. Village and terraced gardens in the Jabal Akhdar of Oman. Photograph: Danny Elder.

Sayyid Shabib bin Taimur, uncle of the ruler, Sultan Quaboos. We were also greeted by a redoubtable British conservationist, Ralph Daly, member of the Sultan's own Court and special adviser on conservation. Ralph had played a central part in the first project to restore the white Arabian oryx – which some think was the unicorn of legend – to the wild. At the time of our visit, however, the emphasis was on a survey of the coastline, as a basis for tourism, fisheries, and conservation. Rodney Salm, who was leading it, took us on a boat trip past a splendid sequence of cliffed headlands, islands and bays just south of Muscat. It looked a wonderful place for a holiday.

One Friday, when all offices shut down for the Muslim sabbath, Danny and I saw other exciting places during a helicopter trip over the Jabal Akhdar – the green mountains – behind Muscat. These are the highest summits in Oman: a towering, broken escarpment that soars three thousand metres from the coastal fringe. But they were not very green, and such villages as lay among them huddled in improbable ravines, or on shelves of rock, wherever springs brought perennial water. Palm fronds jutted from clefts and gullies, and the squat, flat-roofed, mud-brick houses seemed moulded to the slopes and timeless in their isolation. Lower down, more prosperous villages stood beside irrigation channels called quanats, managed with great skill to supply each garden or palm grove in rotation. The master of the process – the 'Lord of the Waters' as such officials are termed elsewhere – was key to communal welfare. It was an ancient model of sustainable resource management. But modern unsustainability was evident nearby. For, visiting an old fort on the valley floor, we were struck by its adjacent grove of dying date-palms. 'Why's that?' we asked our guide. 'It's because of boreholes,' came the answer. 'People have been allowed to sink them to tap underground water and irrigate their land. But this has lowered the water table so that the palm roots can no longer get a supply. So they are dying. The people who are rich enough to sink the wells prosper – and the poor people who depend on communal groves lose their date harvest.'

Sayyid Shabib posed a personal problem, when we ended dinner at his house, and were about to leave for the airport. He suddenly decided that etiquette demanded a present for the Director General of IUCN. He vanished. A few moments later he returned carrying a big red box. It contained a silver coffee pot, in the Arabic style, with a domed lid and long, curved, spout (made, I discovered later, by Asprey's of London). I made suitable acknowledgement and we departed for Geneva (where the Swiss customs decided on the duty to charge by weighing the thing, and estimating a percentage of the value of the silver). I recalled the problems that press publicity over a similar gift had created for Anthony Crosland. There followed debates with the Treasurer of IUCN over whether I should keep the pot, or pass it for use when the DG received visiting Arab dignitaries. I thought of getting a set of little Arab cups for the office, and sending Estelle on a course to learn how to brew the strong, spiced, coffee that should go into them – but in the end it went home, where it remains an ornament of our house as does a splendid *kunjah* (ceremonial dagger) I was given on a later visit. We worried over the presents *we* should take to dignitaries we visited and fell back, I fear, on the less glittering solution of glossy IUCN publications.

Africa. Western Asia. What about the Americas? Yes, we worked there, too, though in North America, as in western Europe, our main effort was to maintain contact with our members and with the government aid agencies that contributed the greater part of our funds. But Central and South America were different. In my time we had a major field programme based on our office in Costa Rica, and extending into Honduras, Belize, Nicaragua and Panama. The work was the usual blend of support for National Parks and species conservation, projects for sustainable development and help with the preparation of strategies. The project I remember best was on the Pacific coast of Costa Rica, among the mangroves at Terraba Sierpe.

This lies on a huge river delta, where over ten thousand hectares of tall mangrove forest spreads among muddy creeks, with tree canopies rising twenty metres above the water. The woods were far taller and more diverse than the scrubby remnants I had seen in the Indus delta and southern China. And they were under threat. First, for fuelwood. Second for timber and poles. Third for charcoal. Fourth, at the landward margin, by clearance for banana plantations. And fifth, from shrimp lagoons.

Legally, the forests were protected, but law enforcement is not easy in such places. What we were doing was helping a group of local people to prove that the mangroves could be used sustainably and conserved at the same time. A block of some 200 hectares had been licensed for use by a cooperative. The Danish development aid agency, DANIDA, was funding the project and Enrique Lahmann, head of ORCA, IUCN's Regional Office for Central America, was coordinating it. The money had been used to supply chain saws to cut the bigger trees for charcoal, and to build new kilns to make it in. Previously, only the bark of these trees had been used, to produce tannin. The cooperative had also been given a lorry. This allowed them to transport their bags of charcoal to market, cutting out parasitical middle-men who would otherwise have scooped the greater part of the profits.

But the onslaught on the mangroves was far from random. No cutting was allowed within 15 metres of the creek banks, so the visual aspect of the area from the water was scarcely changed. Besides bark and charcoal, the project was yielding a coarse fern whose fibres made a good handmade paper. Iguanas were caught for local sale as meat (said to be very tasty). And a walkway had been built so that tourists – increasing in numbers locally – could pass through the forest at all stages of the tide to see the wild life in the water and among the trees. The problems? Too many people might be attracted to copy the project, and so undermine its sustainability. And the banana plantation owners might lure the labour away by offering higher wages for their own, far less sustainable, venture.

Costa Rica is a beautiful, charming, friendly and relatively prosperous country and immensely popular for all these reasons with foreign visitors and residents. There is a substantial expatriate community. But it is not immune from opportunism that thumbs its nose at both the law and conservation. I saw an example of this in around 1993. Maurice Strong, the Secretary General of the Stockholm and Rio Conferences, owned an estate adjacent to one of the National Parks. It was said to include some rather fine forest. This was the subject of some alarming information from our staff, which prompted a phone call.

'Maurice, is it right that you own an area of forest in Costa Rica?'

'Yes, quite right. It's very beautiful, too.'

'Did you know that a lot of the big trees had been marked for logging...'

Deathly hush. Consternation. But I didn't hear what happened after that.

Nicaragua was a contrast. Although just next door, with much the same climate and potential environmental wealth, it is a much poorer country, as was evident when we flew over the frontier and approached the capital, Managua, by its great lake. The city looked like a disaster zone. The ruins of a great cathedral of dark stone towered roofless from barren grassland, and there were other tumbled wrecks of fine buildings. The cause – a great earthquake, followed by civil strife that impoverished the nation and made rebuilding impossible. Yet the environmental resources are there for the using. We were involved in plans for a cooperative project between three countries to promote sustainable use of a broad bay on the Pacific coast. There was a small-scale venture to enhance duck populations on an inland lake. Other projects could have been developed in the forests. And the country is a fascinating one for the naturalist. The Lake of Nicaragua, by the capital, is the only freshwater lake in the world to house a population of sharks – land-locked when the rapid movements of the earth built the Panama land bridge and cut off an arm of the sea. There is still argument over whether the fish could move down the river to the Atlantic (yes, Atlantic, for the lake drains that way although it is very close to the Pacific seaboard). There is obvious potential for 'ecotourism', if the fragile peace can be made robust.

In the 1990s I also became deeply involved in China's environmental affairs. It started with Hainan, an island lying off the south coast, in the South China Sea. It is about as big as Taiwan, but has only 5 million inhabitants. For a long time it was a backward area, to which political dissidents were exiled. The Chinese thought of it as a pristine wilderness, and indeed it had been just that a century ago when the mountainous southern half of the island was cloaked in magnificently diverse broad-leaved rain forests. But the hand of the destroyer had fallen heavily since then. By 1988 native forest covered less than 10 per cent of the island and some rare species, like the Black-crowned gibbon, were nearing extinction.

The island was the largest Special Economic Zone in China, with great incentives for foreign investment. It was important as a source of iron (one hill of almost pure haematite ore was being quarried away at a vast rate). There were coal and gas resources. The pressures of development were heavy. But a group of far-sighted people, led by an energetic Executive Vice-Governor, Bao Ke Ming, his dynamic wife, Wei Saying, and a former Chinese Minister of Agriculture, He Kang, wanted that development to be based on sound environmental principles. Aided and advised by a British consultant and one-time diplomat, Martin Lees, they formed the International Advisory Council for the Development of Hainan Province in

Accordance with the Principles of the Natural Environment. The Council members were to be drawn from China and overseas in equal numbers. He Kang was to be the Chinese Co-Chair, and I was asked to head the International side. Among the Chinese members was Deng Nan, Deng Xiao Ping's daughter, who was Director of Social Development in the national Science and Technology Commission. She looked as like pictures of her father as a woman could. The same short stature. The same broad face. The same strong jaw. And the same toughness.

The IAC kicked off with a technical symposium in Haikou city, capital of Hainan, and broadened into discussion of environmental and developmental objectives. We went on field trips. It soon became obvious that Hainan was no 'pristine wilderness'. Driving out to the north-east, you passed kilometre after kilometre of rather poor-quality rubber plantations, shielded by shelter belts of feathery cypress-like *Casuarina*. There was a nature reserve on a muddy creek where mangroves were recovering from over-cutting, but were still only five or six metres high. On the east side, we visited another estuary where a little holiday resort – a cluster of small bungalows and a restaurant – was threatened by the sea. Once there had been a sheltering coral reef offshore. Dynamiting to stun fish and to quarry rock, used as building stone and to burn as a source of lime for the fields, had destroyed it. The sea, driven by gales screaming in from the east (any part of Hainan can expect, on average, a typhoon and a half a year), had cut the coast back by over two hundred metres. The huts and restaurant were severely endangered.

It was much the same in the forest country. Driving south to the mountains, there was scarcely a patch of semi-natural vegetation in a journey of about a hundred and fifty kilometres. The wetter areas were rice paddy, where peasants in broad-brimmed coolie hats plodded slowly behind their ploughs, pulled by Water buffalo. Flocks of white ducks dabbled and paddled in shallow creeks. The drier ground was covered by poor pastures and scruffy rubber plantations. When we reached the mountains, we found that they were largely deforested or replanted with *Eucalyptus*. The patches of relict native vegetation clung to steep ravines, and the only extensive tracts of natural forest were in two main areas – a central basin called Wang Xia and a western upland, around dramatic granite bosses of mountain, called Jianfengling. In Wang Xia a small forest reserve sheltered the last group of Black-crowned gibbons. But the area was also the home of Li people – one of the ethnic minorities in this part of China – who carved their shifting cultivation plots out of the forest and hunted many wild species for meat. It was rumoured that most of the gibbons had found their way to Haikou market as 'bushmeat' at a time of food shortage.

Lizzie came on a trip to that gibbon sanctuary in the central mountains.

We halted for the night at a spacious, and rather run-down hostel at the iron mine, where the hospitality was generous and the cockroaches abundant. Next morning we bumped along a rough road past some Li villages. There were many children. Deng Nan explained that the minority people were exempted from the one child per family policy that was visibly bearing its limited fruit in Beijing. 'These people are very poor, unhealthy, and live badly,' she commented. 'But they will improve...' It sounded like an instruction. And so to the forested hills – for the 'mountains' of Hainan are mostly on a British scale. We walked along a high ridge through some lovely woods, which included conifers (*Podocarpus* and *Dacrydium*) closely related to those of southern temperate regions. The forest was known to harbour leeches, and Lizzie imagined devouring horrors under every fern-spray. Happily, the weather had been dry, and not a leech raised its toothy rosette towards her. But no gibbons howled either. It was just a good walk through the forest, and a proof that there was a little biodiversity left to conserve.

The mountains and forests at Jianfengling, further west, are even lovelier, with abrupt horns of granite shaped rather like the Sugar Loaf in Rio sprouting from the greenery to a highest point over 1400 metres above the sea. Although there had been commercial logging around the mountains, tracts of undamaged forest also remained and the Hainan government proposed to make this the heart of a tourist centre and focus for conservation. They would transfer commercial efforts to a zone around the mountain's foot, where there were already plantations of eucalypts as well as a fascinating arboretum of local trees. But the tourist industry had other, wilder ideas. At a local fishing resort on the west coast they planned a new city with replicas of the world's great buildings: Taj Mahal or Parthenon by the China Sea, and holiday housing in amongst it all. I doubt if it will happen, but it sounded rather like a Chinese Blackpool...

The Hainan authorities wanted economic growth and prosperity – and were getting it in the urban areas, whose economy was expanding at around 11 per cent per annum. Haikou was growing at an alarming rate. New factories, wide boulevards flanked by oil palms, a new University, a new airport... it was a boom town, changing from year to year. Redevelopment engulfed the old airport even before it had passed from use: one Dragonair pilot from Hong Kong, dropping through cloud, was horrified to find an unlit crane where none had been the day before. The airline schedules changed to day flights only. Away on the south coast, at Sanya, another new airport was built, to take Boeing 747s conveying tourists to the white sand beaches they saw as the Waikiki of the South China Sea. Yet there seemed a gap between the stated desire to develop in conformity with the principles of the natural environment and the dynamic reality. Lizzie was struck by the charm of a row of old merchants' houses in Haikou, with fretted stone facades facing a waterfront full of picturesque fishing boats. We urged Bao Ke Ming to conserve them as a tourist asset and part of the historic heritage but he seemed to have difficulty with the concept. Rather similarly, at Sanya, we tried to suggest that they could improve on Hawaii by developing their lovely white beaches of coral sand at a low density and making sure that the wooded hills remained as a green backdrop to the new hotels. We also urged that light industry be located on the other side of the city, near the new international airport. But I suspect that the economic dragon will be too fiery to quench.

The problem, really, was that although agriculture was well understood (and there is an impressive agricultural university and research centre in the heart of Hainan), nature conservation and the wider concepts of integrated land management were new. A few people, like Minister He Kang, Vice Governor Bao Ke Ming, and the Director of the Hainan Centre, Professor Huang Zong Dao, understood what was needed, but the highly sectoral and rather old-fashioned departments of the Adminstration did not. They still had the attitude that prevailed in eighteenth century Europe: nature needed improvement, and human works were superior. A few years later there were other problems. He Kang became ill; Bao quarrelled with the Governor and senior Communist Party officials and was transferred to Beijing, and the prospects of success in what had started as a remarkable venture looked bleak. I still hope that some of the ideas we discussed will none the less come to fruition.

The Hainan International Advisory Council was a model. And the model, encouraged by Martin Lees, took root in the capital. In 1990 there was a meeting in Beijing to consider the integration of economic development and environment in China. It led to the creation of a China Council for International Cooperation on Environment and Development under the powerful Chairmanship of State Councillor Song Jian. Dr Qu Geping, head of the Environment Protection Agency, was a Vice Chairman. The Council brought together Vice Ministers from many of the key Ministries. Canada funded the international work of the Council through the Canadian International Development Agency and its head, Marcel Massé, became the International Vice Chairman. Charles de Haes and I, as heads of WWF and IUCN, were invited to serve, as were eminent figures like Barber Conable, then President of the World Bank, and Crispin Tickell, then UK Ambassador to the UN.

The early meetings of CCICED were held in the Diaoyutai State Guest House – a compound of spacious buildings set amid lakes and gardens and within a high wall that kept the noise and bustle of Beijing at bay. We were

*A break for tourism! Lizzie pauses on the flag-bedecked
restored section of the Great Wall*

well entertained, as well as worked hard. Lizzie came for one of the
meetings, and we had a chance to see some of the sights of city and
hinterland – the Forbidden City, the Temple of Heavenly Peace, the Ming
Tombs and, of course, the much-photographed restored section of the Great
Wall, winding massively over the tangled hills. We had a banquet in the
Great Hall of the People. I suspect I broke etiquette there, for I had noticed
one interesting thing I will pass on as a traveller's tip. At the start of
receptions in China you will, of course, be offered tumblers of drinks on
trays. The first assortment will be soft drinks – orange, lemon, lime and
Coke. Shake your head. Eventually a tray with some beer will appear. It is
worth waiting for.

One highlight of the meetings of the CCICED was an audience with one of the highest rulers of China. A preliminary meeting I did not attend had met Deng himself, and been amazed by the accuracy with which he could target a spittoon placed on the floor over a metre from him. Once in my time it was the President, Jiang Zemin. But after the meeting in 1990 we went to see Li Peng, then Premier. We had been told that four of us should make three-minute statements describing some of our conclusions. I was asked to cover energy and environment. I was to make a plea for greater efficiency and cleaner industry, leading to reduced emissions of greenhouse gases. I was told to be blunt, and was.

'Premier,' I said, 'are you aware that China could double its Gross National Product without the need to build any more installations to generate electricity, if you only increased your energy efficiency to match that of India? And we have been told that one of the reasons why energy is wasted in China is that it is very cheap, because of state subsidy. Would you consider allowing prices to rise to give an incentive to greater efficiency?'

His face was a study. To be told you were less efficient than the USA or Europe was bearable. To be weighed in the balance with India and found wanting was not. We were rewarded by a twenty minute statement on economic and energy policy in the midst of which Mr Li did accept the great benefits of increasing energy efficiency, and the potential role of a new pricing system in promoting it. And, yes, they are making changes – slowly phasing out extremely dirty coal-fired power stations and building modern, efficient ones. But China does have the largest coal reserves in the world, and I expect that they will use them, greenhouse effect or not.

My last meeting was at Hangzhou, in a lovely setting by the West Lake, a legendary beauty spot near a place that Marco Polo called 'the most beautiful city in the world' but which now has little of architectural merit to distinguish it. We walked by the Grand Canal, built over a thousand years ago and one of the world's most stupendous engineering achievements, as wide as a large English river, snaking seventeen hundred kilometres southwards from Beijing to link with the Huang He and Yangtze rivers. It was flanked by a clutter of houses, factories and shops (one proclaiming, in English, that it sold tasty flaked dog-meat). But the Canal was dirty and smelled bad. Tanneries and metal works along its banks poured filth into the opaque waters. Song Jian and Qu Geping promised a clean-up. The scene illustrated much that was problematical in China at the time, as we heard in a frank briefing from a senior executive of the Central Bank.

Paraphrased, this was an admission that the economy was out of control and over-heating badly. The Provinces vied with one another for economic growth (shades of Hainan). Some were achieving rates of 10 or even 12 per cent per annum. The national telecommunications industry had grown by nearly 100 per cent in 1992. Uncontrolled development sent the cities sprawling over the adjacent farmland, and increasing consumer wealth – in the cities – meant that more costly and sophisticated foods were demanded. Ten years earlier China had prided itself on feeding nearly a quarter of the Earth's people on under eight per cent of the world's farmland. Now the farmland was shrinking, under the impact of pollution, erosion and urban sprawl. They were importing grains – on a mounting scale. The economy was growing too rapidly – they reckoned that seven or eight per cent per annum could be managed, but any more spelled economic overstrain. CCICED recognized that sustainable, environmentally sound, development meant a less breakneck speed. But even so, China remained determinedly on course to overtake the United States as the world's largest national economy by some time around 2020 – if the system did not blow up first.

The Chinese leaders that we spoke to were in no doubt that the economic transition they were seeking depended in part on the success of their 'one child per couple' population policy. In Beijing its consequences were much in evidence in the shape of single children, well-dressed and obviously cherished, accompanied by doting parents or grandparents. People in the west have divided views about this approach. On the one hand, it is the most determined attempt anywhere in the world to curb the soaring human population and bring it into balance with the sustaining capacity of the Earth, and more specifically, China. And because the country is home to so many people the effort will have a real impact on global statistics. In 1990 there were between 1,250 and 1,500 million Chinese. If the policy works, numbers will stabilise at around 1,600 million and then start falling. But there are social downsides. China is not all that bothered about the western worry over a dwindling labour force supporting an increasing phalanx of pensioners, first because people don't retire as we do and second because economic growth is so massive. On the other hand, if the policy continues for a long time consider what it would do to the family. After two generations, a baby would have no brothers, sisters, aunts, uncles or first cousins. There would just be two parents and up to four grandparents. Probably the bleak vision will prove too grim, for once stability is in sight two-child families are likely to become the norm and a more even balance between the generations will be restored. Meanwhile, as China advances towards being the world's largest economy, unconstrained population growth may well make India soon replace it as the world's most populous nation. Which will have a better quality of life?

The Usambaras, Uganda, Zimbabwe, Botswana, Pakistan, Oman, Costa

Rica, China – all brought home to me how the world of conservation had changed in the eight years since IUCN, in partnership with WWF and UNEP, published the first *World Conservation Strategy* in 1980. Although that document recognized that conservation had to cater for human needs, many people felt that it was unduly nature-centred. But by 1986, when William Waldegrave and I both addressed a review meeting in Ottawa, attitudes had evolved and there was much more recognition that conservation could only be achieved within the context of development that relieved poverty and achieved economic growth. The Ottawa meeting not only produced a book whose title *Conservation with Equity* enshrines the new message, but called for a second World Conservation Strategy that would explain how it could be achieved. IUCN took delivery of this mandate, and I found them puzzling over it when I arrived in Gland.

We tried to recruit a well-known science policy analyst and writer as leader of the project. She refused, admitting to doubts about the value of the venture. We were rescued by a former Director General, David Munro. He had presided over the production of the first WCS and agreed to steer the new version if the original compiler, Robert Prescott-Allen, would join him. The team soon got to work, consulting widely, and produced a first consolidated draft in January 1991. I agreed with almost everything it said, but felt it needed boiling down and altering in style. How? I was arrogant enough to decide to do it myself. Robert's draft was loaded into a laptop computer and I went home and sat in the attic. Lizzie became used to this eccentric recluse who appeared from time to time to grab a coffee or munch a meal, while muttering abstractedly about conservation ethics or the economic values of nature or the constraints of the political process. She went out and bought an egg-cup in the shape of an opened newspaper: when the egg was installed all you could see from the front was a brown, bald dome. 'That's you,' she said. 'My alter eggo!' In the end, David, Robert and I agreed on the final text: it was bounced off a lot of colleagues and especially our partners in WWF and UNEP, and *Caring for the Earth* emerged. It was Charles de Haes who coined the sub-title *A Strategy for Sustainable Living*.

Caring for the Earth was a revolutionary document for a conservation organization, for it is essentially social and political rather than a treatise on ecology and the survival of species. Science is its foundation, but the book recognizes that conservation is about securing the human future. How can people and nature co-exist in a world where we use, divert or waste about 40 per cent of the energy that is fixed by green plants on land? The Strategy begins with ethics – the need to respect and care for each other and for the Earth. It has nine guiding principles:

- Respect and care for the community of life.
- Improve the quality of human life.
- Conserve the Earth's vitality and diversity.
- Minimize the depletion of non-renewable resources.
- Keep within the Earth's carrying capacity.
- Change personal attitudes and practices.
- Enable communities to care for their own environments.
- Provide a national framework for integrating development and conservation.
- Create a global alliance.

It sets out 132 actions to build a sustainable society, and 113 targets to be achieved by set dates. It also suggests a series of indicators we might measure to see how well we and the environment are doing.

We launched *Caring for the Earth* all round the world on 21 October 1991. I kicked it off in Sydney, by handing a copy to the Acting Prime Minister of Australia. Our Australian Council Member, Pam Eiser, had written an excellent practical leaflet headed *What on Earth can I do?* and sub-titled *A Personal Action Guide for Sustainable Living.* Although there were some critical reactions from traditional nature protectionists, it caught the mood of the time and was very much in harmony with the approach to the 'Earth Summit' to be held in Rio de Janeiro in the following year.

The formal title of the Rio Conference was 'the United Nations Conference on Environment and Development', or UNCED for short (though wags pointed out that little conceivable was left unsaid there). 'Earth Summit' was journalist's jargon, pardonable given the ponderous official label. It was to be held twenty years after the Stockholm Conference, so the date was fixed as June 1992. The Swedish suggestion of a return meeting in Stockholm was soon swept aside by a demand that this time the world should meet in a developing country, and Rio de Janeiro was chosen. The central theme was to be 'sustainable development' – the buzz-concept of the 1980s.

But Maurice Strong, brought back as Secretary General, was determined that Rio should generate more than buzz-words. As at Stockholm, he wanted a range of outputs. At the highest level, he wanted the heads of the world's States and Governments to adopt a ringing declaration of commitment to a sustainable world. Next, he wanted a practical plan of action. Finally, and again mirroring Stockholm, he wanted new international Conventions on key topics.

Like Stockholm, Rio was planned by an international Preparatory Committee – this time led by a skilful diplomat from Singapore, Tommy

Koh. Sadly, the Declaration they drafted rang about as clearly as a cracked bell. The draft of the detailed Agenda for the 21st Century – Agenda 21 for short – was much better. There were forty chapters of it, and it takes up 470 pages of the official United Nations Report on the Conference. Many Governments have used it as a basis for their own agendas for sustainable development, and for local community action plans as well. As to Conventions, climate change and biological diversity emerged as priority themes, with forests and desertification also championed by different groups of States.

We in IUCN were involved in planning Rio at two levels. First, we had a close working relationship with Maurice and his staff, who were based just along the lake at Conches, in the southern suburbs of Geneva. Indeed, some of us acted as unofficial extra members of the team. Jeff McNeely, our chief conservation scientist and authority on biodiversity, Jeff Sayer, head of our Forests programme, Danny Elder, head of our Marine section, and our international Law Centre headed by Wolfgang Burhenne's wife Françoise, all played an active part in preparing both for Agenda 21 and the Conventions. This behind the scenes work with the Rio Secretariat was, quite frankly, far more productive than attendance at the PrepComs, where as a non-UN body we had little chance of contributing.

IUCN has been in the business of drafting international Conventions for most of its history. Wolfgang, as long-time Chair of the Commission on Environmental Law and with the Environmental Law Centre at his elbow in Bonn, had kick-started the processes that led to the Bonn Convention on Conservation of Migratory Species, the Ramsar Convention on the Conservation of Wetlands, the UNECSO Convention on the Conservation of the World Cultural and Natural Heritage and the Convention on International Trade in Endangered Species. The idea of a wider Convention on the Conservation of Biological Diversity had first been voiced by a Law Commission member, Cyrille de Klemm, at a Parks Congress in Bali in 1982. Although most of these Conventions got taken over by Governments as drafting advanced, IUCN was still very much involved in them and one of my first initiatives as Director General was to convene a meeting of their secretariats to explore ways of improving the synergy between them. Reuben Olembo of UNEP saw this as trespassing on its patch and insisted on taking over the meetings, but we all agreed on the need for greater synergy.

By the mid-1980s, the destruction of the Earth's biological diversity had become a matter of international concern. I think three things combined to push the topic up the global agenda. The first was the discovery that we had a much greater richness of life on the planet, and especially in the tropical rain forests, than we had suspected. The American entomologist Terry Erwin demonstrated this diversity by collecting the faunas of a series of canopy trees, using a fog of pesticide which 'knocked down' all insects and spiders. He found that each tree had an enormous richness of associated life, a good deal of it not described by science. As a result, he calculated that there may be as many as 30 million kinds of insects and other jointed-legged invertebrate animals on Earth. Yet only a little over a million of these creatures have been described and named. Many species appear to have a quite restricted distribution, and some are associated with particular kinds of plant. In some rich rain forests there may be as many as 100 kinds of tree per hectare, and the area to area variation is quite high. The faunas are likely to have an equally intricate distribution pattern.

The second reason for concern was the recognition that the tropical rain forests were being destroyed faster than we had thought – at a rate of around 15 million hectares a year. This led to calculations like that by Peter Raven, Director of the Missouri Botanical Garden, who estimated that if half the world's plant species live in tropical rain forests, and if half the species are lost if the area of that forest is reduced by 90 per cent, at current rates of destruction we could expect a quarter of the world's higher plants to become extinct between 1985 and 2015. Insect losses would be of comparable magnitude. Although we are only known to have lost 340 species of mammal, bird, reptile, amphibian, fish and conspicuous invertebrate since 1600, and 384 higher plants in the same period, these figures must vastly underestimate the true scale of the disaster. Extinctions are likely to be running at between a thousand and ten thousand times the natural rate.

Why does this matter? First, because many people agree that, as the World Charter for Nature adopted by the UN General Assembly in 1982 states, 'all species warrant respect regardless of their usefulness to man.' There is an ethical objection to the destruction by greedy or uncaring humanity of so much of the beautiful richness of life, including many species far older than our own. There are also more mercenary motives. We all depend on the web of life, with its complicated interactions. The world economy is a wholly-owned subsidiary of the world's ecology. Nature provides breathable air, drinkable water, plant and animal food and many medicines. In forest areas, an enormous variety of plants and animals are used by people for one purpose or another. Nearly half the drugs traded across the chemist's counter have their origins in wild plants even if the potent molecules are now synthesized in the laboratory. Tropical forests are, as Norman Myers has put it, 'much more than stocks of wood'. We simply do not know what potential wealth is being logged and burned into extinction in the forests of the world.

So it was natural that conservationists should trumpet concern – and that they should awaken an echo among governments in developing countries, who were jarred by the realization that their forests might be more valuable as shelters for a diverse ecology, or as sources of pharmaceutical wealth, than as neatly stacked log piles by the quayside. There was a demand for international action. The first rumblings were in the shape of seminars, meetings and conferences but it was also realised that the existing Conventions just did not give adequate protection. They dealt with only parts of the problem, and many had far too few States as Contracting Parties. Indeed one idea, floated at a UNEP Governing Council by the United States Ambassador, John Negroponte, even before I went to IUCN, was that we should replace them by a new, comprehensive, measure. Wolfgang Burhenne and I had argued instead for a new 'umbrella' agreement that would not replace the existing Conventions but link them in a comprehensive global framework.

The Commission on Environmental Law began to produce a draft, and IUCN submitted a paper to the UNEP Governing Council in May 1989. UNEP took the action over and convened intergovernmental meetings to negotiate a text. As the preparations for Rio got moving, it was agreed that this should be one of its tangible achievements, alongside a Convention on Climate Change. Many countries began to survey their national living assets and prepare strategies for their sustainable use. Mexico was one of these, and in February 1992 President Carlos Salinas de Gortari convened a Conference in the Anthropological Museum in the heart of Mexico City. Seven of us with invitations were at the World Parks Congress in Caracas, and the only way we could combine the two events was to fly direct – in a small, fast, executive jet which the President generously provided. The Mexicans were good enough to ask Lizzie along too.

The Conference was very positive. President Salinas gave clear backing to the head of the Autonomous University, Professor José Sarukhan, who wanted to prepare a national biodiversity strategy. To see what it meant on the ground, we were all taken to the southern province of Chiapas at the end of the meeting.

We travelled in the Presidential aircraft, sweeping past the legendary volcano of Popocatepetl, and transferred to helicopters that droned their way along a deep river valley and over the canopies of a vast forest. We landed at Yaxchilan – a famous Aztec site sprouting its grey walls and stepped pyramids from the tree tops. The final discussions of the Conference were held in the ancient plaza, under a thatched canopy put up for the occasion. Howler monkeys came in on cue as the President made his final speech (some people said it was really a recording, screamed out through a concealed loudspeaker at the strategic moment). We had just enough time to wander among the ruins and be greeted by a group of representatives of the local people before rushing back to helicopter, airport, and Caracas. It all seemed so peaceful – but this was the region where local discontent was shortly to erupt into revolt.

We all welcomed the concept of a Convention on Biological Diversity, but I was appalled by what I saw of the negotiation process. It was dominated by wishful thinking and professional ignorance. Many governmental teams were led by people who quite clearly did not understand the resources they were trying to legislate about. The problem was that three separate interests and perspectives were being rolled into one process. One perspective was that of 'northern' conservationists. They wanted to stop the destruction of tropical rain forests and other centres of biodiversity. They wanted those centres listed in a global schedule and made eligible for outside help, as World Heritage sites are under the Convention UNESCO administers. Their approach – even if obscured by diplomatic jargon – was protectionist and interventionist. There were hints about barring the products of unsustainable development from world markets.

This was anathema to many developing country governments who saw it as an intrusion into their sovereign right to develop their own resources for their own benefit – and to misuse them if they were so inclined. They rejected any idea of a global list. They became choleric over trade bans. On the other hand, they did want an agreement that would stop northern pharmaceutical companies with superior scientific knowledge coming in, undertaking field research, locating valuable plants and other resources, and walking off with the proceeds. Hence the demand that field surveys to identify such resources must always be agreed with the sovereign State involved – to which a fair share of any resulting profits should flow. There was great optimism that crocks of gold lay where rainbows touched the forest canopy.

The third perspective was opportunist. If the 'north' wanted the 'south' to conserve its forests and other centres of biodiversity, let it pay for it. From this perspective the Convention was to be a mechanism for transfer of funds, knowledge, and technical skills from north to south. Once that mechanism was established for biodiversity, it would serve as a precedent for political pressure elsewhere . . .

Many of these ideas were naive, lacking both a foundation in science and political and economic realism. The northern protectionists failed to understand the impetus of poverty and economic need that forced many developing countries to harvest saleable resources now and worry about the future – in the future. And they ignored the fact that the world economic system, dominated by their own nations, had driven commodity prices for many developing country products downward at a time when their debt burdens were increasing. On the other hand, many developing countries had made a mess of their development process, not least through bad or corrupt government, and had enormously exaggerated notions of the money they might make out of northern chemical companies. They also overestimated the amount of money that might be available to support the Convention on Biological Diversity and other new international measures (though there was some success here when the Governments in the north agreed to establish a Global Environment Facility and to give it 2 billion US dollars). The GEF was to be managed by the World Bank, guided on scientific issues by UNEP, and operated in the field by the UN Development Programme, and biodiversity projects were made eligible for grants from it.

The Governments resisted any efforts by non-governmental bodies like IUCN to suggest ways of making the science better, and the Convention more realistic. It was clear that even an expert like Jeff McNeely would have limited influence on the discussions in the negotiating chamber. So we also attached Françoise Burhenne-Guilmin to the UNEP Secretariat team, to influence drafts from the inside. This did not work perfectly either, because the head of the UNEP Law unit jealously guarded her own patch, but it was more effective than interventions on the conference floor would have been. In the end, a Convention was agreed for presentation at Rio. I still think that we would have had a better instrument if the time pressures had been less severe, and the Governments had engaged in a wider dialogue first.

There was in fact a proven model for what they should have done. In parallel with the Convention on Biological Diversity, a Convention on Climate Change was being negotiated, also for adoption at Rio. But here the Governments had started with rigorous analysis. They had set up an Intergovernmental Panel on Climate Change, and split it into three Committees. The first, made up of many of the world's best climatologists, looked at the scientific evidence that the increasing concentrations of greenhouse gases in the atmosphere were indeed likely to cause climate change. Sir John Houghton, former Director General of the British Meteorological Office, headed it. The second expert Committee reviewed the likely ecological, agricultural, social and economic impacts of the changes the climatologists considered most plausible. The third Committee looked at the options for action. The result was a Convention that was rooted in good science and realistic politics. We should have approached biological diversity in the same way – involving people who knew something about the subject, which most of the delegates to the Inter-governmental Negotiating Committee clearly did not.

The Brazilians made a huge effort to ensure the success of the Rio Summit. One manifestation was a security clampdown such as that dynamic and rather lawless city had never seen before. There were soldiers everywhere. There were tanks guarding the tunnels that pierce the fingers of mountain that fan out and divide the city. The tunnels, we were told, were a favoured spot for robbers, who would block the traffic and circulate, revolvers in hand, to collect the loot much as Dick Turpin did in England centuries ago. They did not get a look in while UNCED was in town. The 'street children' – homeless gangs that slept where they could and had developed many advanced skills when it came to getting money from the pockets of tourists – vanished. We were assured that they were being taken care of by the army, out of town, but many consciences twitched none the less. Crime in Rio was reported to have dropped to one tenth of its normal level.

Things were even stricter in the hotel-land where delegates congregated. There were helicopter patrols along the coasts, and when President George Bush (senior) was in residence at the Sheraton I noticed two warships zig-zagging offshore. There was a triple security barrier around the Rio Centro buildings where the Governments met – a check on the gates, a check and screening to enter the building and a third check to get into the main Ministerial conference halls. When the Heads of State and Government rolled in for the final two days an extra-special layer of security was superimposed.

All this upset the Non-Governmental Organizations. Only some of them were let into Rio Centro (which some dubbed Rio Perifero as it was miles away from the heart of the city). Their main Forum – a kind of environmental bazaar and festival attended by some 10,000 people – was much nearer the real centre of Rio, in Flamengo Park on the shores of Guanabara Bay, looking across to the Sugar Loaf. One or two activists tried to gatecrash Rio Centro. They got thumped by guards. Those of us with a foot in both camps spent a lot of time commuting – or had simply to decide which was to be our venue for the day.

But it was memorable. It was fascinating to see George Bush, Fidel Castro, John Major and François Mitterand – plus many more notables – in the same room. Castro's speech stunned everyone. The Brazilian President, Francisco Collór, who chaired the event with a charm and competence that gave no hint of his impending fall from power and exit to jail, had announced that as over 100 Top People had to speak in two days, they would get eight minutes each. Nobody expected Fidel Castro, renowned for two hour orations, to manage it. Maurice Strong was deputed to break the news.

Fidel Castro signs the Convention on Biological Diversity at Rio, 1992.
Photograph: WWF-Canon/Juan Antonio Gill Pratginestos.

'Mr President,' he said, 'when you speak, you are very eloquent. But you are also very long. This time you need to be very eloquent and very brief.' Castro twinkled. 'You'll see,' he promised.

We did. He strode to the rostrum, a hefty figure in immaculate uniform, great grey beard a-jutting, and raised a hand, gesturing with five fingers at Collór. He completed a fiery oration in 4 minutes, 58 seconds. In total contrast, President Museveni of Uganda leaned gently on the rostrum, pretended to have forgotten his notes, and spoke sincerely about how his country was being rebuilt after years of strife, and of the special place of the environment in the hearts of his people. John Major had clearly concluded that he had to announce some practical actions (his advisers, I suspect, were told to write something that sounded good and would not cost too much). He announced three initiatives: the UK would convene a conference for non-governmental organizations to discuss how sustainable development could really be made to work; there would be a Darwin Initiative to make the scientific knowledge of British institutions available around the world; and there would be a UK national strategy for sustainable development. When these chickens had to find subsequent roosts, I found myself chairing the Conference, while Crispin Tickell presided over the Panel that guided the sustainable development strategy.

George Bush was the real dark horse. During the Reagan Presidency, the USA had earned an unenviable reputation for anti-environmentalism and a negative attitude to things like the Law of the Sea and the United Nations itself. When Bush became President, there was a sign of hope because he appointed Bill Reilly, head of WWF in the United States and an IUCN Vice President, as Administrator of the Environment Protection Agency. Bill was respected as an environmentalist, and we had reason to believe that he would press for a positive US approach at Rio, where he led their delegation. But the vibrations were not good. There were rumours that he had asked for a flexible negotiating position and been rebuffed. George Bush was known to be refusing to sign the Convention on Biological Diversity. But why? What would he say?

Three days before he was due to speak, my hotel telephone rang. An American voice. 'President Bush is giving a small luncheon party before he speaks, and is inviting some key people from the Non-Governmental world. He would be most appreciative if you would be one of his guests.' I thought at first that someone was pulling my leg. No, it was for real. About forty of us gathered and sat down, Captain Jacques Cousteau on the President's left. Bill Reilly and the other senior members of the United States delegation were scattered about. After lunch, Mr Bush tapped the table. 'I'd very much like to hear your views on what we should do to make the world environmental system more effective after Rio,' he said. 'Oh – but please don't go banging on about why I should sign the Convention on Biological Diversity. Captain Cousteau is a good friend of America, and he's already told me off for not doing it. I respect his views, but I am advised that it could be contrary to America's interests, so I am not going to, at least at this stage . . .'

He went round the table. I'm not sure that anything all that profound emerged. I tried to point the contrast between the early 1970s, when the United States was undoubtedly a world leader in environmental action, creating the first Environment Protection Agency and enacting pioneering laws, and the late 1980s when they seemed to have taken deregulation to the point of disintegration. Many of us argued that there should be no conflict between caring for the environment and national prosperity, because they were interdependent. Ashok Khosla of Development Alternatives in India talked about the need for genuine support for third world activities, and the value of the United Nations system. And so on. Then we trooped back to hear the President's speech – which disappointed many. The USA was clearly not in the mainstream of thought or action – but equally clearly, the world had changed since 1970, and the action would go ahead even if the United States opted out.

What did Rio achieve? The developing countries felt that they got rather little out of it. The barriers and pitfalls that they saw on the path to sustainable development remained in place. Nothing much was done to persuade the richer countries to invest in the poorer ones or to transfer less polluting and more efficient technology. The debt burden remained. The world trading system was full of barriers to the sale of developing country products in the wealthier nations. And Rio did not do much to curb the wasteful misuse of resources and excessive generation of pollution in the developed countries. Agenda 21 was, indeed, a good document but Maurice Strong calculated it needed 120 billion US dollars a year to make it work, and there was only $3 billion of new money on the Rio table. In fact, at the time we all went home there was an annual flow of $50 billion in the wrong direction – from the poor to the rich countries – and this was a taboo subject among governments. The oil-rich countries, led by Saudi Arabia but with the United States clapping discreetly on the touchline, did their best to block any mention of targets for reducing greenhouse gas emissions. Nothing material was said about population pressures, even though it was clear that these could lead to famine and international migration on a massive scale. And there was a lot of linguistic duplicity. As I said afterwards at the Royal Geographical Society, 'The fact is that in these contexts some plain, ordinary, honest English words are not held to be plain or honest. You must not, for example, speak of tropical forests as "the world's biological heritage" because this infringes national sovereignty, or demand "new and additional resources" to pay for new actions, because this upsets finance ministers in the richer countries.'

Yet there were positive results. Agenda 21 and the new Conventions on Biological Diversity and Climate Change were important documents. Never before had well over a hundred Heads of State or Government sat down together to discuss the links between environment and development. Never before had two environmental conventions attracted over 150 signatures each within a few days of their being opened for signature. The United States, true to George Bush's word, did not sign the CBD, but it did accept the Convention on Climate Change (this was before targets for action that would cost money were added to it at Kyoto). Governments also adopted what was infelicitously termed the Comprehensive Non-Binding Statement of Principles for the Conservation, Management and Sustainable Use of All Types of Forest. This was a compromise: many developed countries wanted a Convention that would protect dwindling rain forests while most developing countries, led by our Brazilian hosts, wanted nothing of the sort. Deserts had more friends and a Convention to Combat Desertification and Drought Especially in Africa emerged not long after Rio.

But will the Convention on Biological Diversity make any difference?

The loss of biodiversity is largely due to the destruction of rich habitats like rain forests and coral reefs and this destruction is driven by a mixture of commercial greed, ignorance and sheer desperation. All the pontifications of all the scientists and conservationists in the world will avail nothing unless the world's poor have their needs satisfied in less destructive ways, and unless entrepreneurs and crooks are prevented from destroying long-term assets for the sake of short-term gain. Both demand action by Governments, and their record is not good. Moreover, natural areas are terribly vulnerable. It is like climbing a mountain: as Edward Whymper wrote after the tragedy on the first ascent of the Matterhorn, 'a momentary negligence can destroy the happiness of a lifetime.' Decades of steady labour to build prosperous villages alongside cherished protected areas rich in biodiversity can be undone by a few months of war, famine, governmental instability or unscrupulous exploitation. We saw this in Garamba and in Idi Amin's Uganda, and there is a risk now in Zimbabwe. And human population growth inevitably piles more pressure on nature. All the Conventions in the world will be useless if the swelling pan-dominance of *Homo sapiens* does not slow to a halt with room to spare for other species.

Rio did encourage sustainable development – or, at least, sustainable development talk – in many countries around the world. IUCN's work in villages like those of the Usambaras, Elgon, Hunza or Terraba Sierpe and our more ethereal work on National Conservation Strategies were alike swept into this newly reinvigorated vortex. And our work grew in scale and complexity. Lizzie teased me from time to time about my original bold assertion that running the Union would 'be just like falling off a log' after the complexities of Whitehall. I was, of course, quite wrong, because I had failed to appreciate that though IUCN was a small organization in terms of people and budget, it was a very complicated one. It spanned the whole world, and it worked with and through a vast range of other bodies – not all of them members. The Rio endorsement of sustainable development, our track record in many countries and our worldwide network of offices and staff opened the way for take-off.

And take off we did. The budget climbed from around 18 million Swiss francs in 1988 to over 50 million in 1993. When I came, we had an office of about six people in East Africa, and a rather smaller outfit in Pakistan, two people in Washington DC, one in Harare, and a handful in Central America. By 1994, Aban had about forty people in Pakistan and a budget of around 5 million US dollars: the Washington DC office, base for programmes in North America, was about ten strong, there were a dozen or more staff in Costa Rica, and the East African office was moving to a splendid new site in the outskirts of Nairobi, amid gardens and a patch of wild forest complete with occasional leopards. We had smaller outposts in Uganda, Ethiopia, Tanzania, Botswana, Zambia, Zimbabwe, Ecuador, Bangladesh, Sri Lanka and Indo-China, with projects in many other places. We had nearly 400 staff, of whom less than half were in the Swiss Headquarters.

Expansion, of course, brings risks. IUCN prides itself on being a 'membership organization', and we had to carry the membership with us. The old debate between the Union as the champion of nature and the Union as the builder of sustainable development was constantly in the background, and occasionally spurted like flame from a smouldering log. We saw this in 1990 when we met for a General Assembly in Perth, capital of western Australia.

Perth is a lovely city, on the wide estuary of the Swan River, and we were splendidly housed in a conference centre with adjacent casino (off-limits to staff, and scarcely frequented by delegates). The Australians did a marvellous job as hosts, and we attracted well over a thousand people even in this most isolated of the world's capital cities. Prime Minister Bob Hawke welcomed everyone, and the Environment Minister, Ros Kelly, transferred her private office to the Conference Centre so that she could stay for a week yet still handle departmental business in Canberra. Prince Philip came, both as President of WWF International and as one of our own Vice Presidents, and made encouraging remarks about our progress. Old friends like Nigel and Margaret Wace and George Knox appeared, the former driving across the continent from Canberra. George chaired a workshop at which the text of an Antarctic Conservation Strategy was finally agreed. But the debates revealed an enormous range of views on the mission of IUCN, its approach, its relationship with its members, and its future. It was clear that the members wanted much closer links and stronger networks, and saw the Regional Councillors as their representatives at the heart of policy. It was clear we had to strengthen the role of Council, and the visibility of the President – tasks I thought would be aided by the election in succession to Dr Swaminathan of the former Secretary General of the Commonwealth, Sir Shridath ('Sonny') Ramphal. Not only is Sonny a wonderful orator, but he was a world statesman with access to Governments at the highest level.

In the years after Perth and Rio, our work burgeoned. In a few places we grew too fast and over-reached ourselves. Indeed, on the little Presidential executive jet between Caracas and Mexico City I was warned bluntly that our Central American office was going off the rails. We were not consulting properly with other organizations, including our own members. Some of our projects were over-ambitious. There were personality clashes. Aid agencies were getting restive. Arturo Gomez-Pompa, Vice-Chairman of the

Species Survival Commission, confirmed these criticisms when we met in Mexico. I sent people from Gland to investigate, and eventually it became clear that enthusiasm and inventiveness had led people to take on activities for which there was no funding. Strange subsidiary initiatives like a line in commercially-marketed 'green clothing' (ornamented with wildlife images, including sinuous trees that wound from your feet to your collar) were being pressed as a means of raising money to balance the meso-American books. Some of the designs were quite good – but the cash crisis was immediate. We had to write off about 1 million Swiss francs of losses. There had to be staff redundancies, and the programme had to be rebuilt almost from the foundations. Promising ideas for new work in Nicaragua and Mexico were casualties, and many of the enthusiasts I had met on my visits there became disgruntled. But the other strand was a stimulus to work much more closely with our members throughout Latin America, encouraging them to organize their own programme proposals, meetings and networks with IUCN staff in a supportive role. The cultural change worked, and by the time I came to retire the South American region was showing the fastest growth in membership and the most dynamic local activity in the whole Union.

The Rio Conference was not the end of my time in IUCN – I had two years to go when it ended – but in many ways it was a watershed. It gave – or seemed to give – strong endorsement to our central message. It set us on a clear track, parallel to but very different from that of WWF which focussed on saving nature from humans, where we sought to cherish nature as the foundation of the human future. But nobody doubted that IUCN was, and had to remain, a federation of nature conservation as well as sustainable development bodies. The Species Survival Commission, with its 5000 members and 130 specialist groups, remained the world focus for species conservation, and the World Commission on Protected Areas likewise led the global alliance of 'parks people'. No other body in the world had such a powerful and extensive network of volunteer experts. For many members they were the 'real' IUCN.

As the Union grew and diversified, more demands were made of its Council. Like the President, this is elected by the General Assembly, and members see it as the 'cabinet' of IUCN, with the President as Prime Minister. Under its guidance, the operations of the Union are run by the Director General, who is accountable to the Council for working within the policies laid down by the Assembly and to the funding agencies for discharging the contracts they place with the organization. As we approached my last General Assembly, to be held in Buenos Aires, it was becoming obvious that members wanted the Council strengthened, and also wanted IUCN to be 'returned' to them, through much more devolution of authority to the regions.

That final General Assembly was held in Buenos Aires in January 1994. The venue had been settled at Rio – in some embarrassment, for we received almost synchronous invitations from two prospective hosts, the President of Mexico, Carlos Salinas de Gortari, and the President of Argentina, Carlos Saul Menem. Argentina was ahead by a whisker, because they had raised the question at a lunch hosted by the Secretary of State for the Environment, Maria Julia Alsogaray, so Sonny Ramphal and I began by calling on President Menem, and I went on to President Salinas afterwards. We signed up with Argentina, and this in turn meant a planning visit to Buenos Aires and inspection of the excellent facilities in the Sheraton Hotel, right by the docks. It also meant long discussions with Maria Julia, an impressive and forceful character who reminded me a little of Margaret Thatcher!

It may have seemed that a British Director General of IUCN could expect a rather cool reception in Buenos Aires. In fact, it was generously warm. One of the paradoxes of the Falklands war was that throughout it there was very little harassment of the considerable Anglo-Argentine community. Many people recognized that the ties that had linked the two countries so closely in past times, and had almost made Argentina a part of the Commonwealth, would persist. Yes, Argentina does believe that the Malvinas are geographically and historically a part of their sovereign territory. No, they will not give up their claims. But many deplored the invasion under President Galtieri as setting back the process of careful diplomacy which they knew to be the only way those claims are ever likely to be met, and as creating hostility between two peoples that have every reason to be friends.

Maria Julia told me an interesting story.

'My father is a very senior Argentine politician,' she reminded me. 'When we had occupied the Falklands, he recognized that we might well not be able to hold them. He went to see Galtieri.

'"Mr President," he said, "this is what you must do. Get on your Presidential aircraft and go to New York, where the UN General Assembly is in session. Tell them that Argentina is putting the Malvinas under UN trusteeship, and will withdraw our troops in favour of a peace-keeping force without either Argentine or British members. If you do that, the British will never be able to mount a counter-offensive. World opinion would not stand for it."'

It might have worked. But Galtieri was too flushed with victory, and too obstinate, to listen.

We gathered in Buenos Aires just three months before my six-year term as Director General was due to end. My successor had already been appointed. David McDowell was at the time New Zealand Ambassador to Japan, and we had met briefly in Tokyo in November 1993. David stood out in any company, for he was almost two metres tall. He was a historian by discipline, widely experienced in diplomacy, sometime Assistant Secretary of the Commonwealth under Sonny Ramphal, and sometime also Head of the New Zealand Department of Conservation, which he reorganized. He quickly saw that his diplomatic skills would be challenged.

For the demands of the membership for a new-style IUCN rose to a clamour when the Assembly debated a Strategy that the staff, led by an able Trinidadian, Angela Cropper, and a Council Task Force under Jay Hair, head of the National Wildlife Federation in the United States, had developed over the preceding year. Developing country members, especially in Latin America, demanded regional devolution and greater support. Many members wanted resources for the Commissions, as voluntary networks in which they could take part. They were questioning the large proportion of staff employed in the Swiss headquarters. They demanded a larger developing country representation on the staff. They wanted the Council to exercise more power. The message to the new Director General was strong and clear.

The demand for a new style washed over the Presidency. By tradition, holders of this office serve two terms of three years, and also by tradition, if the Director General comes from a developed country, the President should come from 'the south'. Sonny, of course, met the latter requirement (he comes from Guyana, descended from Indian ancestors transported as indented labourers by British colonial administrators, and he served as Attorney General and representative of his country at the UN before moving to the Commonwealth Secretariat). He was also an eloquent speaker with an impressive presence. But his very stature brought many calls on his time. Although he always assured me that he 'would do anything you ask me to do', he was extremely busy, not least in writing the background book for Rio, *Our Country the Planet*, and as co-Chair of the Commission on Global Governance. Council and some members got restive. They wanted a President who would spend time making the Council a more effective instrument of governance. These Council members saw Jay Hair as an ideal candidate. Early in 1993, a bombshell burst in Gland in the shape of a formal letter from US Vice President Al Gore, nominating Jay on behalf of the US State Member. Sonny Ramphal took a dignified but aloof stance. 'Three years ago,' he wrote, 'when you asked me to be a candidate, I explained that I did not seek the Presidency. I do not seek it now. And I must make it plain now, as I did then, that I will not participate in a contested election.' Council had to make a clear choice of nominee, not throw the decision into the lap of the Assembly.

The argument swayed back and forth. All the staff and the two potential candidates left Council to argue it out. In the end Jay Hair was the sole nominee, but in Buenos Aires membership dissatisfaction erupted. Many wanted Sonny (who handled the proceedings with great diplomatic skill) to continue. They were frustrated that the IUCN constitution did not allow the Assembly to over-rule the nomination by the Council. They were even more annoyed at the prospect of an American President and a New Zealand Director General – both seen as representatives of the developed world and of 'white Anglo-Saxon Protestantism'. There was fiery oratory, especially from Tariq Banuri of Pakistan. The rebellion failed. Jay was elected and Sonny's term ended. But a bad taste was left, only slightly assuaged by Jay's promise that he would serve only one term and would ensure that next time there would be two candidates, at least one of whom would come from the 'south'.

On 9 April 1994 I welcomed David Mc Dowell to Gland, and handed over. On 11 April I left for Cambridge. Lizzie and I had been given a marvellous send-off by the staff, and many generous parting gifts. It was the end of the most rewarding six years of my professional life. And so we passed into that curious state that some call 'retirement'.

CHAPTER TEN

Free Agent

RETIREMENT IS supposed to be a quiet time, when you gather the threads of life, prepare to account to whatever Being you believe to exist beyond the time and space that men call real, and have fun meanwhile. I have never found this image attractive. It is self-centred whereas most of us, praise be, reach our mid-60s with new family generations to know and love. And thanks to medical advances, most people nowadays have only slightly less health and strength in their sixties than they enjoyed a decade earlier, and minds and curiosities are undiminished.

We left Switzerland as spring was stirring. Back to Cambridge, to our red brick suburban house that looked across fields and hedges to the Gog Magog hills, all of 70 metres high, crowned by the Iron Age ring fort of Wandlebury. 'When the Gogs start looking big, you'll have acclimatized,' I had written to Elaine Dickinson, one of our IUCN staff who had made the transition a year earlier. On my own test, I never acclimatized.

'But why are you going back to Cambridge?' lots of people asked us. 'It's so flat, cold, grey and dreary after Switzerland. Why not stay here – you've got your residence permit, and you could find quite enough consultancy work...'

Why not? Mainly because of family. Bobbie, my mother, had died in 1990 in her 89th year, after a long period of sad decline, but Lizzie's mother Edith (nicknamed Gully) was still quite fit and nearly 95. Robert was living in a little terrace of houses that dipped to the river at Ely, and David and Karyn had another little terraced house in Cambridge itself.

Karyn? She had crossed the family horizon sometime in 1990 when she came to Queens' to do her teacher's training and met David who was living in College and doing a Ph.D in engineering. Our friends Charles and Jenny Moseley were in no doubt. 'The next Mrs Holdgate,' said Charles. He was proved right when D and K married one shining October day at Dirleton Kirk in East Lothian. There was a great party at North Berwick, near where Karyn's parents, George and Helen Taylor, lived. Karyn was teaching in Cambridge, while David, doctorate safely accomplished, was beginning in accountancy. No, the family drew us back to England. And I recalled what Sir George Godber, once Chief Medical Officer at DHSS, had said of his own retirement to Cambridge. 'The geriatric services there are very good!'

Like a returning spacecraft, we found re-entry to be rather a heated business. First there was a Great Sort Out – as anyone who has tried to put the contents of two houses into one will imagine. The garage looked like Steptoe and Wife's emporium, as we awaited various charities who collected the surplus. But there was further upheaval of our own contriving – for we decided to re-model the house. We like to think that we are quite good at this (I dream that some dilute remnant of a Wyatt gene lurks somewhere within my DNA, and Lizzie has a great feel for space and light). A chaos of builders descended. They were a charming crowd, and did transform what had been a rather dull 1950s brick box, but they left trails of plaster dust everywhere. We celebrated Gully's 95th birthday behind a screen of polythene sheeting. Lizzie became increasingly despairing. She longed for a clean and tidy house, whereas I could retreat into the study and distract myself with writing.

We were getting into the thick of the plaster dust in May 1994 when the post delivered a cream envelope with 'No. 10 Downing Street' on it. I assumed it was about one or other of the things I was thinking about doing in my 'retirement'.

'The Prime Minister wishes to submit your name to Her Majesty the Queen with the recommendation that the honour of knighthood be conferred upon you . . .'

The letter went on 'However, before taking this step the Prime Minister wishes to be assured that this proposal will be acceptable to you.' High-flown language aside, it meant 'please sign and return the enclosed paper confirming that you are going to say "yes".' Not everyone does: I knew one person who strongly objected to titles and refused a knighthood twice. But I decided to be positive. The second decision was trickier – did I tell Lizzie? Nigel Wace once told me that his father, in similar circumstances, had said nothing to his mother, and stunned her by greeting her as 'Lady Wace' when the lists were actually published. I am less good at keeping secrets (though Robert, David and everyone else remained in the dark). The Queen's Official Birthday was a day of celebrations. But the evening was less funny – Lizzie, on her way to answer a congratulatory phone call, went a purler in the dark over an electric flex which our builders had left as an inconvenient trip wire and knocked herself dizzy. I had to call an ambulance in the middle of the night. And the nurse on duty at Addenbrookes' sniffed in a most Puritanical way when informed that we had drunk half a celebratory bottle of wine each. I think she was the sort of person who believed in Judgements. Unfair – it should have been my pride that encountered the fall.

But what were we to do with our lives? One of the potential joys of retirement is that it lets you choose what to spend time on. You can (if you wish) devote all your attention to one topic, undistracted by the demands of a myriad of problems not of your making. And, if you wish, you can do nothing (though observation suggests that to be a sure way to a short and unhappy end to life). We hoped to have time to do things together, and visit places in our own country that we had missed in our worldwide peregrinations. My magic formula was to assume that, after taking out weekends and holidays, there were 210 working days in the year. I planned to devote seventy of them to paid work to augment the pension, seventy to voluntary service, and the remaining seventy to doing whatever we wanted.

Somehow it didn't work out like that. Lots of things cascaded about me.

I was already a member of the Environmental Advisory Board of the Swedish-Swiss Company Asea Brown Boveri. I agreed to serve on the Environmental Advisory Committee of Jupiter Asset Management, helping to guide the policy of their 'green' investment trusts. I was already Chairman of the Government's Energy Advisory Panel. And new requests came thick and furious. Would I be President of the Zoological Society of London – requiring about a day a month? Would I be a Trustee of WWF-UK – about five days a year needed? Would I take over the Chair of the International Institute for Environment and Development from Crispin Tickell – only five days required? Would I like to be a member of the Royal Commission on Environmental Pollution? That was nearer thirty days. A trustee of the National Heritage Memorial Fund (which also administered the Heritage Lottery Fund) – another twenty days? A Governor once more of Arnold School? an independent member of the Board of the World Conservation Monitoring Centre? a member of the Committee for the Prince of Wales' Business and Environment Programme? The seventy days I had allotted to unpaid voluntary service were swiftly absorbed. There wasn't as much time as we had planned for self-indulgence.

IUCN asked me to go on doing things for them. The first was a book. When we were planning the General Assembly in Buenos Aires, we had the idea of taking the output from its workshops and turning them into a single volume on the theme of the Assembly – 'Caring for the Earth and its Peoples'. But John Burke, Director of Communications, had another idea. 'Don't just edit the Proceedings,' he urged. 'Most such volumes are deadly dull. Write a book yourself, around the theme of the GA, drawing on the papers but going beyond them where you feel there's more to be said.' David McDowell agreed, and that took a good deal of my 'free time' in 1994 and 1995. It ended as a fairly hefty volume, *From Care to Action. Making a Sustainable World*. What it says, in essence, is that we do know how to live in harmony with one another and with the Earth that sustains us, but that, as T.S. Eliot put it, 'between the idea and the reality; between the motion and the act; falls the shadow.' Talk, and the production of reports, strategies, books and blueprints, are relatively easy. Changing the way complex societies operate and counteracting the inertia of vested interest can be almost impossible. We are bad at listening to one another, sharing experience and taking a long view. I suggested that big changes happen when people are inspired by visionaries and enabled to follow their inspiration into action. As John Masefield wrote, 'the power of man is as his hopes.'

Another consequence of Buenos Aires was a decision to review the IUCN Statutes. Parvez Hassan, one of the leading lawyers in Pakistan and Wolfgang Burhenne's successor as Chair of the Environmental Law Commission, took the lead, while his deputy, Professor Nick Robinson from Pace University, New York, led a small drafting group. The Council was far from certain about the desirability of involving a former Director General (and especially an opinionated one), but in the end they asked me to be an adviser. That meant a number of agreeable visits back to Switzerland. The revised statutes were high on the Agenda when the General Assembly – re-styled the First World Conservation Congress following our decisions in Buenos Aires – met in Montreal in October 1996. It was a tremendous gathering of over 3000 people, although many just looked in for workshops or the special panel discussions that David McDowell had organized. True to his promise, Jay Hair stepped down from the Presidency and a close run election between two 'southern' candidates led to Yolanda Kakabadse from Ecuador becoming the first woman and the first Latin American to hold the Union's supreme office. Although I was there as an official delegate (of the Zoological Society of London), I had no other responsibilities and could revel in the freedom of not being Director General. For Lizzie and me it was really a marvellous party with hundreds of old friends.

It is difficult to know when to end a personal memoir (a biography is easier, because it has a natural conclusion). I have decided to stop in January 2001, when I completed my Biblical span of threescore years and ten. In the seven years following our return from Switzerland, a mass of things happened. I got deeply involved in UK energy policy. As a member of the Royal Commission on Environmental Pollution, I found myself probing what we should do to use soil sustainably, manage transport, avoid damaging climate change, set environmental standards and adjust the environmental planning system. I also found myself at the centre of international policy on forests. The Heritage Lottery Fund, WWF, the World Conservation Monitoring Centre, the Zoological Society, IIED, ABB, Jupiter and IUCN provided many interesting diversions. And the turning wheel of fate brought us back to the northern hill country where I had found so much early inspiration.

Involvement with energy policy started before we had even left IUCN. It began back in 1991, when Colin Moynihan, who had been Minister for Sport in the final year of my time at DOE and went on to a Ministerial post in the Department of Energy, asked me to serve on his Renewable Energy Advisory Group. He wanted to do more to establish wind, wave, tidal, solar and suchlike 'green' energy sources. He appreciated that I was based in Switzerland, but his office said they would try to time at least some meetings to coincide with my visits to the United Kingdom.

I agreed. Of course the Minister's Private Office never found it possible to take my schedule into account when fixing meetings. A Minister's diary is appalling at the best of times, and mine was almost equally horrendous. It was not surprising that a year later, having attended no meetings, I felt obliged to write to Colin and resign. 'Don't do that,' he said. 'You're ideally placed to give me independent advice on our draft report.' That seemed the least I could do. I received it, was unhappy about it, and began to write a detailed critique. Then – the 1992 General Election came, and Colin lost his seat in Parliament. What to do? I wrote to Michael Heseltine, now President of the Board of Trade and head of the reconstituted Department of Trade and Industry, within which the Department of Energy had been reincorporated. I sent my critique.

Phone message. 'The President is most grateful for your letter, agrees with your criticisms, and would like you to take over as Chair of REAG and guide the group in the completion of its Report.' Some of the members thought this was a bit odd, or even off-side, and did not receive me with the greatest warmth. The Press had fun by describing me as 'an expert on penguins' – clearly the ideal qualification for assessing energy needs in a British winter. But in the end, we did produce what I still think is quite a good document. And it led straight on to other things. A White Paper on the future of the Coal Industry had been produced, partly as a consequence of the parliamentary rebellion over pit closures. In it the Government promised that there would be an annual Energy Report surveying the national scene, prepared under the guidance of an independent Energy Advisory Panel. I was asked to be its first Chair, working to Tim Eggar as the responsible Minster and Charles Henderson as the Deputy Secretary and head of the Energy side of the DTI. We started in 1993, and the first Report was published in 1994.

The EAP was a rather odd outfit. Its members were a bright bunch, from many backgrounds – energy industries, academia, research, consultancy and the city among them. But it had a very limited role. It commented on suggestions from the DTI about what might go into the Government's document. It was not an independent 'think tank'. It took no evidence. It did not publish its own ideas – it was just an almost-anonymous appendage to the Department. And early on I recognized that cultural dinosaurs still roamed the DTI . . .

Thirty years ago, most of British industry really did not want to know about the environment. The Department of Trade and Industry was, if anything, even more reactionary than industry itself. Its officials seemed to take delight in blocking initiatives to get sulphur out of power station flues, or lead out of petrol, or dumped wastes out of the sea. Their attitude was that anything that could impair the competitiveness of our firms by driving up their costs was wrong, and its advocates unpatriotic. Now, in 1994, Government had signed up to 'sustainable development', as endorsed at Rio. It had accepted the reality of the greenhouse effect. It had agreed to reduce our national emissions of carbon dioxide. It had even signed up to the Precautionary Principle. These were matters of public policy to which all Departments of Government were officially bound. But there were still voices in DTI that spoke the language of an unregenerate past. Words like 'possible' or 'hypothetical' got inserted before 'greenhouse effect'. The draft Energy Report tended to minimize what was said about environmental issues and especially their international dimension. I found myself, as supposedly neutral Chairman, grinding the environmental axe vigorously.

There were amusing moments. Minister Tim Eggar came to a meeting one day. We explained what we were doing, and asked him what he would think if the Panel from time to time did its own evaluations of energy issues, and sent him our opinions. And what would his view be if we occasionally made our views public (after consulting him of course)! He rose to the bait enthusiastically.

'I think it could be a very good idea for you to engage from time to time in your own thinking and analysis. And yes, I would certainly have no objection to your going public. But I would like to know what you were going to say first . . .' DTI officials quailed visibly. They clearly had a vision of the Panel Getting Out Of Control.

Mary Archer was one of the members of the Panel (she had also served on the Renewable Energy Advisory Group). I respected her clear mind, scientific knowledge and articulate contributions to our discussions. We were also fairly near neighbours in Trumpington. As a consequence of this acquaintance, Lizzie and I found ourselves among the galaxy of the (mostly) great and (generally) good at the Archers' legendary summer party in the grounds of the Old Rectory at Grantchester, where Rupert Brooke had seen 'ghosts of former curates go, on lissom, printless clerical toe.' There were no deceased curates in evidence on that summer's party-day, but most of the top brass of Toryism shone in burnished splendour. And there were many other celebrities: at lunch Lizzie and I were delighted to find ourselves flanked by Speaker Betty Boothroyd and actor Donald Sinden, who were deep into anecdotes of the theatrical world. It was my only meeting with Jeffrey Archer, whose books had helped make aircraft and foreign hotels more bearable. I was impressed by his energy and evident charm. Whatever mistakes he may have made, one could see why his friends stuck to him.

The Energy Advisory Panel did not break much new ground in developing British policy. But the Royal Commission on Environmental Pollution certainly did. When I became a member in 1994 I couldn't help thinking back twenty-four years to 1970, when I had attended its very early meetings under Eric Ashby's courteous and shrewd leadership. Since then the Commission had got bigger and its reports longer and wider-ranging.

But the essence remained the same: a group of highly gifted people from many disciplines who were willing to take the time to probe deep into complicated and sometimes controversial areas of policy. Several of the members were old friends from my time in the Department of the Environment. The Chairman, Sir John Houghton, was the distinguished physicist and climatologist who led the section of the Intergovernmental Panel on Climate Change that dealt with predictions of how greenhouse gases might affect worldwide weather. Sir Geoffrey Allen had been Chairman of the Science Research Council in my time in Whitehall: we shared a taste for light verse and had from time to time engaged in Chestertonian duets at not too serious meetings. Professor Richard Macrory, environmental lawyer, had been closely involved with the Centre for Environmental Technology we in DOE had helped to set up at Imperial College. And the Secretary, David Lewis, had been a member of the Environment Protection command in my time in the Department.

The Commission had just finished a big study of the environmental impact of transport. It was hailed with enthusiasm by the anti-road lobby, because it emphasized the environmental damage caused by cars and lorries and argued for measures that would damp down the continual growth of road traffic and the expensive congestion that resulted. Among these, it suggested that private transport should be made more expensive, especially by a steep increase in the tax on petrol. It wanted other measures to clean up cars and lorries and enforce tight speed limits. It argued the case for more and better public transport. I was rather glad I had not participated, because I felt then, and still feel, that some of the conclusions were naïve. There were, and are, perfectly logical reasons why road transport has grown: it is the only transport mode that can take people and goods from any door to any other door, at a time of the traveller's choice. I believe in cleaner, more energy-efficient, vehicles and more economical use of road space. I believe that the best way to travel from most city centres to most other city centres is by rail. But Britain and all other modern European states have become irreversibly road-dependent, and some parts of the Commission's report seemed to me to fly in the face of history.

My first Commission study was much more down to earth, for it was on the sustainable use of soil! Somehow, though almost all our food depends on the fertility of the land and contamination is a wasteful barrier to the use of thousands of urban acres, nobody had taken a look at how we cared for this invaluable resource. The Commission called for a national soil protection policy. It demanded tighter controls on the spreading of wastes like sewage sludge on land and called for a challenging target for reducing the amount of waste that was dumped in holes in the ground. And we were pretty blunt about the need for more effective clean-up of the derelict land that is a blight in so many towns and cities.

The study took nearly two years from the first announcement to the publication of the 250-page Report. In the hope of brisker action, we then took a second look at transport because members were pretty dissatisfied with the Government's response to their previous would-be jam-buster. We emphasized that the country was on course for worse pollution and noise, more carbon dioxide to stoke up the greenhouse effect and more and more traffic jams. The Commission did not doubt that road transport would remain dominant, but did think that people and things were going by road simply because there had not been enough investment in reliable, attractive alternatives. We said we needed an integrated transport system, and more investment in cleaner, quieter and more efficient cars and lorries. We urged that taxes should provide an incentive to buy and use 'greener' vehicles.

The difference between the Royal Commission and the Energy Advisory Panel was very obvious. The Commission was independent and authoritative. It took a long time to puzzle its way into and through issues. It invited evidence from a wide range of bodies – and was open to inputs from anyone who thought they had a point to make. It met many of the chief advocates of policy change for formal or informal discussion. Its reports were thoroughly referenced. Every word was crawled over. And the Reports were taken very seriously both by Government and by many sectors of the community – they were even scrutinised in Brussels!

However, it wasn't always all sweetness and harmony. When we moved on to the third topic I was involved with – the process of setting environmental standards – discord often threatened the mutual respect which in my view is essential in such a body. The standards study was particularly difficult because it was full of intangibles. What is a standard? Why do we have them? How far are they expressions of robust science, and how far are they reflections of social values? How far should they be based on consultation as well as the judgement of (often self-styled) 'experts'? Unlike most reports, this one did not set out a string of recommendations, but it did suggest the broad directions in which we believed the protection of the environment should evolve. I am not sure how much impact it has had, or can have.

It was easier when we looked at energy. Although some critics dismissed the Twenty Second Report, *Energy – the Changing Climate*, as out of date by the time it appeared, for most people it brought home starkly how difficult the choices were. Do nothing about greenhouse gases – go on burning coal, oil and gas at ever-increasing rates – and the climate would not only get warmer but droughts, storms and floods would increase and sea level would rise by about a metre. That meant crisis for millions of people who live on coastal plains and coral islands. It would not be jolly in Britain, where more than half our best farmland is below the 5 metre contour. But to stop the worst consequences, we needed not just to hit the weak targets set in the Kyoto protocol to the UN Convention on Climate Change, but to reduce our use of fossil fuels by 60 per cent by the year 2050. We hit the headlines with four scenarios of how this could be done. They pointed up the hard questions. Did people want a new generation of nuclear power stations (which emit no greenhouse gases)? If not, were they willing to cover a tenth of the land outside National Parks and Areas of Outstanding Natural Beauty with wind farms, or have two hundred such farms, each with 100 turbines, offshore in the shallow seas? Would people accept a great barrage across the Severn, which could contribute almost a tenth of national electricity needs? Or should we grow willow and other crops over perhaps three quarters of a million hectares of land, to feed new style power stations supplying heat as well as power? Should the roofs of our houses incorporate tiles that mopped up the energy of the sun to supply heat and light? On any scenario, it was clear that we had to be vastly more efficient in how we used energy.

The final report I was involved with tackled another difficult topic – environmental planning. By this we did not simply mean the Town and Country Planning system which regulates whether you or I are allowed to build a new house or a developer to scatter match-box villas in the local Green Belt. We were bothered about the many overlapping policies that affected land, whether for agriculture, forestry, water supply, energy or nature conservation – and the impact of pollution control practices on all of them. We criticised the existing system as giving inadequate protection to the environment. Most of those who gave evidence to us condemned it as too bureaucratic. We demanded a new and clear purpose for town and country planning and new 'spatial plans' that joined up the different functional strategies. We argued for more and better information about the environment, made available to everyone so that people could join in an informed debate about how they wanted their land to be used. We spent a long time debating whether the town and country planning system should extend to cover changes in land use by farmers, and decided otherwise – but we came down strongly in favour of a new approach that would help farmers to care for the environment by providing 'joined up' payments for all manner of conservation activities awarded on the basis of a simple farm plan.

How much difference did the Commission make? The Government (of whichever political party) generally responded positively to the reports, while evading the most awkward and expensive implications. The Press was generally positive (although they took little notice of the 'dull' soils, standards and planning studies and got excited over the more controversial analyses of transport and energy futures). But as my eight years on the RCEP drew to their end I found myself worrying about it as a body. Was it taking on impossibly wide and awkward topics? Was it going too far from the central theme of pollution? Was it becoming rather like Antarctic exploration now that all the territory was mapped – ever deeper examination of lands and issues whose shape was known? And there had been a change in public attitude to such bodies, in the name of 'transparency' and 'accountability'. Could the process of appointment change without reducing the ability to recruit Commissioners with both broad and deep knowledge, and willingness to give the considerable amount of time that was needed? Should the Commission be more open to public participation, for example by conducting open hearings? Should it cease to be a mainly British body, and address global concerns? I do not know the answers but I remain convinced that all countries need authoritative bodies like this, able to review major policy areas in depth, gather and sift evidence, and publish their findings in a format which allows their reasoning to be scrutinised and, where inadequate, criticised.

The Heritage Lottery Fund was different again. Although it had grown from the National Heritage Memorial Fund, created to safeguard the nation's cultural heritage as a worthy tribute to our war dead, it had been vastly enlarged by becoming one of the 'four good causes' receiving Lottery money. The Chairman, Lord Rothschild (son of the architect of the customer-contractor principle), told me when he asked me to join that we might have £50 million a year to hand out: in reality the sum was over £250 million. It went on a vast range of things, from art galleries, historic buildings and municipal parks to conservation sites and the purchase of individual works of art that might otherwise have been lost to the nation. My particular interest was in the conservation sites, and while some applications sought money to safeguard areas that were already rich in wild life, others were more imaginative. One I remember most vividly was by the River Lark near Lakenheath in Suffolk, where the Royal Society for the Protection of Birds wanted to buy 300 hectares of farmland and turn it back into wetland. Several of us went to visit it (Jacob Rothschild had established the sound principle that a Trustee went to see every major project that came forward).

It was a dull, flat, tract of farmland but the potential was obvious. The river flowed along one side, and there was a patch of relict fen woodland called Botany Bay just next door, from which fenland plants could spread back to the new site. It lay low, and could easily be flooded. The idea was to turn most of it into reedswamp, to encourage bitterns and other marsh birds like bearded tits. There was only one ornithological problem. Part of the site was covered by poplar trees, originally planted to provide matchsticks for Bryant and May. The company had sold the land long ago, and most of the trees had been replaced by sugar beet – but the remaining poplars supported a number of breeding pairs of Golden oriole, a European bird that is rare in Britain. Dilemma. If the land was flooded the poplars would have to go, and take the orioles with them. If the poplars stayed, the project could not succeed (and we could not fund it). The orioles were given notice to quit. I have been told that the site is now an exciting new wetland. I hope that some bitterns have started to boom there.

Most of my other 'retirement jobs' were dominated by Committee rooms, and as these are not an exciting habitat, I will pass lightly over my involvement with WWF-UK and the IIED. The Board of the World Conservation Monitoring Centre was also conference-table based, but it faced serious challenges. The Centre had originated in IUCN, and mainly as SSC's species information unit, later broadened to cover National Parks and other protected areas and special habitats like coral reefs and mangroves. In 1988 – just as I was joining IUCN – it had fallen into financial crisis and we rescued it by making it a joint venture of IUCN, UNEP and WWF. But as the years went by it proved more and more difficult to persuade the three partners to inject the core funds without which it could not operate. As the twentieth century ended, WCMC became an integral part of UNEP. It is now one of only two places in Britain where the pale blue flag of the United Nations flies.

The Zoological Society of London was very different. For one thing, it was rarely out of the headlines. In 1992 it had been in such dire financial straits that its Council believed that they would have to cease trading and close London Zoo. The resulting row rocked the Society to its foundations. A vote of no confidence ejected the President and most of the Council. Thanks to the Emir of Kuwait, who gave it one million pounds, and the much less publicised generosity of one of its Fellows, David Blackburn, it pulled through. Field Marshal Sir John Chapple became President, and a distinguished zoologist whom I remembered as a Research Student at Cambridge, Professor R. McNeill Alexander of Leeds University, became Secretary (in the ZSL the Secretary is also a kind of Honorary Chief Executive). Then, John Chapple was appointed as Governor of Gibraltar. Neill Alexander and the Clerk to the Council, Peter Denton (who had been in the DOE in my time) met me in Cambridge. Would I take over?

I was, after all, a zoologist by original training, and I had been a Fellow of the ZSL for many years. I had been involved with Roger Chorley and John Phillips when Solly Zuckerman made his bid for Government funding. I felt some responsibility for what had happened afterwards. So I agreed. I was assured that the turmoil of recent years was over and that the Society was, to quote John Chapple, moving from a period of survival to one of revival, to be followed by 'thrival'. I hoped he was right.

The ZSL has a long and complicated history. It began life in 1826 when the founder of Singapore, Sir Stamford Raffles, returned to London. Raffles was a keen naturalist and collector – his name is still attached to the world's largest and most repellent flower, *Rafflesia arnoldi*, which is a parasite that pushes out blossoms over a metre across and attracts the flies that pollinate it by smelling of decaying carrion. In London he joined with Sir Humphrey Davy the chemist (we learned at school that he 'abominated gravy, and lived in the odium of having discovered sodium') to found a Zoological Society for 'the advancement of zoology and animal physiology and the introduction of new and curious subjects of the animal kingdom.' Although Raffles died suddenly that same year, the momentum was kept up and the Society received its first Royal Charter in 1829. By 1994 it was not only a learned body where zoologists gathered for scientific discussions and consulted an outstanding library, but it operated a major Research Institute, an overseas field conservation consultancy (which had taken on the captive breeding and re-introduction of threatened species in Saudi Arabia) and the two animal collections at Regent's Park and Whipsnade in Bedfordshire. London Zoo, however, was the biggest part of the business and its economic failure could still drag the remainder down.

It soon became evident that the calm and security were relative. The ZSL was still in a pretty jittery state, and management was not very cohesive. The

Council, like the Fellowship of an Oxbridge College, was a real mixture of talents and eccentricities. Everyone was dedicated to the future of the Society, but they had many different visions of what that future should be, and even more diversity when it came to what should be done. There was also, shall we say, some lack of mutual respect and regard. Council members were not unknown to seek an interview with the President and complain about one another in pretty flamboyant terms. The Press was always on the lookout for signs of new and entertaining strife.

The Society suffered from two central problems. First, it got most of its money from the visitors to London Zoo, and this was on a cramped site on the edge of Regent's Park, difficult of access by public transport. The zoo buildings were a clutter of styles and because many were by distinguished architects they had been 'listed' for their heritage value – regardless of their merits as places in which to keep animals. Other buildings – like the 'concrete mountains' of the Mappin Terraces (which also roofed the aquarium) needed major refurbishment. The site was too small to display many big animals – including elephants and rhinos – in the settings they deserved. Yet if the Society slimmed the range of species, focussing on small animals, attendance would probably decline. The dilemma remains.

The other problem was organizational. The structure was complex, with five operating divisions each with their Directors and Boards or Committees, but with no overall Chief Executive, apart from the Secretary, Neill Alexander – and he had a major University Department to run.

We soon agreed that we had to have a salaried Director General, and after a good deal of debate in Council, proceeded to the appointment in 1995. Richard Burge took over at the end of that year (three years later he moved on to become the Director of the Countryside Alliance, being succeeded by Dr Michael Dixon). And we did make progress. Annual surpluses replaced deficits. Thanks to a generous donation from Lord and Lady Paul in memory of their daughter Ambika who had loved visiting the Zoo, but had died of leukaemia in early childhood, a new Children's Zoo was built. The Mappin Terraces were given a low-cost facelift and reopened as a place where people could watch Sloth bears, dwarf deer and monkeys. A new Millennium Conservation Centre incorporating a 'Web of Life' exhibition of animal biodiversity was opened by the Queen in June 1999. As I write, early in 2002, our Director General, Dr Michael Dixon, is leading negotiations that should make the Society a partner in a wonderful new National Aquarium in Dockland.

The opening of the Web of Life had one marvellous moment. Her Majesty was being taken round by a senior member of staff, who was earnestly explaining the displays. We paused in front of a glass pane that

HM the Queen opens the Millennium Conservation Centre at London Zoo.
Photograph: Zoological Society of London.

allowed a view into the tunnels of a colony of naked Mole rats. My
colleague explained their social structure.

'And there's a big, fat white queen in the centre of the colony,' he said. A
few seconds later he obviously caught the import of his words and hastened
on . . . 'just like the ant queen!'

No visible muscle of the Royal features even twitched.

The United Nations was another part of my past that refused to let go.
After Rio, the Governments had set up new organizational machinery. One
part of it was a Commission on Sustainable Development, where Ministers
would discuss issues of environment and development and review the
implementation of Agenda 21. Another element was to be a High Level
Advisory Board on Sustainable Development, to assist the Secretary General
(or keep him up to the mark, as the case might be). The members were to
be independent 'eminents' from the various regions of the world, and in
September 1993 I found my supposed eminence recognized. Indeed, I
became Rapporteur (Secretary) in support of the Co-Chairs, Bernard
Chidzero, the senior Minister from Zimbabwe, and Birgitta Dahl, formerly
Environment Minister of Sweden and now Speaker of the Swedish
Parliament.

I suppose I should have felt honoured, and even flattered. As it was, I soon felt disillusioned. The HLAB found real difficulty in getting to grips with its role. We met in a rather dark panelled room in UN Headquarters in New York. The thirty members soon fell into three groups: those who enunciated familiar ideas from established viewpoints, those who said very little and looked bored or bemused, and those who really tried to make the Board do something.

The then Secretary General, Boutros Boutros-Ghali, fell into the third category. Our rare discussions with him, usually lasting only about two hours in a three or four day meeting, were the most memorable part of the business. Boutros-Ghali was a courteous Egyptian academic and former senior Minister with much French gentility about him (he had studied in France, spoke good French, had published many writings in that language and preferred French culture to English). He was 72, and considered by some to be too old for the job. His subsequent ousting by the United States was, however, more to do with his outspoken championship of the UN and his condemnation of the USA as principal defaulter on the dues they had a solemn obligation to pay. In HLAB he came across as a wise thinker, under pressures that would have crushed many far younger men. One of his problems was 'peace-keeping'.

'The United Nations is bankrupt,' he proclaimed once. 'Yet I have to run seventeen peace-keeping or other humanitarian operations – all in places where member states have let the situation get out of hand, and where we have been called in as a last resort. Somalia? Bosnia? Rwanda? Burundi? Afghanistan? How on earth can we do more than tie the cracks together? And become more indebted?

'I see the role of the UN as conflict prevention rather than peace-keeping,' he went on. 'That is why I attach great importance to sustainable development. It is the only long-term solution, and it is there that we should be investing our money. That is also why I consider your role as an Advisory Board so important. The more we can cure poverty, ensure the equitable use of natural resources, stimulate sustainable economic growth and build international agreement on the use of shared environmental resources like great rivers, the more we will do to prevent war. That is what I would like to devote my time to. But now I have to catch a helicopter, to catch a plane, to try to calm the conflict in Bosnia . . .'

The HLAB tried. But it had only one real channel of influence – the Secretary General – and he was too harassed and distracted to lead the campaign we needed. True, we were warmly supported by Nitin Desai, the gifted Indian Under Secretary General who had been Maurice Strong's second in command at Rio and now ran the Department for Policy Coordination and Sustainable Development in New York. True, our reports went to the Ministers in the so-called High Level Segment of the annual meetings of the CSD. But as our first two-year period of office came to an end, I discerned no real signs of success. Bernard Chidzero's health had failed, and he had to step down. Birgitta Dahl assumed the Chair with characteristic energy. But my doubts remained and I decided not to seek a second term. Stephan Schmidheiny, the Swiss businessman who had created and led the World Business Council for Sustainable Development, did the same. The HLAB has now been disbanded. It remains one of the good things that might have been.

But the UN has many tentacles. Just before Christmas 1994, Klaus Toepfer, German Environment Minister and Chairman of CSD at the time, telephoned. Would I do him a favour and Chair the inter-sessional consultations on what the UN calls 'sectoral issues' – the state of the Earth's forests, deserts, biodiversity and mountains and how we could achieve sustainable agricultural and rural development within the wider context of the integrated planning and management of natural resources? Old colleagues in the British Department of the Environment urged me to say 'yes', and retained me as a retired part-time Deputy Secretary 'for the duration'. Back to New York, in a cold, raw, March for a meeting that was made relatively lively by the Philippine delegate, who was Chair at that time of the Group of 77 and China (a consortium of the developing world). He was seminary-educated and spiced his interventions with Latin tags. I remembered enough (thanks to Grandpa and to 'Bumps' Haythornthwaite long ago) to respond in kind – breaching the rules since Latin is not among the eight official languages of the UN. When it came to our report to the CSD I searched the Oxford Dictionary of Quotations for a supertag to end with, rather as one searches the wine list for a special bottle at a farewell dinner. Nothing less than Cicero would do for Mr Guerrero. *Vulgo enim dicitur: Iucundi acti labores.* It is commonly said that accomplished labours are pleasant. Especially when viewed from an aircraft leaving New York.

But oh! the labours weren't accomplished! Our report urged the establishment of 'an open-ended intergovernmental panel on forests under the aegis of the CSD'. It was to:

> . . . provide an assessment of action already undertaken to combat deforestation and forest degradation and to promote management, conservation and sustainable development of all types of forest, including environmental and socio-economic impacts; and against that background to propose options for further action . . .

Clear? That's UN-speak for you! It means 'look at what's happening to the world's forests, and why, and what needs to be done better, and how to do it.' And 'open-ended' meant 'let any government that wants to take part do so'. A few months later I found myself drafted as Co-Chairman from the 'northern' countries (which, paradoxically, include Australia and New Zealand). My initial counterpart for the 'south' was to be the Permanent Secretary of the Environment Department of India, a country that lies, of course, entirely in the northern hemisphere. But the UN knows what it means by 'north' and 'south' (just as Tristan Islanders know that 'to the west'ard' means 'to the left' and 'to the east'ard' vice versa). Like Humpty Dumpty, it uses words to mean what it wants them to mean. Unlike Humpty, it does not pay them extra.

The IPF met first in New York in September 1995. I was delighted to find Mulumba's father, Professor Matthias Semakula Kiwanuka, as His Excellency the Ugandan Ambassador to the UN! But in the conference chamber itself politics were far more visible than trees. Various fairly junior diplomats were clearly concerned to advance causes that were only peripherally connected to forests, but for which the forest cause might be a handy lever. Much of the fuss was about how to increase (or constrain) the flow of money from rich to poor countries, or how to get better market access in the 'north' for the products of the 'south'. In Rio there had been talk of 'new and additional resources' to promote sustainable development – and this phrase had become a special slogan for many developing countries, and a point of friction for others, especially the United States. It was easier when the debates became more technical, as they did in Geneva in March and September 1996. Forest scientists replaced New York diplomats and there was sensible discussion about how to promote national plans to manage forests better, how to diagnose why forests were being degraded or destroyed, how to use traditional knowledge, and what to do about forests threatened by desertification, pollution or simply excessive human pressure. Another theme was how to value forests – recognizing that if this were done, the economic models might favour keeping them rather than turning them into logs for export.

The 'indigenous peoples' made a special contribution to the debate. In the 1980s and 1990s it became an article of faith that people like the Amazonian forest dwellers, the North American First Nations, or the aboriginal Australians had a special and superior environmental wisdom. Sometimes it has been expressed in romantic, and indeed inspiring, statements like the famous 'Chief Seathl speech' – allegedly a letter written in 1855 to the President of the United States about the sale of ancestral lands, but actually a film script dating from 1971 or 1972. Some of it harks back to Rousseau and the image of the 'noble savage'. The core of the argument is that indigenous peoples understand their lands better than those who have sought to expropriate them, have wisdom that must be heeded and rights that must be respected, and must be listened to and never contradicted.

I go along with some of that, but by no means all. The environmental record of indigenous peoples is mixed. It was the indigenous peoples of Europe, from Neolithic through Iron Age times, that destroyed the continent's forests. The extinction of large mammals in North America, Eurasia and Australia seems to have coincided with the advent of the first waves of hunting peoples. The advent of rifles was followed by a massive over-kill of caribou by some Canadian First Nations. The ancestors of the Maori exterminated the seventeen species of giant birds – the moas – in New Zealand. And who is indigenous? The UN definition says that the term applies to peoples with a distinctive culture and traditions and a distinctive language, who have been inhabitants of an area for at least several centuries. On that basis, many people in Wales, Ireland and the Western Isles of Scotland are indigenous. So is virtually everyone in Asia and Africa. Indeed it is easier to turn the definition around and ask who is *not* indigenous? The descendants of the colonial and post colonial settlers in North, Central and South America – mostly Europeans, but now increasingly also from east Asia. Similar colonists in Asia, Australia and New Zealand. Most of the Russian settlers in the Eurasian Arctic.

And this is the heart of the matter. For the deep concern over indigenous rights today arises because of the expropriation of land, slaughter of original inhabitants, and destruction of their cultures. There are many ghastly stories to be ashamed or angry about (as is evident in Fuegia). There is a real need to listen, with sensitivity (as Robert Chambers has said so eloquently). But a sense of grief and guilt should not lead us to uncritical acceptance of every protestation of superior environmental wisdom by indigenous peoples. Things have to be judged fairly, on their merits. I am not sure that they are being, in the United Nations, in Canada, in Australia, in New Zealand or in the United States.

Talking about forests is one thing. Seeing them is better in every way. In October 1996 I had the chance of a brief visit to some forests that were the scene of controversy. In British Columbia.

It came about through an old friend of Lizzie's, Günter Hansen, who had been at school with Robert's father, Hartmut, and had got to know Lizzie when Hartmut was dying. In 1995 they made contact again, and Lizzie began to visit Vancouver where Günter, now in his late 70s, was living. She started to write his life history. Günter had trained in agriculture and horticulture and was fiercely proud of the beauties of British Columbia and the magnificence of its woodlands. 'You ought to see our forests,' he insisted. 'A lot of nonsense is talked about them. The Greens – especially the Sierra Club – are going around saying that whenever an area of original old growth forest is cut, its biodiversity is destroyed. The Indians are claiming ownership of big areas – yet when they get it, they sell the logs off faster than anyone else, because their lands are Crown land, not subject to BC law. It's a mess.'

He offered to arrange a tour. He contacted Dr Patrick Moore, one of the founders of Greenpeace but himself of a logging family, and now an adviser to the Forest Alliance of British Columbia – an industrial consortium promoting responsible forestry. We were offered a visit to the northern end of Vancouver Island. In the end Günter did not go – the schedule looked too demanding, and his health was not good. I flew to Port Hardy one beautiful day in late October.

I had thought of Vancouver Island as a green, forested, landscape lying offshore from the Canadian Rockies. So I was unprepared for the clusters of bold rock peaks, heavily capped with the new snows of winter, that jutted from the wooded lowlands. I had also not appreciated how little of BC had been cleared for agriculture or grazing. Nobody had made sheepwalks on the island – which retains over 90 per cent forest cover. And what forests! Immense stands of tall, quick-growing conifers: Western red cedar (which isn't a cedar), Hemlock (which is no relation to the plant Socrates drank), Balsam (which is really a fir), Douglas fir (which isn't), and Sitka spruce. Stands of old-growth, many characterized by spiky Red cedar whose leader shoots have for some reason died back, giving way to laterals that then suffer the same fate, leaving the ancient tree topped like a cathedral with a multiplicity of spires. Wet places with bogland and Lodgepole pine. Streamsides with alder – virtually the only broad-leaved tree in evidence.

We jumped into a helicopter and swept down the canyon of the Marble River and out over Quatsino Sound. The land was a mosaic of old-growth and second growth trees. In some places there were signs of erosion, where forests had been cut from steep slopes. But over large areas good modern practice was evident. Clear-felled patches were limited to 40 hectares, and it was ordered that streamsides were to be left untouched and that no block might be cut unless it would be surrounded on all sides by green canopy. Rates of regeneration, and of growth of planted trees, were rapid. I saw hundred-foot stands of Douglas fir that were under a hundred years old. Vancouver Island is fortunate in having a wealth of native conifers that provide fine timber, so nobody needs to import and plant exotics – it is rather the Vancouver trees, such as Sitka spruce and Lodgepole pine, that are being used in Britain where we have no quick-growing, good-quality native conifers.

It rains a lot on the island, and grey curtains were sweeping across Winter Harbour as we drove to Pat Moore's summer home on the waterside. We went out anyway – dry weather walking is a rare luxury in that pluvial climate. We squelched past an immense Sitka spruce, a good three metres in diameter, and reached the shore, where Pat demonstrated how to make a horn out of a kelp stalk. Cut across the round float chamber, and that gives you a resonant horn mouth: slice across the tubular stipe about a metre along, and blow! Each kelphorn has its own note, so an algal orchestra is possible. The mournful sound resonated across the harbour, somewhat disturbing the sole audience – a Sea lion fishing in the living kelp offshore. Later, we drove out with Pat's father, Bill, who had lived there all his life. They were, I discovered, Ulstermen by origin. Bill was a 'logger poet' – and every year he and his fellows got together and read their new verses. He gave me two of his – which have strong echoes of Kipling. And he took us out in the rain to a fine stand of ancient trees, protected because they bore marks carved there decades ago by First Nation people.

Nearby, the Coho salmon were running, spawning and dying in the shallows of a river. The predators gathered for an immense free meal. About thirty Bald eagles sat around on stumps and branches, one so replete that he did not bother to move even when we walked under his branch, fifteen feet or so below. Gulls screamed in the shallows, pecking at the carcases. There should have been Black bears too – this is bears' bonanza time when they gorge on the autumn salmon and thicken their fat reserves before going into hibernation. But they were not around – maybe they had already departed for post-prandial slumber.

My main question was whether there were any signs of permanently reduced biodiversity in the mosaic of cut forests of different ages, if enough old-growth was left uncut as a reservoir and sanctuary? BC policy is to place 12 per cent of the whole Province in protected areas – and in some places like the west of the island, around Clayoquot Sound the proportion has been raised to 40 per cent. Some steep and remote slopes are protected naturally by terrain and isolation – though logging by helicopter is widening the area of accessibility. Only long-term monitoring will tell, but I came away impressed by the possibility of combining conservation and sustainable use, and with a profound disbelief in some of the extreme claims of the conservationists. I also had a lot of sympathy with Robert Prescott Allen, who had tried to reconcile the various warring factions. Like Boutros-Ghali, he found that you could not reconcile people who resolutely held to the sole truth of their own vision.

The final meeting of the Intergovernmental Panel on Forests was held in New York in February 1997. I was apprehensive. The atmosphere was clearly going to be highly charged politically. Our new southern Co-Chairman, Manuel Rodriguez of Ecuador, our Canadian head of Secretariat, Jag Maini, and I had tried to boil down the record of the Third Session in Geneva to 45 pages of text as a basis for our report, but would Governments insist on inserting their wrecking amendments everywhere? What about the follow-up machinery? In the end, they did agree to commend the technical conclusions from our two Geneva sessions and bless the Inter-Agency Task Force that had brought the UN bodies with forest interests into something like harmony. They also agreed that the work of the Panel had to be continued by a new Forum (though I was quite clear I was not going to Chair it), and that the vexed question of whether or not to seek a new Convention on Forests should be left to that Forum to resolve. So ended my last contribution to the work of the United Nations.

Just as we were in the middle of our work with the Panel, I found myself caught up in a quite separate forest furore. It came through my involvement with ABB. This firm prided itself on its environmental sensitivity – but it was dominated by engineers who did not really understand environmental issues. In July 1996 it became known that the company had agreed to lead a consortium to build the Bakun Dam in Sarawak, Malaysia. I wrote a warning letter to Percy Barnevik, then both President and Chief Executive Officer.

'Large dams, especially in the tropics, have been widely condemned in the environmental movement,' I explained. 'This one will be attacked as unnecessary as a source of national energy, as outmoded technology, as damaging to an area of great ecological importance, as the cause of displacement of about 8000 indigenous people, and as technically illegal because the environmental impact assessment does not comply with Malaysian law.' At the same time, I knew that the political debate in Malaysia, which had see-sawed for a decade, had finally come down in favour of the dam. I had heard about this when in Kuala Lumpur for a UNEP Global 500 Forum conference in October 1995. The Deputy Prime Minister, Anwar Ibrahim, who had opened our meeting, and the Environment Minister, Datuk Law Hin Dieng, had both gone out of their way to explain the project – and express concern about the conflict they foresaw with the world environmental movement.

Barnevik was clearly surprised at the strength of the likely hostility the company would encounter. I am not sure that it had occurred to him that environmental responsibility embraced not only how well the Company managed its internal affairs, but also the kinds of business it went in for. He sent Göran Lindahl, who had led the negotiations in Malaysia and would shortly take over as Chief Executive, for a discussion over dinner in Geneva.

We agreed that the political decision was one for the Malaysian and Sarawak Governments, but that it was for ABB to decide whether the contract was worth the environmental disapprobation. But I think that Barnevik and Lindahl also appreciated that if they were involved in building the dam they ought also to press for conservation and sustainable use in the catchment upstream. Not long afterwards the news broke, and the green world began to splutter.

'Dr Holdgate,' demanded a journalist at the World Conservation Congress in Montreal, 'how can you continue to claim to be a conservationist if you do not publicly repudiate the action of this Company?' 'Surely you appreciate,' said someone else, 'that association with ABB and commitment to conservation are incompatible?'

I disliked the idea of the dam, but had to accept that the Malaysians must have the last word when it came to developing their natural resources. Moreover, reports suggested that it would not flood any primary, old growth forest since the valley land had already been logged or cultivated. The immense catchment of 1,500,000 hectares seemed far more important, because it was said to include over 30 per cent of the untouched primary forest in Sarawak. But nearly half of that had already been approved for selective logging. The issue was whether we could influence the Malaysians towards an integrated land use plan for the catchment that would permanently safeguard the areas of highest biodiversity, maybe linking such conservation with an ecotourist scheme based on the reservoir, or whether there was absolutely nothing to do except ensure that the construction consortium minimized its own environmental impact whatever happened elsewhere. It was an uncomfortable situation, but would I help the environment by resigning from the Company's environmental board?

On 27 January 1997 I set out to visit the site with Jan Strømblad, the head of Environmental Affairs in ABB. We droned all day in a little helicopter, following the river above the dam site and sweeping across the catchment. It was a revelation. Far from being untouched primary forest, much of the area was criss-crossed by logging roads, some sending yellow scars of eroding soil down the hillsides. Big twin-engined Russian helicopters were hauling logs from the steep slopes. While there were areas of high diversity which could have been made attractive to ecotourism and valuable for conservation if they had been placed off-limits at once, it seemed unrealistic to expect anything other than further destruction. As for the dam site, a Korean company was driving huge tunnels through the hillside to allow diversion of the river – and one of these, thrusting through a zone of shattered rock, had partly collapsed, fortunately with no loss of life. The whole thing looked to be an environmental disaster in the making.

It was not clear what ABB could do about it. I was immensely relieved when the economic down-turn appeared to put paid to the whole scheme – at least for now – but I came away with gloomy forebodings about the future of the rain forests of Sarawak.

By early 1997 I was clear of my commitments to the UN, and there even seemed to be a chance of reclaiming those seventy days of free time. But David McDowell had another idea. 'You know that IUCN will be fifty years old in 1998,' he said. 'I think we need a history, setting the Union in the wider context of the development of the modern environmental movement. Would you write it?' That led to an even more fascinating period of research in the archives at Gland, which revealed that the birth of the Union had indeed been tempestuous. The Ligue Suisse, its first parent, had jockeyed for position against a Dutch International Office for the Protection of Nature. The British, led by Max Nicholson, had been highly sceptical of the whole business. Julian Huxley had led UNESCO to the rescue – and may have forfeited a second term of office in consequence. There had been squabbles over money. Max Nicholson's pen picture was vividly true:

> In dealing with IUCN, one must always bear in mind that there never has been, and undoubtedly never will be, any other human organization remotely resembling it. Its peculiarities, subtleties and complexities are sometimes mind-boggling.

For my part I likened IUCN's progress to that of a hot-air balloon, 'launched to sail serenely through the skies – only to descend with little warning and strike financial rocks, often ejecting the Director General (the chief pilot) in the process. Refuelled, recaptained and relaunched, new heights have been gained and new progress made – until the next crisis.' The book – *The Green Web. A Union for World Conservation* – appeared just too late for the fiftieth anniversary celebrations in Fontainebleau but was launched there in summary. I am delighted that IUCN has now taken to calling itself 'The Green Web' as a catchy (and apt) description of the World Conservation Union.

True to form, scarcely had President Chirac and the other dignitaries left Fontainebleau than David McDowell was out of the pilot's basket, to be succeeded by Maritta Koch-Weser who came from Germany via the World Bank. And she herself did not long survive the Second World Conservation Congress, held in Amman in Jordan in October 2000. The Congress was opened by Queen Noor, Patron of the Union, in the magnificent Roman theatre carved into the hillside in the heart of the city. Despite involvement as Chair of the Programme Committee, I snatched a visit to the great Roman city of Jerash, passing the place where, according to legend, Jacob wrestled with the angel long ago. But my most enduring memory is of a banquet on the shores of the Dead Sea under the stars, looking across the water to the twinkling lights of the West Bank. Four days before, Ariel Sharon, in the midst of a posse of guards, had forced his way onto the Temple Mount, crowned by the Al Aqsba mosque that stands on the site of the ancient Jewish temple. The fury and revulsion that followed sparked Palestinian intifada. Those peaceful lights beyond the mouth of the Jordan gave no hint of the tragedies that were to follow.

We told ourselves repeatedly that there was little point in being back in Britain if we did not enjoy its environment and culture. We thought of retirement as a chance to see our own country, after so much trotting about the globe. Our first year back, 1994, was largely sacrificed on a builder's altar, but we did get to Norway and Sweden. Lizzie loved the wild, open coasts and islands north of Ålesund. 'We've got environment like that in Britain too,' I said. 'Let's go to the Northern Isles.'

So the long twilit nights of June 1995 – the season known in Shetland as the 'simmer dim' – had taken us to the West Highlands, with a call on Pete and Fran Tilbrook in the Black Isle and a sweep through the west of Ross and Sutherland with its towering rock peaks. 'We'll get there ahead of the midges,' I promised – and we almost did. And so by ferry to Orkney, to that land of lush pastures and fine cattle, grazing among the monuments of an ancient past. Maes Howe, old as the Pyramids and clearly built by a cultured people. Skara Brae, with the built-in stone furniture of a Bronze Age village preserved by drifting sand. Chambered tombs galore. Great standing stones. And ruined broch towers on every headland. 'Where's the broch of the day?' teased Lizzie.

The bird cliffs and headlands of Shetland are the nearest thing to the Subantarctic that I know in the British Isles. We sat on Hermaness in warm sunshine, and peered out over Muckle Flugga, white with gannets, matching latitude for latitude almost exactly with Signy Island at the other end of the world. Bonxies dived at us just as southern skuas do. We peered through a telescope at Albert Ross, the solitary Black-browed mollymawk that had somehow got across the tropics and spent each summer of twenty years on his earthen nest mound, waiting for a female that never came. 'Poor bird – must be hard to retain your dignity amid all those squawking gannets.'

As the years passed, I have felt an increasing 'pull to the north'. In the spring of 1996, when Lizzie was in Vancouver, I went back to the limestone country of Cumbria and re-examined the vegetation around Sunbiggin Tarn. I met with David and Karyn and we walked on the Lakeland hills. Lizzie and I decided to look for a cottage as a base and retreat in the midst of that green and lovely countryside. Later that year we found it in the hidden

*At home in Hartley, spring 2003. From left to right: Robert, Lizzie (holding
Caroline), Michael (in front), Martin, Katherine (in front), Karyn, David.
Photograph: David Holdgate.*

village of Hartley, near Kirkby Stephen. A grey stone cottage that had once
been a tiny smallholding, with its byre and hay barn downstairs and simple
living quarters above, standing by a beck that is full of life and sound as it
trips down under a little arched stone bridge on its way to the Eden river.
We took possession in November 1996. It was a cold autumn with early
snow. From the crest of a little knoll above the village, I looked once again at
the white wall of the high Pennines, bespattered with shifting light as the
north-west wind drove the clouds from a clear, cold horizon. It was over
fifty years from that vision on the Drybeck road, but this land could still tug
at the heartstrings. It was not yet the end of wandering, but part of me had
come home.

Since then, our ties to the north country have strengthened. David and
Karyn have moved to Edinburgh – where Katherine and Michael were born
in 1998 and 2000 to be followed by Caroline in 2003 – and this has meant
many visits to that magnificent city. Links with Blackpool were renewed
through my Chairmanship of the Governors of Arnold School – vastly
transformed and enlarged from those meagre days of war and now one of
the country's top co-educational independent schools. We have become
involved in local conservation, and especially, in a Conservation Foundation

created by our friend John Strutt. Although Lizzie's affection for her native Suffolk and her home of Clare remain undiminished, and she has poured some of it into her own little book of childhood memories, in the autumn of 2000 we finally left Cambridge to settle in Cumbria. We had learned from past experience, and our cottage was enlarged and refurbished before we moved into it!

Behind the house, our own fields rise to a broad, low, swell of land that shelters the village from the west winds. From its crest you look across to the little town of Kirkby Stephen lying in a bowl of hills. Eastwards, limestone scars and peaty slopes rise to the Nine Standards Rigg, where a row of great cairns of unknown origin prick the skyline. The young river Eden comes tripping down from the vale of Mallerstang, where the great gritstone scarps of Wild Boar Fell and High Seat face one another across a deep, green trough. The broken walls of Pendragon Castle and Lammerside Castle blend history and romance. It is still the fair, green country of my childhood and the curlews still call in springtime across the echoing moors.

Some Books to Read

HERE ARE A few books that go more deeply into some of the subjects covered in what is, inevitably, a selective and compressed narrative.

Chapter Two: Unsuspected Isles in Far-off Seas

Crawford, Allan B. (1982) *Tristan da Cunha and the Roaring Forties*. Edinburgh and London: Charles Skilton and Cape Town: David Philip (the most recent general account of the history of the Tristan Islands by a man who has been deeply involved in the action).

Holdgate, Martin (1958) *Mountains in the Sea. The Story of the Gough Island Expedition*. London: Macmillan (the full account of the Gough Island Scientific Survey, now out of print, but in various libraries).

Wace, Nigel M. and Holdgate, Martin W. (1976) *Man and Nature in the Tristan da Cunha Islands*. Morges, Switzerland: International Union for Conservation of Nature and Natural Resources (an attempt at evaluating the linkage between people and environment, and suggesting a way towards 'sustainability').

Chapter Three: In the Footsteps of Darwin

Bridges, E. Lucas (1951) *Uttermost Part of the Earth*. London: Hodder & Stoughton/Reader's Union (a unique account of Tierra del Fuego and its vanished indigenous peoples, by a man who lived among them).

Darwin, Charles (1955) *The Voyage of the Beagle*. London: J.M. Dent (Everyman Series) (one of the finest books of observation ever written by a travelling naturalist).

Moorehead, Alan (1971) *Darwin and the Beagle*. Harmondsworth: Penguin Books (a good and well-illustrated brief account of the Voyage).

Chapter Four: The True South

Bonner, W.N. and Walton, D.W.H. (1985) *Key Environments: Antarctica*. Oxford etc: Pergamon Press (a good factual introduction to Antarctic science).

Cherry Garrard, Apsley (1922 and many subsequent editions) *The Worst Journey in the World*. London: Chatto & Windus (the most vivid and readable book from the heroic age of Antarctic exploration).

Fothergill, Alastair (1993) *Life in the Freezer. A Natural History of the Antarctic.* London: BBC Books (one of many beautifully illustrated popular books about the Antarctic and Subantarctic).

Fuchs, V.E. (1982) *Of Ice and Men.* Oswestry: Anthony Nelson (a history of the British Antarctic Survey).

Chapter Five: Conserving Nature

Boyd, J. Morton (1999) *The Song of the Sandpiper. Memoir of a Scottish Naturalist.* Grantown on Spey: Colin Baxter (a personal memoir by an outstanding conservationist).

Moore, N.W. (1987) *The Bird of Time. The science and politics of nature conservation.* Cambridge: University Press (another personal account by a man who was a formative influence on nature conservation policy).

Sheail, John (1998) *Nature Conservation in Britain: the formative years.* London: The Stationery Office (the factual account by a professional historian).

Sheail, John (1992) *Natural Environment Research Council: A History.* Swindon: Natural Environment Research Council (another factual account).

Worthington, E.B. (1975) *The Evolution of IBP.* Cambridge: University Press (the only overview of a largely-forgotten event).

Chapter Six: Cleaning Our Environment

Johnson, Stanley (1973) *The Politics of Environment. The British Experience.* London: Tom Stacey (a politician's account of the events leading up to the creation of the Department of the Environment and the Stockholm Conference).

Meadows, D.H., Meadows, D.L., Randers, J. and Behrens, W.W. (1972) *The Limits to Growth.* New York: Universe (the book that caused such a fuss at the time of the Stockholm Conference).

Peyton, John (2001) *Solly Zuckerman. A Scientist out of the Ordinary.* London: John Murray (a very readable description of an extraordinary man).

Ward, Barbara and Dubos, René (1972) *Only One Earth: the care and maintenance of a Small Planet.* London: Andre Deutsch (the seminal book for Stockholm, and one of the best overviews of the Earth's situation in 1972).

Chapter Seven: Science and Policy

Jordan, Andrew (2002) *The Europeanization of British Environmental Policy. A Departmental Perspective.* Basingstoke: Palgrave Macmillan (a scholarly analysis of the evolution of environmental policy in the DOE, and about the only book about the workings of this side of the Department).

McCormick, John (1989) *The Global Environmental Movement.* London: Belhaven Press (an excellent overview of the evolving environmental movement in the 1970s and early 1980s).

Tolba, Mostafa K. (1992) *Saving Our Planet: Challenges and Hopes*. London: Chapman and Hall (a relatively popular and digestible summary of the big overviews of the state of the world environment that proliferated in the 1970s, 1980s and 1990s).

Chapters Eight and Nine: Back to Nature and Caring for the Earth

Chambers, Robert (1983) *Rural Development. Putting the Last First*. London etc.: Longman (a lively new prescription for tackling rural poverty).

IUCN, UNEP and WWF (1991) *Caring for the Earth. A Strategy for Sustainable Living*. Gland, Switzerland, IUCN (also published as a 'popular' illustrated volume in 1993 by Mitchell Beazley, Reed International Books Ltd, London etc.)

Holdgate, Martin (1999) *The Green Web. A Union for World Conservation*. London: Earthscan (a history of IUCN, written for its 50th anniversary in 1998).

Ramphal, Shridath (1992) *Our Country the Planet*. Washington DC: Island Press (the 'overview' book for the Rio Earth Summit).

Index